A Place in Words

Cover and text design by Matthew Robertson
Photographs © 2017 by Kellie Hindmarch

Printed and bound by CPI Group (UK) Ltd, Croydon, CR0 4YY

First Printing: September 2017

10 9 8 7 6 5 4 3 2 1

ISBN 978-1-5272-0733-2

A Place in Words
25 Years of Creative Writing at Bath Spa University

Contents

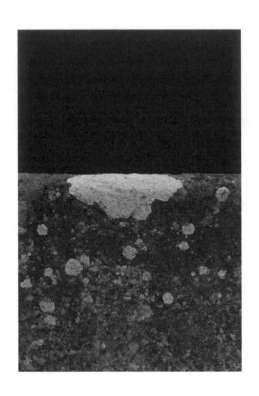

Introduction

TESSA HADLEY

A twenty-fifth anniversary is such a nice one to celebrate: twenty-five is seriously grown-up, but still youthful. And that's just how the Bath Spa Creative
Writing courses feel. We've been doing this for a long time and we've learned
so much through practice. When Creative Writing began, with our MA, it was
a very new discipline inside universities in the UK: its forms of learning and
teaching hadn't set hard, anything seemed possible. Those few visionaries
who founded the writing courses and taught them were, in the best sense,
making things up as they went along (just as novelists and poets have to
do). Well, now Creative Writing courses have proliferated, and there's a lot
more experience around, as well as the inevitable outgrowths of commentary
and theory.

But the Bath Spa courses still feel fresh too. Partly no doubt that's because
of the students who bring to the beginning of each new year their unique sen-
sibilities and their passions for writing, as well as their high hopes and fears.
Partly it's because of new staff who've brought their different writing selves
and their ideas for change. Better than that, though: even the staff who've
been here for a quarter of a century don't find the teaching ever growing stale,
because writing itself is always new. There's such a fresh delight always, for
staff and students alike, in seeing a new novel or story or poem that's never

existed before come into its being, take on its right form and tone and life out of its beginning as an idea or a hunch or a fragment.

The pleasure to be had inside the best of those workshops, from a group of committed readers and writers working at white heat together, has to be experienced to be properly appreciated – whether they're reading and critiquing each other's work, or reading and exploring some of the published writers we study together (How did she do that? Why did he do it that way?). I'm convinced that some of the best literary critical discussion happens inside those classes coming at literature as it were from underneath, through its makings, asking the how-to questions, and I know for sure that developing as a reader is an essential part of becoming a writer. The students learn from reading one another's work, as well as their own.

I have had the pleasure both ways: I began at the very beginning, as a student on the MA course when it was only in its second year, and I've been involved in teaching Creative Writing at Bath Spa ever since (and I'm not alone, a number of our staff have had this privilege of experience on both sides). My year on the MA made all the difference in the world to me as a writer. Not because – that old chestnut! – you can actually teach anyone to write. You can't. There's no toolkit of easy skills, no secret formula to make it obvious. Each writer has to find her or his own way, like each book or story or poem, through patient particular work. But what a Creative Writing course does, makes all the difference; it embeds that solitary, slow writing apprenticeship in a real world of committed, informed, participatory readers and writers and editors.

Suddenly I wasn't writing to myself. It sounds like a small thing, but it was everything. Others were leaning over my shoulder and pointing out what wasn't working, what was: because I had an audience I could hear myself – what I sounded like, what I had to say, when I was failing to say it – for the first time. Writers have always found their own communities, because they needed just this kind of support, this participatory audience, this collaborative creative reading: in the great cities, among friends, in cafes or around journalism. Jane Austen read her novels to her family. Creative Writing courses are just a new form for an old cultural necessity. And the courses, I am quite certain, have done something too to help open up access to achievement and publication, broken up some of the old coteries in the world of books.

I'm not going to try, on this commemorative occasion, to name all the names of those who have played significant roles in our Creative Writing story; there are just too many wonderful writers and teachers who've at some point given their time and imagination and passion – and of course their dogged day to day administrative work as well – to making the courses as exciting and successful as they are. And there are too many students who've given themselves so wholeheartedly over to the risk and adventure of writing and made the course worthwhile, for them to be listed here; we're very proud of them all, and some of them have gone on to publishing success, some to glittering careers and prizes and critical acclaim. The anthology in itself helps compose these lists, and is a tribute to all those individuals. But it seems to me that there a few names have to be named, and any introduction would be incomplete without them.

The MA course began in sadness; brilliant Les Arnold, whose idea it was, long before Bath Spa was even a university, died much too young and unexpectedly, before he could even see the first year's intake through. Poet Jeremy Hooker took on the direction of the course under that shadow, and set his stamp of serious high aspiration on it from the beginning. It's impossible to imagine the MA without Richard Kerridge, who has been part of it always, managing change and continuity with consummate intelligence, his passion for the course and for good writing unflagging. Steve May and Paul Meyer built Creative Writing as an undergraduate subject; Tracy Brain established it as a PhD, with Gerard Woodward.

At a crucial point in the MA's expansion, Richard Francis joined our staff and helped to build our exceptional relationship with the commercial realities of contemporary book publishing, without losing any of our writing freedom, or aspiration to excellence. (Of course not! Because excellence is what publishers want too.) It was his idea to push students towards writing at greater length, so that their novels were well on the way to being finished by the end of the year. More recently Philip Hensher has wielded his formidable talent and authority in making a strong commitment to the course and its future. First Philip Gross, then Tim Liardet and Carrie Etter, have kept the poetry torch burning brightly. The MA course to begin with included writing for young people and children, but after a few years this area was made a separate MA; this has been so ably and inspiringly led by Julia Green, who has established the pattern for a rather different discipline, and had dizzying success in terms of publications. And now there are MAs too in Scriptwriting and Travel and Nature Writing, and an MRes in Transnational Writing.

There are so many others, staff and students, whom I'm hungry to mention: but if I began, where would I end? (Dear erudite stylist Colin Edwards brooded most helpfully over the novel I wrote on the course.) I feel such gratitude to Creative Writing at Bath Spa. It was at the beginning of my being published, and it's been a part of my life ever since, offering such a rewarding counterpoint to the solitude that is also of course essential for a writer. I have loved working with colleagues and students over all these twenty-five years, in a shared passionate engagement with good books.

Deleted scene from *The Power*

NAOMI ALDERMAN

AUTHOR'S NOTE *if you want to know, this happens just after Tunde's in Delhi.*

TUNDE

'How does he seem to you?'

Emmanuel cleans his nails with the file on the bedside table. He curls it carefully under each one, cleaning out the day's dirt. He sighs.

'I don't know. Subdued.'

'Have you spoken to him?'

Vivian dips her fingers into the oil and twists her hair, dividing each section into two strands, wrapping them around each other until they look to Emmanuel like the glossy braid on expensive furniture. The room smells of coconut. She can twist the whole head of hair without looking in the mirror, but Emmanuel likes to watch her, fingers swift, deft and precise. He has always found her competence almost unbearably attractive. He has to stop himself smiling because he knows that she will take it as laughing at her, and that's not it at all.

Emmanuel says: 'I tried to ask him what happened.'

'He told you nothing happened. He held out his hands and said: "nothing happened."'

Emmanuel laughs. They are both remembering the same thing, they do not even need to speak it aloud. Tunde coming home from school at six years old covered head-to-toe in bright red paint. Walking in through the front door, carefully not touching the walls, not sitting down. And Vivian saying to him: 'Tunde, Tunde what happened?' And six-year-old Tunde spinning round on the spot very slowly, head up towards the ceiling fan, following its lazy motion with his body, saying: 'nothing happened, Mama, nothing, nothing, nothing.' They had had to telephone the teacher, and even she at first could not explain it, until she remembered that he'd asked if he could take a little bag of powder paint home from school to show his sister, and she'd double-wrapped in plastic for him. His interest and desire to paddle his fingers in the soft powdery paint must have overtaken him between the school gate and the house. He has always been like this: curious and thoughtful, active and self-contained, a boy with a few good friends rather than a crowd of acquaintances, one whose first instinct is to say 'Nothing happened. Nothing. Nothing.'

'Has he talked to you about going back to school?'

Emmanuel shrugs. 'He's making money,' he says, 'it's good money. Advertising. Exclusive deals.'

They have looked at the YouTube channel. They do not quite understand it, or how it can translate into actual money, but Emmanuel has examined the figures closely. Over one million subscribers. Each one is worth ten cents a year. It is good money, it is growing.

'It will not last forever,' says Vivian, 'it is a craze.'

She finishes putting her hair up, ties it back with a silk wrap. Turns off the light around the mirror. Comes to bed.

They lie in the dark, her head against his chest, his arm around her shoulder. Tunde is in his room down the hallway. Very faintly, they can hear the sound of him talking; he is recording a piece from his bedroom. They could ask him not to do it now, but neither of them would interrupt him, and besides, there is something comforting about the sound of it. Here he is. Safe and sound. There is something in the way he's been since he came home that's made Viv wonder if Tunde will always be safe and sound. It's not a worry she's had before. She does not know what to do with it. It is like an unexpected gift of an ugly candle or an ornament; she did not anticipate it, does not want it, has nowhere to put it. It rattles around from place to place, this unasked-for feeling that there is something she should be doing for Tunde, but she does not know what it is.

She lies in the dark, staring at the ceiling, remembering the laughing little boy he was. How he learned how to do a handstand – somewhere, at school, from the other children – and showed her again and again, laughing.

She says: 'Do you think something happened to him? While he was away?'

Emmanuel says: 'What would have happened? We saw him every day on the video.'

'Why has he come back?'

'He said, he wanted a rest. He has been travelling so much.'

'But you said it yourself; he is subdued.'

'Stop worrying!' says Emmanuel. 'Always worrying. Worry about me!'

She nudges him in the ribs and he chuckles.

Viv has not developed the power. Her younger daughter Temi tried to show her, but nothing came of it. Here in this room, things are as they have always been. Temi and her friends practise in the garden after school. They see on the news that there have been attacks in rural parts of the country; kidnapped girls rising up against their captors. And they have nodded and said: Good. Good for the country, good for the women. It is safer now than it was, it is better. But here, in this house, not much has changed. Except that Viv has this feeling, in the centre of her, where Tunde once was lodged high up, his feet pressing against her ribs from the inside. A feeling that she should talk to him about the world and its dangers. But this is not a conversation to have with a boy. She would not know the words.

Charles laughs with his mouth open, making a little gesture, rubbing his right thumb very quickly against the tips of the first three fingers of his right hand.

'It's good,' he says, 'it's good. I know a girl who can do it straight out of her pussy.'

'Fuck you do,' says Isaac, 'she'd zap your prick and then you'd die of pain.'

Charles leans very close to them.

'You mean no girl ever gave you a little something to get your motor running? You don't know anything boy, nothing at all.'

Charles is three years older than Tunde and Isaac. He'd had sex when he was fourteen anyway, he says so. He's been having sex with girls since before all of this started, he's seen the change. Charles claims to like it better now.

'Did you ever have a girl who can do it all of the colours of the rainbow?' he asks.

Tunde is sick of this. He thought he'd come back home and his friends would want to hear his stories, that he'd be the hero, the celebrity. He'd thought, after Delhi, that he should just go home for a little while, to be among his family. He had an image in his mind of his childhood bedroom, somehow in his imagination it would be as it had been when he was ten years old, not even as it had been when he left for Riyadh. But something has changed now, in them or in himself. He cannot just be Tunde, the studious one, anymore, the one who listens to Charles's stories. Or is it that Charles's stories are different now?

Tunde leans back on the sofa, beer in his hand, puts a half smile on to his face and says: 'In Beijing, I saw a girl dip her fingertips in gold powder, and turn it to mist with her sparks. The gold fell like rain.'

'Oh, I forgot,' says Charles, 'you have *travelled*. Tell us of your travels, oh mighty Phileas Fogg, explorer of the world.'

Tunde drinks from his bottle of beer.

'I knew you wouldn't understand,' he says, 'this country. You know in China there are scientists learning more every day about how it works, to see if they can turn on the genes in men that would let us do it? Did you know that? And here ... do you still think Charles that if you fuck enough girls with your magic penis you'll get the power yourself?'

'Come on now,' says Isaac, 'come on.' He cracks a smile: 'Even if there's no magic penis, surely this plan of fucking a lot of girls is worth a try? Tunde, someone must push forward the boundaries of scientific knowledge.'

He frowns and nods sagely. Keeps nodding far beyond the point of seriousness. Keeps on nodding and stroking his chin until they both start laughing.

There's a party that night at the house of one of Charles's friends from university. There are always parties, through the summer and into the autumn, until the last stragglers go back to college; almost every night there's something to go to. Sometimes 'a party' means seven people and a PlayStation and a crate of beer; those are Tunde's favourites, especially now that he's a little bit famous. He's had a good summer here, mostly, impressing girls with his stories, he hasn't had to work hard at all to have a steady stream of interest in joining him in bed. He's noticed they chase him now, in a way they never used to; he can't quite tell if that's because of YouTube or because of some other thing that's changed in the air of Lagos since he was last here.

This is not one of those parties, though. It is the Saturday night before the Sunday morning when a large group will be going back to college. They drive over the bridge to Victoria Island; they give their names at the security gate of one of the large houses, they park the car and they can already hear the music from the house, booming across the swimming pool.

They drink. They smoke the Chesterfields Charles brought with him. There are girls here who have seen Tunde online, he can feel it. Two or three girls here he's slept with already, who seemed eager enough for another go-around, but he sees someone he likes the look of walking through the crowd. She's wearing a gold dress, loose on the shoulders and tight on the hips. He works his way towards her. He's lost Isaac in the crowd but Charles positions himself on the arm of the sofa, to watch the action.

Tunde says: 'Hey. Hello,' to the girl. She smiles at him, faintly.
    'I haven't seen you around,' he says. She shrugs and says 'Aha'.
    'Of course I haven't been around much myself,' he says, 'I've been travelling you know. I make videos. Online videos. I put them online. I was in Delhi last month, and before that Singapore and before that Beijing.'
    She looks both bored and slightly panicked. She pulls her phone out of her pocket.
    'I've got to ...' she gestures at it with one finger ... 'yeah'.
    'Yeah OK,' says Tunde.

He sinks back on to the sofa. Later. When she's not surrounded by friends, maybe later he'll find something to say to her. At the end of the beer.

Charles says: 'You could never have a girl like that, not if you travelled to the moon and to Mars.'
    There is a desperation in his voice. Tunde sees now that Charles has ridden him like this because he is *jealous*. Because whatever it is that girls want now, that is what Tunde has. It would be good to be kind in this moment, to place a hand on Charles's shoulder and say: I too am afraid. But Tunde is drunk and in any case, could Charles hear the words?
    Instead, Tunde says: 'Maybe I couldn't get a girl like that, but you couldn't have anyone. Not one of them will give you a second glance, my friend.'
    He raises his beer in mock salute, and Charles is on him. Punching, not hard but vigorous and constant. Punching him in his belly and his chest and his legs with a strong, thick fist; making a grunting sound.

Tunde at first is too startled to do anything. But Charles's face, next to his face, Charles's heavy breathing, Charles's knee pinning down his leg, and he thinks 'I have *always* hated you. I have always hated you.' Charles and his supercilious smile and his need to always know best and his fucking stories about girls. Tunde brings his knee up into Charles's stomach with a thwacking force. Charles breathes out beer-and-cigarette breath into Tunde's face, winded. He jerks back. Tunde wriggles his right arm free and gets Charles on the chin, a solid uppercut. Charles opens his mouth and there's blood. And now it's on.

Tunde pushes Charles off him with his feet. Stands up. He's shorter than Charles, and lighter, but he's agile and fit and he's had less to drink. Charles is shaking his head, already dazed.

'Come on,' says Tunde, 'are you going to fight? Or are you afraid?'

Charles is up with a roar, and somewhere Tunde's aware of Isaac pushing his way through the crowd saying 'stop, stop'. But Charles is on him again, trying for a bear-hug. Because he has the advantage of weight and height, he wants to crush Tunde into the ground. Tunde tries to sidestep but there isn't room and the rug on the floor is slippery. Charles gets him by one arm and one leg and hurls him to the ground. He scrapes his back on the base of a lamp. And there it is. Delhi, and the woman on the roof. And Tunde is suddenly more angry than he thought he had in him. He snarls and he goes for Charles's face, punching and punching, and Charles is bleeding, his nose is beginning to swell, and Tunde does not stop. Around him there's a sound like a far off roll of thunder. He's dimly aware that a crowd is gathering, that there are people shouting 'fight, fight', and at the same time there are people saying 'someone stop them, stop it'. Charles raises his hands to cover his face, and Tunde scrambles into a half-crouch and kicks at his side, thinking I can turn him over, I can jump on him. Fucking Charles with his snide remarks and his little digs and his stupid fucking face.

And then. He is frozen. It is very sudden, and very cold, and to begin with it does not hurt at all. His spinal column has turned to water and the water has turned to ice and it is all very pure and perfect. There are frost fingers working their way up into his skull, and along his arms, and down through his buttocks; like the patterns on a window on a frozen morning. Like Lichtenberg figures. Like ferns unfurling, leaf-budding. And then it begins to hurt. As if the pain were an organ or a limb of his body, as if a seed of pain had sprouted along his vertebrae, its tendrils penetrating every vacuole and orifice. He turns his head.

It's Enuma. He hasn't seen her since the summer before last. If anything, she's even more beautiful than she was then. Seventeen and ripe and perfect. She's laughing at him and shaking her head. It's her ice crystals in his spine, it's her headache blooming across the base of his skull like ink in water. She's hurting him even as she's holding him steady.

'Tunde,' she says, 'fighting?' She presses her lips together as if to conceal a smile. She shakes her head again. Turns to the group of women who are with her. She says, to them, 'Don't you know Tunde, that boys shouldn't fight with their clothes on? We like to have something to look at, you know.' And the women with her all laugh. They lick their lips.

Enuma lets him go. He crashes to the floor. His nose is bleeding her pure, icy blood. His eyes are popping with her red, prickling fire.

She leans down and puts her face very close to his.

'Don't make me come here again,' she says, 'to fix this.'

Another girl lets Charles go. Tunde looks at Charles. Charles looks at Tunde. They are both afraid, and they are both hard, and they are both ashamed and they look down and away and the crowd is laughing at them even as it disperses.

In the morning, in the house, his sister Temi is making eggs. There is a soothing rhythm to her work; she performs the steps just like their mother, her weight shifted on to one hip as she reaches for the cooking oil, her face solemn and composed. She cracks the eggs into the bowl: one, two, three. She slices the tomatoes, halves then quarters. She makes sure everything is ready before she pours the oil into the pan, just like their mother, cooking calmly, as if it were a ritual. She salts the tomatoes. She cuts the chilli with small scissors. She turns on the gas and then, with a flick of her finger, ignites it.

Tunde feels he cannot move or breathe. It was the way she brought it out from her thumb and forefinger. It was the way she did it so easily. She must have done it a thousand times before. She is not afraid that anyone might see her. His parents must have seen her do it. Here in his own home, this has happened. Temi is singing a little song, softly, as she tips the eggs into the sizzling pan. He remembers wrestling with her, not two, not three years ago. Wrestling for fun, letting her win, being careful with his strength. And now this.

She turns around.

She says: 'Want some, Tunde?'

The Buzzard and the Babe

DAVID ALMOND

Two ladies in a garden before a house on Windy Ridge.

'You're Davie, aren't you?' one of them asks in a low voice as the boy passes by.

She's Leticia Spall, he knows her. The one beside her is unknown. They both have arms folded beneath their breasts. There are dazzling hip-high flowers, perhaps dahlias, glowing all around them.

'I see your mother's face in you,' says Letitia. 'I see your father's, too.'

Davie wants to move on but the words cause him to hesitate.

'I knew you when you were a babe,' she continues. 'I remember one day I slipped a coin into the covers on your pram. You were a bonny bairn. I see that bonny bairn in you, as well.'

She smiles and leans closer.

Her companion smiles as well.

'I didn't know you when you were a bairn,' she says. 'But that's not too surprising. I come from Hexham, from the far side of the hill, and didn't know these parts at all until I came to know Letitia, and began to come across the hill to spend my time with her. My name is Ellen, Davie. I am pleased to meet you, son.'

The ladies lean towards each other, their shoulders touch.

25

Behind and above them, a bedroom window of the house is wide open, a white net curtain drifts before it in the gentle breeze.

An orange butterfly lands on Letitia's shoulder. She whispers to it that it is welcome there.

Davie smiles, moves to move on.

'We were talking of the buzzards,' says Letitia.

'Of the buzzards?' says Davie.

'Aye,' says Letitia, 'and of the vulnerability of all babes.'

'Look high,' says Ellen, 'and peel your eyes.'

They all turn their faces to the summit and to the light beyond. There are larks there, Davie knows, that are invisible.

'They are there, the buzzards,' she says, 'if you're able to look hard enough.'

So Davie looks as hard as he is able, and turns his eyes and mind from the two ladies, from gardens and allotments and from playing fields and drifts of poppies, and from the hill above him which he will climb, and yes, at last he sees them, two dark birds with wings outstretched, wheeling in the blue. Two tiny birds, which must be massive to be seen from here so far below. Two massive birds above the place to which he seems to be heading as he wanders through the day.

'We talked,' says Letitia, 'of a tale that was told to me so long ago that I was little more than a babe myself.'

Davie turns his eyes from the distant birds to the nearby lady.

'I was told,' she continues, 'that one summer morning, bright and warm as this one is, a buzzard dropped from its distant sky to the air above these gardens. It dropped down to a basket on a table in which a little babe was fast asleep, and that it took that babe in its claws and carried it away.'

'And I said,' says her companion, Ellen, 'that such a thing would be impossible. A little babe, no matter how tiny it might have been, would be an impossible thing for a bird such as a buzzard to lift. What do you think, bonny lad?'

'I suppose,' says Davie, 'that I think it'd be impossible as well.'

'And yet,' says Letitia, 'I was told that such a thing indeed was true. And in my bairn-ness, I believed it. And I was told that the mother and the father and the brother of the babe rushed out of this house and from this gate, and hurried upwards across the fields, all the time calling to the bird above to give them back the little bairn they loved so much. But the bird continued upward, and the tiny babe continued dangling from its claws.'

She pauses, to allow Davie to look once more towards the sky above the hill, to imagine there the upward-flapping bird, the dangling babe. Would the babe, he wonders, have been screaming? Would it understand that now it was exposed in air when once it was at home on earth? Would it perhaps accept that this was just the fate of all babes born on to this earth?

And he imagines the frantic family on the earth beneath. He imagines them howling at the sky, holding out their arms in case the babe should fall.

'A bird,' goes on Letitia, 'can fly through air much quicker than a man, a woman or a boy can run across the earth. Soon, because of shrubs and trees and rocks and the uneven pathways, they could not always keep the bird in sight.'

'Can you imagine it?' says Ellen. 'I'm sure that I cannot. Perhaps a buzzard could carry a babe as far as a garden gate, perhaps even as far as an allotment row, but surely it couldn't carry a babe as far as that! Couldn't carry it, as Letitia told me, until it hovered a hundred feet over the summit of the hill with the babe in its sharp claws, while the desperate family sprinted, gasped, grunted in useless hot pursuit.'

'But that's the tale that was told to me,' continues her companion, 'the tale that has lodged itself deep in my heart, so that at my age now, I hardly care if it's true or not. I care only for the strangeness and the beauty and the terror of it. The bird went out of sight, Davie. The sky was empty but for the everlasting larks. And the family reached the summit and they wept to know such loss. And then they roamed the high land, until the boy, the brother began to call. "There! There! Hear it? Hear it?" And he led the mother and the father towards what he had heard, the weeping of a baby.'

'They found it?' asks Davie.

'They hurried to the sound. And oh, they found a baby lying on green turf beside a trickling stream.'

'A baby?' says Davie. 'It wasn't theirs?'

'Ah, at first they said they couldn't be certain.'

'Couldn't be *certain*?'

'They said at first they thought the baby's crying voice had changed its tone. They thought the eyes were a brighter blue than they'd been before. And when they came to it, it did not stretch its arms out to them as it would have done before. But then they calmed, they knew that it must be their own babe.'

'Who else's could it be?'

'No one else's, of course. They said afterwards that their perception of the babe had been confounded by their terror. They said that it wouldn't be surprising if a babe did not undergo some changes after the experience of such an ambushment, and such a flight into the sky. They lifted the babe, they carried it home to Windy Ridge, where it was loved, they said, as no other babe has ever been loved, and it grew and flourished as all babes seem to do in this place.'

She reaches out and tousles Davie's hair.

'As you do yourself, Davie, despite all toils and torments.' She narrows her eyes as she peers at him. 'Oh, I remember you, the bonny babe beneath the covers in the pram with everything before him. And I see you now, all grown up and walking in the gorgeous light with everything before him still. I see the babe, the boy, the man you will become. I see the changes that have happened and the changes still to come. Your mother must be proud of you. Oh, how you have changed.'

Her companion laughs.

'Of course he's bliddy changed,' she says. 'But it didn't take an ambushment by a buzzard on a summer day to bring the change about.' She bites her lip and stares into Davie's eyes. 'Or *did* it?' she asks. 'Have you been lifted from the earth in terror, lad?'

Davie laughs out loud at the thought.

'I don't think so,' he says. 'I don't remember it!'

They watch him and wait.

'And my journey to the summit of the hill,' he says, 'is much slower than the baby's or its family was.'

'It was the babe herself who told the tale to me,' says Letitia.

'The babe?'

'The babe who, by then, had grown into a woman old enough to have babies of her own. She had been told that this had happened to her many years ago, before she could remember anything.'

'And she believed it?'

'She said that she believed it. Ha. And she said that sometimes she believed that she was not the babe they had pursued, but was a babe from somewhere far across the hill, laid down there by that buzzard or another buzzard. She said that maybe she was the wrong baby. She talked of going on a journey sometime, to find out if there was another baby dropped down by a buzzard. She wondered if the real she was someone else to be discovered somewhere else.'

She touches the orange butterfly. It flaps and floats away from her shoulder.

'Anyway,' says Letitia Spall. 'What are such tales but beautiful distractions on such a perfect day as this.'

At the bedroom window, the white net curtains drift. The ladies lean together, smiling.

Ellen winks.

'Perhaps,' she says, 'the tale she tells is the tale of Letitia Spall herself.'

The ladies laugh.

'Tell your mum that I was asking after her,' says Letitia. 'My sympathies to her and to you for your sad loss.'

She leans to him and tousles him again.

'Like the babe,' she says, 'what is lost might be discovered again, but in a different form, and the form might simply be a tale that could be lies and could be truths and could be lovely bits of both.'

She pushes a coin into his hand.

'Take this,' she says. 'It's like the coin I slipped between the covers in your pram when you were a tiny babe. It's for the future, as I whispered down to sleeping tiny you, before you knew there was such a thing as future at all.'

Davie thanks her, and sighs, and turns away from the happy pair.

'Don't let the buzzards take you!' says Letitia Spall.

He laughs. He wanders on. He imagines the buzzard's claws on his shoulders. He imagines dark wings beating above his head. He imagines himself being lifted, his walking feet rising from the earth. He feels the warm breeze at his back.

No Map

JANINE AMOS

It began at a harbour-side cafe: a Sunday morning, sunshine on the water, a group of friends daydreaming about the future. We asked each other, 'What would you do next year – for yourself – if you could do *anything*?'

'I'd take the Writing for Young People MA at Bath Spa University.' The words leapt out, surprising me.

It was an impossible dream for a single parent with bills to pay. I ran my own business; there were writing deadlines to meet, contacts to maintain. My next few years were all mapped out, weren't they?

My friends ignored that. 'Do it. Just give them a ring, find out. Dare you.' The seeds were sown.

At bedtime, I ran the idea past my son. 'My mum – a *student*!' he whooped, full of questions and enthusiasm. 'Go on,' he challenged before snuggling down, 'I dare you!'

A double-dare – how could I resist? And so, without thinking it through, and very unlike the organised, reliable parent I'd become, I applied. Upstairs, safe in his pyjamas, my son slept on.

A busy few weeks later, I hared across Bristol to Newton Park in my lunch hour for an interview, in the rain. The car was hot, the windscreen misted up and a lorry blocked my view. I realised I didn't know where I was going. Literally. I had no map (and definitely no satnav).

It took forever. The traffic was crazy and panic set in: I'd blown it – I'd never find the place, I'd bc late for my interview. What on earth did I think I was doing in any case? I ought to be saving money for my child's higher education, not my own. Selfish, greedy mother, I should pull out, right now.

Twice round the roundabout, palms sweaty on the wheel, a quick stop at *The Globe* to ask for directions, and at last I began crawling along a scarily narrow driveway on to the campus.

Greenness swallowed me up. The rain stopped and my breathing slowed. I rolled down the windows: scents of damp leaves and freshly washed countryside filled the car. Could I see sheep in the distance?

A heron swooped across the field to my right and landed softly in the grass.

At that moment, I knew. I knew that I really, really wanted a place on the MA. I knew that the time was right for me to explore my craft and that, somehow, I'd keep a roof over our heads, if I could just have this year – for myself.

And so I drove on. I wasn't late for the interview and I did get a place – and that whole greedy, map-less year was one of the best I've had, so far.

These days, every time I travel along the drive on to campus, I keep my eyes open for a heron. Sometimes I see one, often I don't – but there's always the possibility that I might. And I never use a map.

Five Poems

The Present Moment

Miroslav has informed me
that a moment is three seconds,
precisely.

He could only imagine eternity,
and the present worried him
like a bit of string.

But now the metronome
and the flashing palindrome
have confirmed.

The subjective present's
three seconds is as real
as his shoe size, and in this

he finds a great deal of comfort.

Now that it is measured
he can picture
the present moment.

*

Miroslav has been writing
about angels
and this bothers him.

They are responsible for atomic fusion
but he does not want them
to save anyone.

While to him the soul is soft and red
open to the air from under
the skin.

He has spent time mourning
the last cell thrown away
in his laboratory.

But he knows that he is happy
for three seconds
after removing a tight pair of shoes.

Nightmare of the Pines

I had only gone in once, into the thick, dark forest of pines along the gravel drive to the camping ground. I had only entered two or three rows deep, could still see the creep of light on the floor-edge, but only just. The light extinguished quickly in the swath of boughs, like a candle blown out. I went in with a friend, but lost her voice. I lost direction. Nothing filtered down. Nothing gave a signal. I thought I was heading towards the dust-crack edge of light but only found more darkness. The needles of the pines ran their nail-points down my arms. All of them so close. I couldn't run.

For years I dreamt of running down a gravel road at night, unending pines on either side. I ran from something that pursued me from behind, the fear was blinding. My legs would dissolve, crumple, stop beneath me and I'd tumble, trying to stand up again. As time went on, there were headlights behind me, the only light on that gravel road. The darkness of the pines on either side. Nothing filtered down. Nothing gave a signal. The headlights coming close. I couldn't run.

Solvent

The morning light is indecipherable,
limp grey gauze in layers growing thick
with rain. I am coffee-deep into the day,
but slow and occupied with solitude.

Amidst the dark mid-morning of a Monday
in a Midwestern state famed for roadways,
there is no one near the pool at this hotel.
Green ripples wobble up from the water
over the ceiling from below my form. A storm
launches, pouring rain on to the glass windows
in a roar, beads thick as black pearls,
the lightning making a canvas of each pane.

Eight laps, a headstand, some mermaid
moves and my body's borders begin
to blur until I'm mostly water, water made
of green light and a slight chemical sting.

Water, electricity, and the gauze of my flesh,
slowly fuse with the darker clouds that slip past
until the rain has stopped, until a white towel
and a cloud break gather me back into myself.

Meeting the Moon

Seeking six days for the very spot, I found chalk arrows pointing away from each other. I found dandelions. I found a pathway, I found the moon rising in daytime. I found the dimension of impasto petals thick with light. Tracking the moon's cycle, I found a rolling orb, sunflowers for spokes, palette knifes for handlebars. I saw the evening ride and lift against cerulean clouds. The wheels spun over swimming grass blades, swirling tree limbs. And off the evening rolled behind the stone wall. I waved to the astronomer, and we walked away in opposite directions.

The Constellation's Prayer

My daughter,
    I pray for you a lighthouse—

though my blue supergiant heart
    has the brightness
of a million suns
and my four angles

are strong in the carpenter's
square,
    I am set to supernova
in a million years.

Long may you be carried
    in the spiral arms beneath me.

I pray that you will only
gather
    the right stones
into your orbit.

I pray that you will circle
a planet
    fit to view your light,
fit to ballast

your extreme seasons
your circuit like a belt
your uneven sphere
shaped by your own gravity.

I pray that you shine
    past all
measure, past all
        Enlightenment.

Not Like in Denmark

SUSAN BEALE

Scandinavian Airline System's flight 903 bumped on to the runway in New York, half an hour late, just before 3 p.m. on an overcast afternoon in June 1990, and Camilla Jurgensen, seated in 27H (a window seat), nearly burst into grateful applause. The eight-hour flight from Copenhagen had been a trial of nerves. The final descent was through thick and soupy cloud cover. In the murk, the unfamiliar sounds – a whizzing whorl, followed by a thump beneath her feet – gave her a start.

'The landing gear,' explained the young man seated next to her, an American.

Camilla forced a smile. She knew he meant to reassure. Still, she wasn't one to go striking up conversations with strangers.

Air travel was not Camilla's cup of tea, which was why she politely declined invitations to join her neighbours on their package holidays to the southern coast of Spain. A week or two at a cottage on the Danish mainland suited her just fine. She could go by car and bring her dog Rex. What more could anyone wish for?

She stared out the plane's porthole at tarmac and strips of ragged grass between the runways. It didn't look all that different from Denmark.

'This is America,' she reminded herself, clutching instinctively at the heart pendant her late husband Ken had given her on their twenty-fifth wedding anniversary. 'I am in America.'

Ken had always wanted to go to United States. How strange that she should be the one making this trip. But, of course, it was all because of Preben.

The news that her only son would go on assignment to New York had come as a shock. She had barely adjusted to his living in Copenhagen, a train and a ferry and another train journey from her village on the island of Fyn. With everyone talking about a new, unified Europe, Camilla had worried that he would take a job in Brussels or Frankfurt or even Berlin, now that the wall had come down, but New York! One heard of such violence there. Of course, when she had voiced her concerns to Preben, he had laughed and told her she had been watching too much *Cagney and Lacey* on Danish television. His firm's office was a long way outside the city, he said. And anyway, it was only for two years, three at most. By the time he returned, the bridge and tunnel project linking Fyn with Zealand would be finished, cutting the travel time between her village and Copenhagen in half.

Camilla exited the plane slowly. Hours spent sitting had left her stiff. She was a little weary – no surprise since it was late evening back in Denmark – but that would surely disappear the moment she saw her darling boy. She couldn't wait, even if there wasn't anything particular she needed to tell him. She kept him abreast of all the news in her twice-weekly letters, written on flimsy blue airmail paper – 'they are to build a shopping centre in Vissenbjerg'; 'Hette Andersen will have a new baby'. Preben's letters were less frequent, and, frankly, less informative. Boys were like that, her friends all agreed. Occasionally, he phoned. What joy to pick up the receiver and hear his voice on the other end of the line, as clear as if he were next door! But they never spoke for long. Camilla worried about the expense and the trouble it might cause Preben with his boss. Soon, she would see him. She smiled, thinking of the special treat in her carry-on bag, plucked fresh from her garden that morning.

The line at immigration was long and zig-zagging. Bedraggled people shuffled forwards in tiny steps, dragging or kicking their hand luggage. When, at last, it was Camilla's turn, she approached the desk with a smile that the man in uniform on the other side did not return.

'I am here to see my son,' she announced, in her best English, when asked the purpose of her visit. 'He has a very good job with a big American firm.'

The man grunted. He peered closely at her visa and passport, before stamping the latter so hard it made Camilla jump. It was not like in Denmark.

She proceeded to the baggage carousel. A small dog came over, a beagle. It sniffed her carry-on, wagged its tail, and sat down next to her.

'Sweet,' Camilla said, patting the dog's head, thinking of Rex, back home. She hoped the Mortensens would visit and walk him often. She didn't want Rex to be lonely.

A short, big-bosomed brown woman in a dark blue uniform approached.

'Is this your bag, ma'am?' the woman demanded, pointing to Camilla's carry-on. 'I'm going to have to ask you to come with me.'

'What took you so long?' Preben asked when, at last, Camilla walked through the gate into the arrivals hall. 'Your flight landed ages ago. Did you get lost?'

'*Min skat*,' she cried. 'They took all my strawberries!'

Danish strawberries were the sweetest, the tastiest in all the world and the ones that grew in Camilla's garden were particularly good, everybody said so. As a boy, Preben's fingers used to be stained pink each year from late May through July.

'*Mor*, you can't bring fresh fruit to America. It's not allowed.'

'Yes, yes, I know that now,' said Camilla, not meaning to speak so sharply to the son she had just flown six thousand kilometres to see. 'The lady with the dog was *very* clear about that. What do Americans have against fresh fruit?'

'It's the insects,' said Preben. 'The medfly destroyed crops in California.'

'Oh, but that was *southern* Europe!' she said, a little hurt that Preben was taking America's side in the matter. 'Danish insects will do them no harm.'

Preben closed his eyes and put a hand to his forehead, as if to check his temperature.

It was not like in Denmark. The blast of heat and humidity that hit Camilla when she left the air-conditioned airport came as a complete surprise since the sky was a shade of grey that, in Denmark, signalled cold and raw weather. She moved sluggishly, as if through water, to Preben's car, which was bigger than the one driven by Ebbe Holm, who was a managing director. Camilla had never seen such roads, not even in Germany. Six lanes in each direction, clogged with cars. Every flag-post flew an American flag, just like on television. How exciting Ken would have found this, Camilla thought, her fingers brushing her heart pendant.

The traffic thinned as they left the city. Six lanes gradually became two. Trees appeared at the roadside. Soon, they were driving through a forest. The clouds lifted and everything became very bright. After an hour, they passed a sign advertising a restaurant.

'Hungry?' Preben asked.

A waitress brought them glasses of ice water that they didn't ask for. It was too cold; it tasted funny. The laminated menu was full of pictures and went on for pages. The waitress spoke very fast. Preben said he would have the bacon double cheeseburger. Camilla, not knowing what to choose, said that she would have the same. Two enormous plates arrived.

Camilla picked up her knife and fork; Preben ate American style, with his hands. Juice dripped between his fingers; bits of salad and burger oozed out the back end of the bun.

It took two more hours to get to Preben's house. Camilla's eyelids would not stay open. Preben showed her to her room immediately. It was large, with windows on two walls. Camilla opened them wide, to let in the fresh air. She slept fitfully. Mosquitoes buzzed in her ear; they bit her. The next morning, she was covered in welts.

'America should not worry about Danish insects,' she said to Preben. 'Their own are far worse.'

'That's why the windows have screens, *Mor*.'

'But … fresh air?'

'Blows through the screens,' he exclaimed, with an exasperation that was most upsetting. This, after all, was the same person who had once caused a snail infestation when residents of his shoebox 'zoo' escaped, leaving trails of slime throughout the house.

It was not like in Denmark. The television had one hundred and thirty-six channels and nothing interesting to watch. There was not a word of Danish news, when one could read about America every day of the week in Denmark. No fresh bread, not even at breakfast. Preben toasted bagels or waffles in a small countertop oven. The houses were made of wood, like summer houses. Preben said they were perfectly warm in wintertime, but Camilla did not think this could be so and made a mental note to knit him something thick and woollen.

On the third day of her visit, Preben announced that a friend was coming to the house for dinner. Camilla offered to make Preben's favourite *frikadeller*, but Preben said not to worry.

Eric, the friend, arrived at half past six. He had a boyish face and a lovely smile, and carried a bag of groceries.

'Pleased to make your acquaintance,' Camilla said.

'Fornøjelsen er helt på min side,' Eric replied with an American twang. The pleasure is all mine.

Camilla clutched at her heart pendant.

Inside Eric's bag were the ingredients for dinner, a speciality dish from his home state of Arizona.

'Authentic southwestern food,' he said, handing her a glass of Pinot Grigio. 'Not the horrible Tex-Mex you get here.'

He took control of the kitchen, seeming to know where everything was. He instructed Preben on how to slice vegetables and mash the avocado, while keeping an eye on the pots of beans and rice, and the meat sizzling in a skillet. When satisfied that everything was cooked to his liking, he rolled it all together in a warm tortilla.

'Burrito,' he said.

Camilla leaned in close and gave it a sniff.

'The tiniest smidge of chili,' he said, 'for flavour, not heat.'

'There's ham in the fridge, if you don't like it, Mor,' Preben said.

But she did like it. In fact, she ate it all.

Eric cooked for them again and again, each time something strange and new, everything delicious. He joined them when they went to a baseball game, and on long drives to the Finger Lakes, Connecticut, and Pennsylvania. Camilla sat in the back of the car, toying with her heart pendant, watching her son's face light up whenever he looked at Eric, and Eric's grow dreamy when he turned Preben's way. They talked nonstop. If one of them told a joke, the other laughed long before they got to the punchline. When Eric wasn't around, Preben found ways to say his name, savouring the taste of it on his lips as if it were his favourite liquorice.

For the final days of Camilla's visit, they went to New York City. Eric came too, of course. They saw Rockefeller Center, and Central Park, the top of the World Trade Center – which swayed alarmingly in the wind – and the Statue of Liberty.

'I thought it would be bigger,' Camilla said and then laughed at herself because that was what the tourists said about the Little Mermaid statue in Copenhagen Harbour. Preben got tickets to Sunset Boulevard – for Eric's sake, Camilla suspected, because Camilla could just as well see it in London. The DFDS ferry went from Esbjerg to Harwich.

They rode the subway out to Coney Island and ate the famous hotdogs, which were not as good as what you got in Denmark, even Preben said so.

'Tivoli is nicer,' he told Eric.

'At the Chinese Pagoda, you can get a beef spring roll with mushroom sauce and a beer for 35 kroner,' Camilla said.

'Sounds fantastic,' said Eric.

Later, Camilla wondered whether Eric even knew what a kroner was.

Too soon, they were standing in the departure hall. Camilla prepared to say goodbye to her darling boy. The situation seemed to call for more than a standard farewell.

'I'm happy, *Min skat*,' she began, before pausing, the words catching in her throat. 'I'm happy that *you* are happy.'

'See you soon, *Mor*,' he replied.

'Yes, yes,' she said, not believing it. From behind the glass on the other side of security, she saw Preben and Eric walking away, their heads together, deep in conversation.

The overhead compartments rattled and swayed as the plane barrelled down the runway for take-off. Camilla, in seat 27A (also a window seat), feared it would break apart; instead, everything settled once the plane left the ground and began to climb. Camilla looked out the window at the New York skyline and thought of Preben and Eric, preparing for their dinner at a chic restaurant.

'My son is in love with an American,' she told the grey-haired man in the seat next to her.

The man looked up from his book. 'Congratulations,' he said, in Danish-accented English.

She nodded and fingered her pendant, thinking of Ken, the six thousand kilometres between Fyn and New York, and the grandchildren she would never have. It felt like someone had laid a slab of granite on top of her chest.

Camilla ordered a double vodka tonic from the drinks trolley. She had wine with dinner. Halfway through an after-dinner cognac, she leaned over and interrupted the grey-haired Dane's reading, once again.

'A little piece of my heart is back there, in New York,' she said, in English, despite knowing her seatmate was Danish. 'I am old and not so flexible. It will snap off, and ... and I will bleed to death.'

The man looked at her in horror. Camilla sat back in her chair and closed her eyes, exhausted. When she came to, her mouth was agape, her throat dry, in a way that suggested she could have been snoring. The cabin crew was making final preparations for landing at Kastrup. The Danish man avoided eye contact. Camilla took the opportunity to grab both armrests as she braced for what turned out to be an uneventful landing.

The officer at passport control could not have been nicer. The baggage area was free of little dogs sniffing around, looking to steal the bagels she had brought back for the Mortensens.

The sight of her little house with its white plaster walls and half-hipped roof of red tiles made her smile. Rex trotted down the hall to greet her, his round black eyes seeming to say, '*There* you are!'

Some days later, when the worst of the jetlag had passed, she invited the Mortensens for a Danish lunch. They sat outside, beneath the covered porch, drinking beer and schnapps and eating open-faced sandwiches on rye bread. Her mouth filled with the flavours of pickled herring, breaded plaice, liver paste, and *frikadeller*: the tastes of home, comfortable and safe. She had missed them these past few weeks, so it was puzzling that it should be at that exact moment, while Rex slept under the table at her feet, and a cool, afternoon drizzle fell on her prized strawberry bushes, that images of Eric's cooking came so vividly to mind — the tenderness of the marinated meats, the buttery taste of the avocado, the zestiness of the lime and fresh coriander. Next time, she thought, she would ask him to add a little more chilli.

Rip Off

I didn't exactly want to become a criminal. I didn't plan it as such - certainly not on such a scale. It was just that I always had a fondness for mechanical things, ever since I was a boy. That's what started it; I saw this old ticket machine in the window of the Sally Army shop, and it appealed to me. Normally I never went in there because my ex-girlfriend Lou, who I had a lot of respect for, said they traced missing women, which was bad. Maybe not bad if they were runaway teenagers, though even they might have had their reasons, but bad if it was someone who wanted to be missing, like to get away from a violent husband. I'd seen my dad belting my mum when he had a few in him, and I used to wish she'd take us and leave. I left once he put his fists up to me.

So, I never usually went in there, but there it was, in the window, sweet as a nut. It even had a kind of cartoon face, with two screw heads set apart like two eyes above the straight mouth slot where the ticket came out. When I went in and asked to try it on the old dear looked a bit surprised - but when she saw how it looked on me I could see she was taken with it too. It was light and comfortable, with a nice wide strap that fitted over one shoulder and across my back.

- Fits like a glove, she said. You really look the part.

And I did. I even looked in the mirror; I thought I looked a bit like Gary Numan on *Top of the Pops*. I stroked the curve of it, like an extra belly. I turned the handle on the side and out slid a ticket with a sound that made my teeth feel sweet.

I tore off the ticket and gave it to the old dear.

- That'll be fifty pence, please.

- Go on with you, she said. Old people like to have a joke; they've got time for it and they're less uptight. - More like five pounds, my love.

It was three pounds, which seemed a bit steep, but it turned out to be the best investment I'd ever make. When I got home I worked out the mechanism – pretty simple really; you just set the letters and numbers and it printed them. The serrated edge to the mouth slot allowed the printed section to be torn off neatly. Detail. Maybe it is boring – Lou always said it was – but it's all about the detail.

At first I didn't have a plan, I just wanted to try it out. Usually I wore black trousers anyway, and I had a black Harrington jacket from when I'd gone to college in Manchester. Put together, they looked quite official – not exactly a uniform, but understated and smart enough to be taken for some kind of work outfit. What I wanted was to be unnoticeable, official.

My next challenge was where. It was spring, and sunny, so I thought of the Downs and the way people parked up there to look at the view, especially along that bit nearest the Gorge. That would be a pleasant place to wander about, and I'd never seen any police or traffic wardens up there. It didn't take long to set the machine with 'Parking: Downs' and the date: '24 March 1979'. It took me longer to decide what to charge. Enough to be believable, but not so much they'd complain or argue. Thirty pence, I decided – enough to buy a book. I put on a shirt and tie under my Harrington and chose a thick plastic bag for the ticket machine. On the bus, I held the machine inside its bag on my lap. It felt precious.

Clouds were blowing across the sky as I walked across the open sweep of the Downs. I remembered walking there with Lou, how she was tall and talked louder than was necessary. She'd had brothers to compete with. I'd liked her, but she'd got cross with me for not being ambitious, and left me for some muscly bloke just back from Palestine, very right on. Anyway, there weren't many cars about up there. I felt nervous, kept messing with the bag; what if someone went and got the police? I could say it was for charity, but I knew that wouldn't wash. Labradors and spaniels were being walked by ladies with hairdos that reminded me of Margaret Thatcher. These people could afford thirty pence. The dogs ran and the ladies strolled about in a healthy, middle-class way that reeked of privilege. Unwitting privilege.

Before I approached anyone I went and read the noticeboard near the men's toilet, just to make sure there was nothing about parking on it. Then I went into a cubicle even though there was no one else in there, and got the ticket machine out. Putting it on made me feel serious, excited. Butterflies fluttered in my stomach. About half a dozen cars were parked at intervals along the road that curved along the edge of the Downs and the steep drop into the Avon Gorge below. I straightened my back and approached the first one, jangling the change I'd brought in my pocket. Detail. Smile, I told myself, but not too much – try for one of those brief, official smiles that end at the eyes. Turning my head to look out over the Gorge, I practised the smile.

The car was an ugly Austin Maxi in a nondescript green. The woman in it was nondescript too – fortyish with brown hair and a sweatshirt. She looked like somebody's mum – what was she doing here? An assignation? Assignations were probably good – she'd want to pay up and send me on my way. In an appropriately leisurely fashion, I walked up to her window and bent down. She was smoking a fag so it was open.

- Morning madam. Thirty pence for the parking, please.

She looked surprised. My heart was going a bit, so I straightened up as if I had all the time in the world, leaning back on my heels in that way that waiting officials do. I placed my hands on my ticket machine patiently.

- Oh, she said. - Hang on.

She stuck her cigarette in the corner of her mouth and leaned over to her handbag. I looked along the road. I could always run. Her hand appeared with three 10p coins in the palm. I pocketed the cash, turned the handle and tore off her ticket.

- Thank you.

She nodded and took an uninterested drag on her ciggie. Wow. It was that easy.

Out of all six cars, only one put up any resistance.

- This is new, isn't it? Charging for parking up here?

He had a posh voice. Some men like to show they know what's what.

- Council policy, I replied as if I'd said it hundreds of times before. - Thirty pence, sir, please, I repeated, just to remind him what a paltry sum it was and how petty he was being. He was sitting in a black Audi with the pink expanse of the *Financial Times* propped against the steering wheel in front of him. People who think they're clever question things, but sometimes it just makes them look like arses. Anyway, he paid up.

Strolling away, I tried to look as casual as possible. It was a buzz, even for thirty pence. I gazed down into the Gorge, watching a gull fly above the surface of the river. The thick banks of mud made me wonder what it'd be like to jump into the silk of them – but I had more to do. There were plenty more cars further along, by the wooded area where lone men nonchalantly wander off among the trees. Those sitting in their cars would probably cough up smartish, no questions asked.

They did. Morning sir. My official smile began to feel well practised. When I'd made ten pounds I went and had coffee and cake in Princess Victoria Street. It was almost too easy, but I could see there were flaws. Approximately every tenth car, someone questioned the charge.

- It used to be free on the Downs.

- I didn't know there were charges. Why haven't we been informed?

It would only take a few letters of complaint to the council or the paper for suspicions to be raised. I could keep at it for the afternoon, but it would be too risky to do more than a few days. As I was enjoying it, I went back to it. In fact, the tricky customers were almost the best; it was fun finding new ways to deflate them, developing a nice jobsworth kind of dip at the knees as I responded.

- Oh, I know, sir, you can't get anything for free any more, can you? That's the way the world's going …

Sympathy was good; who can argue with you if you agree with them? At around four o'clock I decided to call it a day. I'd made just under fifty pounds – not bad at all. As I walked past the zoo, a woman was packing her kids into an estate car near the edge of the parking area. A picnic hamper spilled over the pavement. She was leaning in, organising the kids in the back. I remember thinking she must be one of those perfect mums, taking them to the zoo, picnic and ice creams, everything organised. Nice bum, too. I stopped and picked up the hamper, handing it to her as she turned round. Maybe I was frowning, thinking about my own mother.

- Oh my God! She was flustered, wide-eyed. Quite attractive in that posh, groomed sort of way, like a pony; bouncy, shiny haired, a lot of teeth in her smile. I still had the ticket machine on; I'd got used to it. - Should I have paid? I'm so sorry! She smiled apologetically, shoving the hamper into the back and grappling with her shoulder bag. - How much?

- No problem, madam. I didn't see you earlier; have you been here all day?

- Sorry – I didn't realise. I wasn't avoiding …

I nodded, all understanding and calm.

- That'll be one pound then, please.

As she drove off, I cast a calculating eye over the parking area. It was quiet, maybe only fifty cars or so scattered over the large grassy area in front of the zoo. Most people were leaving. I doubled my day's takings. There was room for a lot more cars. I went home and thought it through, and the next day went and got BCC embroidered on my jacket – Bristol City Council, maybe … My name would be Bob. I introduced myself at the zoo's ticket office once the morning rush was over.

- Hello – Bob Numan – parking attendant. Nice to meet you. There's been some concern about the levels of crime up here. Apparently there's been a few break-ins; bags left on seats, broken quarter-lights, that kind of thing. I'll be here from now on to keep an eye on things.

I was careful not to actually claim I was from the council; I was straightforward and workmanlike. The woman in the kiosk liked me, I could tell, but I was careful not to be too friendly.

- I'd better get on, then. But if anyone reports any further problems, refer them to me, all right love?

After a couple of days I got a camp chair. In the summer I made a sign and sat under the shade of an oak when I wasn't collecting. One pound for cars and five pounds for coaches. Everyone seemed happy, and the vehicles were safe so no one complained. I made over three hundred pounds most days. When winter came I invested in a wooden hut and a heater, reading books when it was quiet and thinking what I could do with the money. Obviously I couldn't pay tax. The seasons came and went, and sometimes I wondered how long I could go on without getting found out. I lived quietly, putting the cash into different banks then shifting it into investments. After a few years I got a Swiss bank account. Sitting in my hut all winter, I read travel books about Peru, Cuba, Madagascar, Tibet, and sometimes the *Financial Times*.

For almost thirty years I sat there, always polite, keeping myself to myself. I was known for it. Well, I didn't want to give any cause for complaint, did I? It probably made me a different person, living with the knowledge I could be caught. Of course it affected me. I couldn't have a girlfriend; women ask too many questions. Close friends were too risky. I never got blasé. Shady, under that tree. Every day I changed the date on the ticket machine – until, after a few years, I got an electronic machine that was smaller, lighter – but I missed the beauty of the old one.

On the news it said that when I left, the zoo rang up the council requesting a replacement parking attendant.

- What attendant? they asked.

Apparently, I had over three million quid.

That's My Boy

GAVIN JAMES BOWER

Driving back from the funeral and missing my father so much I had to swerve to avoid a car in the outside lane, forcing myself to listen to *Thin Lizzy Greatest Hits* – that, a set of dumb-bell weights and an old but well-maintained vacuum cleaner the haul from his now-empty two-up two-down – and choking on tears and memories of how, as a child, I would say 'taking over' when I meant overtaking, my father laughing at the mistake, the way fathers from where I come from do, gently chiding sons into shape.

'*That's* my boy,' Dad would say, tongue literally in cheek as he reminded me how his father, too, had told him if he ever pulled on the blue-and-white stripes of Sheffield Wednesday, their team although not mine, he would watch from the terraces, Hillsborough's Spion Kop, and announce to no one in particular, '*That's* my boy.'

'I'm clever at school,' I would say, defensive, even then not much liking being on the wrong end of a piss-take. This, of course, just made things worse. 'Do you want a *jink*?' Dad would say. 'We could go on a bike ride, or is your bike *too heavy*?' No speech impediment, no lisp or stutter or problem with my r's, though I inexplicably failed to pronounce the *dr* in the word *drink* for years – and when I say years I mean years, the aberration eventually teased out of me, but not before I started secondary school.

The incident with the bike ride involved a traumatic hill climb, the mountain stage of the Tour de Burnley, fairly steep and fairly constant, on a brand new mountain bike boasting, if I remember right, front suspension. Like my own, admittedly replica, Sheffield Wednesday shirt this bike, understandably given my age, 13 at the time, was two sizes too big. In the retelling, the machine manufactured itself a lead frame and wheels of granite, too much even for the racing hero of my childhood, the perpetually yellow-shirted Miguel Indurain. Cycling up that hill I complained out loud, mid-pedal, that the bike was too heavy for me, wind in my face and tears mixed with screaming shame as my father and older brother, reaching the summit, looked back at me and laughed.

A 20-pence piece on my desk as I write this, from the year 1982, the year of my birth; my father kept one on a chest of drawers in his bedroom, another coin, copper I think, with the year of my brother's birth; and another with the year of his marriage to my mother; and more, for all I know, spent now the house has been sold and the chest of drawers gone, a coin for every sentimentally-charged year of his life. I am haunted by misleading memories of my father, memories and gaps in memories and the 32 years of my life with him in it to remember and reconcile this ghost, this sketch of a man, with something resembling the truth. I have coins on a chest of drawers and bike rides and the soundtracks of car journeys – Thin Lizzy and Status Quo and Eric Clapton and Dire Straits and Chris Rea and Joe Cocker and the Beatles – but not my father to chide me into remembering and getting it right.

My father died a few months before my daughter was born, his first and only grandchild, and a few months after that I started a new job, a new career, as a lecturer. He knew I was applying for work outside London, where I had lived for 10 years, spending money like it was going out of fashion, most of it my own but some, from time to time, his – a deposit for a new rented flat here and there, the odd 20-pound note thrown in now and then. He prided himself on occupying a position of financial strength until his death turned the tables, but more than that his presence offered security now absent. Between the chiding and the piss-taking, in moments of sober clarity that were more frequent towards the end of his life than when he was still married to my mother, when I was no longer a child but a grown-up son, he repeatedly and rather grandly pronounced teaching would suit me, bemoaning my path into publishing via a series of what he called 'Mickey Mouse' jobs. He, too, had worked his fair share, a favourite of his bitterly recalled whenever we would drive into Manchester, a city inferior in every way to his beloved Sheffield – a 'shithole', 'all top show' and 'fur coat, no knickers' – and pass a warehouse where for a short time he sold plastic bags of elastic bands and pins and tacks and the kind of nonsense you ignore in aisles of newsagents, removable plastic strips impermanent on not-quite shelves. For a while, between well-paid work for a 'piss-head' who ruined his own father's firm and finding a steady gig selling cars, my father had a succession of these 'shite' jobs. He even sold incontinence pads, though, sitting here now smiling at the thought, I might be making that up. He enjoyed mixing stories of his woes with those of friends, one, a salesman himself, who told him at the tail end of a particularly lengthy session: 'If I don't sell, I don't eat.' This sort of thing really did it for my father.

He would order copies of my books in shops and make his friends buy them off him at full price, as much a sign of pride as his own usefulness. He was, I know, proud of me; though in the months after his death I would question this truth, uncertain, memories of his chiding me and those coins he kept on the chest of drawers and the photos of me from my short-lived modelling career, this not a source of ridicule but in his sitting room, where everyone could see; and his saying how teaching would suit me and the letter he gave me the night before I got married spelling it out, a letter I have since lost but that ended with his best advice – 'Don't fuck it up!' – and my daughter now one and a half and me, still teaching, not just people to write but only the other day to swim, holding her tiny body afloat and remembering how I, too, would climb my father's broad back and hold on like life, all of life, depended on it.

Fair Italy

CELIA BRAYFIELD

... and now, fair Italy!
Thou art the garden of the world, the home
Of all Art yields, and Nature can decree:
Even in thy desert, what is like to thee?
Thy very weeds are beautiful, thy waste
More rich than other climes' fertility;
Thy wreck a glory; and thy ruin graced
With an immaculate charm which cannot be defaced.
— Lord Byron, *Childe Harold's Pilgrimage*, 1818

The sun rose behind the mountain and golden light flooded into the valley, casting hazy shadows under the olive trees, glistening on the roof tiles of the village. A line of white birds flew northward from the distant lake. When the sunlight reached the grey crag that rose above the myrtle scrub on the far side of the valley, it would be 11 o'clock. Not that there was a timetable. James sighed, feeling free and content. Perhaps Keats travelled down this very valley on his way to Rome. Perhaps he passed the ruined tower that crowned the perfectly mounded hill that overlooked the road, with a line of pines stretching along the ridge beside it. The pines planted by the Romans. The tower built by

57

the papal guards to defend the province against the Florentines. Keats, who died at 24. He was thirty years older than Keats already.

The monastery bell rang the hour and the notes floated down the hillside. A swallow flew over the swimming pool, perched on the infinity ledge and splashed water on its wings. James wondered about a monograph, a conference, an exhibition, *The Grand Tour Revisited*, long hours with archivists in Florence, a research grant, thousands of euros, hundreds of thousands even.

No, no. That would never happen, not now. Dollars, rupees, yen, that was the future.

But this was a holiday. James turned over and saw Kristina, his new partner, and Molly, his daughter, placed like a living Hockney with the blue of the pool in the background, the space between them almost vibrating with tension. They were so aware of each other. But amicable. Perhaps, after all the 'Fine', and the 'Of course, no problem', and the silences and the averted eyes, they would make a family after all, one of those enviable, modern, reconstituted unions of people who shared values, time and property instead of just genetic material.

They bowed their heads over their screens. Kristina was sending emails, her lovely, tapered fingertips swiping rapidly. Molly was doing something appropriate for a ten-year-old. Earphones on, head nodding unrhythmically. James picked up his book and let the measured wisdom of Sir Harold Acton soothe his anxiety.

In her office, where the blinds were lowered to keep out the glare, Philippa made a call to the water company. How were they? This ugly weather. Would this heatwave ever end? The clients were taking three showers a day. You could almost see the swimming pool evaporate before your eyes. This summer was a disaster. First the referendum, then the pound was worth nothing, and now this. Yes, yes, Italy should learn, no good can come of a referendum. Yes, yes. She could wait until Friday for the next delivery. Thank you, thank you, thank you so much. She ended the call. At least somebody was making money. Was there a leak by the pool pump? A ripe fig fell off the tree and hit the terrace with a plop. Must remember to get rid of it before the wasps descended.

'Darling, would you?' On the opposite side of the pool, Hetty held out a bottle of tanning lotion towards her husband, who put down his copy of the *Financial Times* and smoothed the stuff over his wife's freckled shoulders, proud that he still felt tenderness for this silly, twittering creature whose flesh puffed like pizza edging either side of her swimsuit straps.

'What is that child doing? Is she playing a game? She hasn't looked up from that thing all morning.'

'Nor has his wife.'

'She's not his wife.'

'She'll have to go home, I suppose. What is she? Slovenian?'

'Slovenian, Slovakian. They'll all being going home soon.'

'He should get rid of her now, before the child gets attached. Plenty of work at home for them. Isn't she some sort of doctor?'

'Bio-medical science. Whatever that might be.' He squeezed her upper arms gently, a warning. 'Sound travels over water, darling.'

'Why don't we go to Calegrano's for dinner?'

'It's a long way.'

'I know it's a long way but I do so hate being here with them and having to listen to them and him going on about bloody paintings, trying to show off. That poor child must be bored rigid. There's an atmosphere, darling. Surely even you can feel it?'

'But why should we be the ones to make arrangements? We're civilised people. We may dislike ...'

'Dislike? He's a traitor. And besides, they hate us just as much as we hate them.'

He said nothing, hoping the conversation would expire. She rolled around to face him. 'Go on, darling. I'll drive. Do you want me to do your back? Can't have you looking like a lobster all holiday.'

On the terrace below some wasps, heavy with the juice of the fig, got into the air and blundered upwards, making for their nest in the olive grove.

Philippa pleaded with the plumber. 'This afternoon? Before you go to the other job. I'm going crazy, losing water here. It's a thousand euros every delivery. I can't afford to lose water.'

Molly took off her headphones and felt her ears were sweaty, so she put down her iPad and jumped into the pool. Kristina, eager to be friends with her lover's only child, tapped Send in a hurry and followed her, her long, pale quadriceps slicing the water without a splash. She moderated her stroke to keep pace with the child and Molly, seeing an adult eager to have her approval, felt content and smiled into the dazzling light.

At the shallow end, Kristina found a wasp struggling on the water's surface and scooped it out on to the grass. James said, 'Careful. Somebody might tread on it.' But Molly caught her eye and smiled. And then they swam some lengths side-by-side, two pliant forms in dark sports swimsuits.

On the lower terrace, Philippa scraped up the fig pulp and dropped it in the compost bucket. The secret of her marvellous roses, still billowing pink and white all around the gardens in spite of the brutal summer heat, was the compost. 'English Country House Holidays in Italy.' And an English country house must have roses.

With her husband's back anointed, Hetty rolled back on her sun lounger and pulled her Panama hat over her eyes to keep out the glare. She heard a wasp cruising above her and flapped it away.

'Live and let live,' she heard him say. 'They're coming for the fruit at this time of year.'

'Well I wish they'd get on with the fruit and leave me alone.'

She sat up again and immediately felt something in her thigh. Not quite a burn, not quite a prick. 'Oh damn, it's stung me.'

They thought of themselves as outdoor people, veterans of shooting parties and race meetings, supporters of the farming community even if he had been in the oil business, owners of working breeds even if their dogs were pets, unfazed by rain, mud, gales or insects. And one did not complain. Making a fuss was for other people so her husband said, 'Oh, bad luck.' And Hetty bit down on a whimper.

The burning sensation was stronger. She got up and, with short, annoyed paces, walked to the shallow end and splashed her leg with water.

'That looks bad,' said Kristina, seeing the patch of red flesh as she got out of the pool. 'It must be really painful. Maybe I can get you some ice from our apartment?'

'It's only a sting. It'll wear off in a minute.' Not a good idea to be grateful to a foreigner. But her whole leg was throbbing.

'Maybe it's an allergy.'

'We are not allergic in our family.'

Molly caught the note of determination in Kristina's voice and picked up her iPad. In any case, she was stuck at a really annoying level in her game so she decided to Google 'wasp sting'. 'Water,' she said. 'Calamine lotion. Ibuprofen – I'm sure we've got some of that.'

'I can get it. Let me ...' But Kristina saw James frown, which puzzled her.

'Please ...' Hetty felt dizzy and sat down abruptly on the edge of the pool. At this point, her husband put aside his newspaper. He saw his wife with her hand at her throat, gasping, swallowing, scratching her arms. Most unlike her.

Molly read on. Allergic reaction. Severe allergic reaction. Itching, swelling, dizziness. Immediate medical treatment. 'Daddy?'

Her father had turned away, as if he was embarrassed. She went around him and held the device above his book. 'Daddy, look. It says ...'

'Don't be silly, Molly. She's been stung, that's all. It's bound to wear off. You can go and get the After Bite if you want to be helpful.'

'But it says "immediate".'

'Don't make a scene, Molly.'

'I'm not. I'm not.' It was so easy for brave princesses. All they had to do was widen their eyes and toss their hair and people believed them.

But Kristina was putting on her jeans, struggling to get the garment over her damp skin. 'James, she's right. I know this, it is the allergic response. This can be serious. She must go to hospital now. She has half an hour before she can't breathe. I can drive her if someone can tell me where.'

'But, surely ...' James stood up, intending to explain that there was no need to over-react, and Hetty's husband lumbered over from the far end of the pool, intending to calm the situation, but when they saw Hetty herself, now scarlet from the neck upwards and barely able to croak through her swelling throat, the men hesitated.

Philippa came on to the pool terrace, calculating that she would have an hour of peace before the plumber came, while the guests went back to their apartments to dine on *insalata Cosa Nostra* and ask each other why the same foods eaten at home in England were not nearly so delicious. She took in the anxious child, the two uncertain males, the stricken Hetty and Kristina's expression of determination. 'What's happening?'

'My wife has been stung by a wasp. I'm sure ...'

'No, excuse me please.' Kristina was wriggling into her shoes, left foot, right foot. 'I know this situation. This lady is having a shock reaction and we must go to hospital with her.'

'Surely ...' Philippa saw her hour of hard-earned sybarism endangered.

'It says it here.' And Molly held out her iPad, the symbol of ultimate authority.

'I've got some arnica.'

Hetty's husband, feeling his wife's terror almost as if it was his own, summoned up the necessary courage. 'I'm most awfully afraid, Philippa – well, I think – better safe than sorry. No need for you to do anything. I'm sure we'll be able to find the hospital when we pick up the satnav signal at the bottom of the hill.'

'Can you phone the emergency room for us?' Kristina now had the car keys in one hand and was handing a towel to Hetty with the other.

'She needs to put some clothes on, doesn't she?' Now Philippa felt the cold shadow of TripAdvisor creeping over her sparkling swimming pool and her rose-covered pergolas.

'No time, no time. It's emergency.' And Kristina swept the towel around Hetty's shoulders, her husband found her sandals and the trio fled to the car.

Molly, not daring to ask if she could go too, ran up the driveway and opened the gate for them and shooed back Philippa's Labrador as she closed it. The noise of the engine and the skidding tyres gradually faded as the vehicle hurtled down the *strada bianca*, puffs of dust rising through the trees.

Five hours later, at the time normally marked by the soft noise of people uncorking Prosecco, Kristina and Hetty's husband returned, he to collect clothes for his wife before returning to the hospital, she to find James making supper. There was a petulant edge to his movements and Molly had retreated to her bedroom.

'I was hoping to see the Piero della Francesca *Resurrection*,' was all he said as he put the food on the table. 'It's a very moving work. You would like it.'

'We can go tomorrow.' Kristina distributed forks, spoons, napkins.

'I suppose we can.'

She was puzzled. Had she shown too much cleverness, made him feel stupid? The three of them ate in silence, Molly making big eyes of warning at her. So afterwards she let him sit out on the terrace with the whisky, and remembered her mother looking doubtful and saying, 'If a man is divorced so soon, there must be a reason.' There was nothing in England for her now, in any case. If she did her doctorate in Germany it wouldn't be so bad. The thesis would still be in English.

James watched the stars over the Tiber valley and a profound grief took hold of him. His life was nothing. His scholarship, the glittering hoard of knowledge he had gathered over the decades, the jewels of insight and the precious nuggets of research, was worthless now. Painting, sculpture, writing, none of them had any currency. The new world despised beauty, ridiculed knowledge, denied memory. The wisdom of centuries just thrown away. He had no place here.

In the morning Hetty and her husband returned. Once his wife was settled in the shade and resting, he marched up to the pool terrace to do his duty, find Kristina and take her slender white hand firmly in his sun-speckled paw, saying, 'My dear. I have to thank you. You have saved my poor wife's life. Very much appreciated. We are in your debt.' Which left James standing stiffly, not knowing what to say, because the wrongness of the whole affair overwhelmed him. Such debts could not be contracted between opposing sides. A tiny voice suggested that if the stupid woman had died there would be one less Brexiter in the world. He suppressed it but the thought shocked him. Was he no better than them, after all?

Molly felt sad, as she often did. When a brave princess saved someone's life there was feasting and merriment and comedy animals being funny. Her mother was rather against princess stories.

In the afternoon, the Canadians appeared, newly arrived from Rome and complaining about the roads. 'But we are so looking forward to meeting some English people and hearing all about your Brexit,' the wife said.

'Yes, well.' Hetty's husband felt he should say something but his words only made the silence louder.

The Canadian husband searched his stock of cultural references for a more successful gambit. 'Do you have much Mafia activity here?' He pronounced it Mahfiah.

Philippa, watering the geraniums in their Tuscan pots, said, 'They're a southern thing really. Naples. Sicily.'

'How far is Naples?'

'About four hours' drive.'

'Quite close, then.'

Hetty's husband went to see if his wife needed anything. James decided that it might be to his last opportunity to visit Piero della Francesca's *Resurrection*. He could explain to his daughter that once the story had meant something.

As the sunlight took on the honeyed glow of the early evening and the clouds above the distant mountains darkened, the Canadians felt a chill, picked up their towels and went back to their apartment, wondering if they were imagining it or if autumn came earlier in Europe.

Singing Under a Monsoon Sky

JESS BUTTERWORTH

The bulldozers arrive on a Wednesday. I've stopped at the edge of the forest with Vijay on the way home from school. We sit on giant boulders kicking our legs back and forth. I'm supposed to be in music practice.

'Miss Dhasmana didn't have to send me home,' I say.

Vijay shrugs. 'She was angry you forgot your flute again.'

Grandma gave me her wooden flute for my eighth birthday. I open and clench my fist, remembering the way it fits perfectly in my grip. Usually I carry it everywhere but recently, with Dad working away from home, I've been forgetting things.

I gaze through the trees at low clouds covering the Himalayas, secretly pleased I have an hour before I'm due home to help with cooking.

'Want to play sprint?' I ask.

He nods, leaps off the boulder and dashes into the trees.

I jump down and straighten, ready to chase after him.

It's then the air shakes with the roar of engines. I recognise the sound instantly from the construction sites Mum worked on when we were younger. But there's no planned construction going on near us. I know, because someone from home would be working there.

My heart sinks.

65

Rumours spread in the past week. Whispers from traders and teachers that people wanted us gone so they could build hotels on the land. But I never thought they were real. How *could* they be true?

Shouts come next. Screams fill the air and even through the merging of voices I can pick out my sister Ruchi's, and Mum's.

Someone would have warned us first, wouldn't they?

Vijay glances at me, his eyes wide, head tilted, listening.

'Quickly,' he says and beckons me towards home.

We run, propelling ourselves forward. I skid on the slippery path through the trees before we reach the rice paddies. I take the shortcut and leap over ditches. Vijay's jumper is tucked into his backpack. It flies out and lies on the ground. We don't stop.

I reach the road and dash straight across, dodging a cow lying in the verge, over to the bridge and our home beyond it. My bag bumps against my leg. A car horn beeps after us. My breaths are short and quick as the bulldozer engines get louder.

The stream below us becomes a raging river at this time of year. Concrete tower blocks line the other side of the bank. On this side is our small piece of land. Tents spread across it. The fires are lit for cooking and colourful clothes hang on lines to dry. Homemade jewellery stands are propped close to the road. I smell wood smoke and cooking lentils tainted with petrol fumes.

Three bulldozers plough through our homes, crumpling the tents. I press my hand against my mouth. Behind them everything is flattened. They leave a lake of debris: ripped tarpaulin, snapped frames and crushed pots and pans. They churn the earth up and coat everything in mud.

People dash around us, passing belongings to each other, chucking cooking pots and clothes out of their tents and ushering children out of the way. My tent stands in the corner furthest away. There's no one near it.

'There's my dad,' says Vijay.

'Go,' I say. He nods and dashes towards him.

'Mum!' I shout, spinning around and looking for my sister and her. 'Ruchi!'

I spot Mum helping Bela's grandma to the road. The old woman trips and I rush to them. Mum and I kneel next to her, take an arm each, and gently lift her up, urging her onwards. Gravel and stones coat her palm. There's no time to stop and brush them off.

'You're here,' says Mum, turning to meet my eyes.

The bulldozers plough forwards, closer and closer to our tent.

We rest Bela's grandma at the side of the road with the elderly and the younger children.

'Stay with her,' says Mum firmly, before turning and running back into the crowd.

I hesitate. I have to keep helping.

'I'll be fine,' says Bela's grandma, shaking my hand away. 'Go.'

I hug her quickly and follow Mum.

Half of our homes have disappeared now. Anger strikes through my chest. I storm up to the bulldozer at the front.

'Stop!' I shout and stand with my hands on my hips.

The bulldozer hasn't reached my tent yet. I've lived there all my life. No one is going to take that away from me.

I stare at the yellow machine and the person behind it. They're not the eyes I expected to stare back. I recognise them from town. He doesn't look mean or angry. I plead back at him with my own.

I feel a squeeze on my shoulder. Vijay's by my side.

'Stop!' he shouts, over and over again, and punches his arm into the air. My heart thuds.

More people join us until we're a crowd, blocking their way.

'Riya!' Mum grabs my hand tightly and yanks me back from the front of the crowd.

For a second I think it's working. The man switches his engine off and I cheer. We all cheer.

But then the police arrive.

And I know they're not coming to help us.

There are three times more of them than us. They push us backwards to the roadside and quickly form a perimeter of men and tape. The engines start up again.

What did we do wrong?

Mum's lived here for forty years.

The policeman looks over the top of me. I only reach up to his chest.

We didn't have any time to prepare, to gather our belongings.

My flute.

I lunge to the side and duck under the tape.

A policeman grasps my collar and I wriggle free, dodging his snatches.

I reach our tent and dive inside. My eyes dart back and forth until I spot my flute lying in the crack between my bed and Ruchi's. I grab it, along with Ruchi's school bag and a bundle of clothes.

'Be quick, Riya,' shouts Vijay from outside.

There are only a few tents left now. Metal scrapes over rock. I dash back to Mum, Ruchi and everyone else. The sky is dark and stormy.

Monsoon rains pour. There's nowhere to shelter and we huddle together as the raindrops pour down our faces. If we lived any higher up the mountain, everything would be damp all of the time, any lower down and the heat would be unbearable. This is the perfect place.

After it's over, Mum and a few people pick through the debris. The colours run in the rain. I can't bring myself to do it. Everything from my whole twelve years is gone in an instant. Even the bright pink bougainvillea flowers have been trampled. Their petals dot the ground.

'Where do we go now?' asks Ruchi.

I squeeze her hand. 'I don't know.'

'Can you play?' she asks, pointing to the flute and resting her head on my shoulder. 'Not now, I need to think.' I wonder how we'll tell Dad.

'Please play,' says Vijay, and everyone around him nods in agreement.

I lift the flute and blow across the top of it, playing the tune Mum used to sing to me before bed. The notes ring out into the clouds.

A few people join in, humming and singing along, while others pick through the mess of broken tents, gathering anything they can salvage. All that's left is to rebuild and start again.

The clouds hang lower and lower until we're inside the damp air. This will always be the land where we stood together, singing under the monsoon sky.

from *Storm-Wake*

LUCY CHRISTOPHER

To Moss, storms always had a smell. Churned-up saltwater and seaweed, the damp wood on the tide, even the far-off sulphur of lightning … but this storm had something else, too. It was sweeter. *Wilder*. Moss pushed her hair sideways and looked up at the cliffs. Tiny pieces of colour were everywhere, as if the rocks held gemstones. The colours danced on the wind.

Her hair flew back in front of her face, tangling in a hundred different sailor's knots. But she'd seen right.

Stormflowers.

Opening.

Again, she shoved her hair clear to see where the flowers grew thickest, all around Pa's cave. Wind was pulling at their petals, rattling their stems. The storm's sweetness was *this*. There were pink ones, white, others gold – petals floated from the rocks to settle on her shoulders. They'd never opened like this before. She heard a high-pitched sound, too. Pa had always said that the flowers would sing. When they wanted to. When they were ready.

She tried to see Pa at the cave entrance. Now she knew why he wasn't down on the beach with her, exploring for Wash-up. Pa was doing this. Somehow – finally – he'd opened the flowers.

She dropped the collecting-pot and ran. Fast, fast, faster, leaping the sharp stones on that part of the beach. Quick, quicker, she skidded through their camp and took the well-used path up to the cave. She was huff-puffing before she'd got halfway. As she spread her arms, so that she was almost touching the wild-moving pine trees, she was imagining how, later, beside the campfire, Pa would dance and sing and swirl her. Would tell stories, 'til the fire went low, of the world where they had come from, of where they would go back to, also, one day. His smile would be wide beneath his bird-beak nose, his blue-grey eyes soft.

Now, she felt lighter. Now, she ran faster. She went quick-spinning and leaping beneath those petals, all swirling and falling. Until, flinching, she saw the sky smash.

'Lightning,' she whispered, savouring the word like a treasure. 'Sky's on fire.'

Was what Pa would say. She spread her arms wider until her wrists brushed the pine needles and felt their cool zing.

Sky's!

    On!

       Fire!

She loved Pa's sayings and how his voice tilted when he spoke them; she liked to test how they felt in her mouth. A bigger, second flash came, but she didn't cower, didn't lie flat on the ground like Pa had taught her and wait for it to pass. She stood still, feeling the wind claw, smelling the petals, hearing the sea churn above the reef. And, still, that singing – that high-pitched, beautiful singing! From beyond the volcano at the top of the island, she thought she heard the wild dogs howl in answer. Perhaps the lizards even hissed in their caves, too. Today it felt like everything on the island made noise.

At Pa's cave, the heavy cloth across the door was half pulled back. Inside, the wind was not so vicious. When Pa turned, his teeth caught the light from the candles and glinted like the petals did. He held out his arms and she ran for them.

'How did you make them open, Pa?'

He smiled wider. 'Luck? Timing?'

When she breathed in, she caught smoke and earth, those smells always stored in Pa's coverings no matter how hard Pa washed at them. She crouched to Jess too, and breathed in her smell of running and rabbits. The dog licked her ear. Soon, Pa took Moss's hand and pulled her to the table to see the glass vase. She reached to touch it, thinking, as always, how special it was that something so big and fragile had survived their rough journey across the sea. Underneath its lid, a mixture swirled.

'Opened petals?' she asked. 'All crushed up?'

Pa nodded. 'I mixed them with saltwater and sand. I told them dreams and stories! When they'd had enough, they opened.'

She frowned to understand. Then she repeated the words he'd told her, when he'd been crouched close to the fire one night, 'Island feeds on stories'.

She'd read those words in his Scrapbook, too.

'Clever Moss-bird.' He tapped her on the nose. 'I found those buds again – the ones on the volcano. I sang for them. Perhaps I got the song right; perhaps they were ready to work.'

He hummed for Moss. It sounded more like a bird's song than the rowdy-loud sailing songs Pa sang beside the fire after palm wine. Two notes, up and down, getting faster and higher in pitch until it was like a finch trill.

'You knew the tune?'

'I dreamt it up. Finally, it came right.'

Pa put the flowers he'd picked on the table, in a line. She'd never seen a stormflower open fully. Before, when the island had storms, the flowers had only opened halfway, and she and Pa had peered inside the closed-in petals to see their yellow hearts. Now, their centres shone, and their petals glinted lively-bright as fish scales.

'When the flowers opened,' Pa continued, 'I knew a storm would follow. Like the old story said. Now, we can send these flowers back to the rest of the world. Will you help?'

'Heal the floods,' Moss murmured, repeating more of Pa's words.

'Fix the darkness.'

Gently, Pa picked up one of the smallest, most orange, flowers and held it out for her. Glow-bright, it was.

'The pollen,' Pa explained, '... making it glint.'

But she knew that; Pa had told her a thousand times.

Healing pollen.

Magic pollen.

Pollen to change the world. To make them famous.

To heal Pa, too.

When she breathed in, the pollen's sweet smell rushed inside her and tickled the back of her throat. Still, though, Pa's hands shook.

'Try it now,' Moss said. 'Eat it! See if it does anything!'

He ruffled her hair, got his fingers caught in it. Carefully, he took the flower between finger and thumb. Snapping the flower's head from the stem, he put it inside his mouth. His eyes widened as he chewed.

Moss squinted as she watched him, waited for his Adam's apple to bob down his swallow. Did Pa look any different? Could one flower make him better? How many flowers would it take to make the rest of the world better, too?

Pa laughed at her expression. 'Do you want to try?'

She took a pink flower. Closer up, its smell was sweeter than the honeycomb she fetched from the hives. It wriggled in her fingers and felt almost … alive. There was a sound like giggling. Was it coming from the flower?

'We can't eat something that laughs!' she said.

Pa's eyes went crinkle-kind. 'Sing to it. Let it know you mean good.'

She copied him – those two bird-trill notes – moving her mouth in the same way he did. Jess barked at the sound. And the flower went still in her hand, almost as if it were listening. She turned it this way and that, seeing its million shades of pink.

'It's too beautiful,' she said. 'It giggled!'

'So? You giggle too! Sometimes you do. What seven-year-old wouldn't when I do *this* …' He reached forward to tickle her ribs and she squirmed away, giggling louder than the flower had. The flower trilled again. She wanted to spin and spin with the whooshing feeling inside, dance with that flower.

When she opened her palm and looked back at the flower proper, it seemed to buzz on her palm. Something felt different inside as she watched it, like her pulse beating faster and stronger.

'You're so full of stories and dreaming,' Pa said. 'The flower loves it, it gets energy!'

She laughed again. And the flower moved. It rushed from her hand towards her. Her mouth opened wider with the shock of seeing it, and it dived straight in. There was an explosion of sweetness on her tongue.

'See?' Pa said. 'It wants to be closer to your stories inside.'

It made her mouth tingle. Made her want to laugh and laugh and spin and swirl. Made her want to sit beside the fire and tell stories with Pa, read from his book. Draw pictures with sticks; dance in spirals. Pa had been right: these flowers were full-magic. Now, she felt full-magic too

Pa tipped dirty rock-pool water from a scallop shell on to the table. 'Watch this, Moss-bird.'

The flowers rushed towards the water, their petals darkening as they took in the brown liquid.

'They drink it?' Moss felt her eyes widen.

She understood then – why he believed in the flowers. 'They will make the waters go down.'

He looked at her slowly. Nodded. 'Send the darkness away.'

He laughed, his noise so like a startled bird that Moss jumped. She felt the zing of petals against her cheeks. A sway inside her. Had the flower changed her, too? Healed her of something she didn't even know she had?

'But what do I know about flowers like this?' Pa continued. 'What does anyone? A new species, Moss … a new chance. And we're the explorers!'

There was hope in his eyes, and happiness. She dug her fingertips into Jess's neck fur, steadying herself. The flower did not have an unpleasant taste, but it was strong. It made her want to shut her eyes and do nothing but dream. When a gust of wind tried to pull petals from the table, Pa caught them quickly.

'If I can get this mixture right, maybe we'll heal the world without even leaving the island.' There was a glint in Pa's eye, as if a piece of pollen were caught there. 'If I can send it back on those storm winds …' He picked up the vase and tilted it. Inside, the mixture glinted and buzzed like a million fireflies pressed tight. 'Perhaps the person who first discovered poppies or willow bark felt like this once. We could be on the brink of something that could change … everything!'

'How will you know if it's working?'

Pa looked towards the cave's mouth, to where, when the cloth flapped back with the wind, Moss could see the sea swirling and storm clouds coming quicker.

Pa shrugged. 'We'd need a sign.'

'Maybe we'll see the other land – that will be the first thing.'

'You remember it?' Pa ruffled her curls again.

Moss frowned to remember that other island, smaller than theirs, so far away on the horizon-line. The memory of that place was hardly there; instead, it was more like a half-remembered dream.

'When did that island disappear again?' she asked.

Pa smiled. 'Long time ago. When the waters rose to cover it. Maybe …' He was thinking hard. '… maybe only when that land comes back will we know that it's safe to return to the rest of the world.'

Pa took the lid from the vase, and such sweetness came into the air that, instantly, Moss smiled again.

Pa put his hand out to steady her. 'Easy, my bird.'

His hand was warmer than before. He squeezed her shoulder before picking up more flowers from the table. He crushed them and dropped them into the swirling mixture, which turned a deeper shade of orange. He licked his fingers, not wasting a driblet of the flower juice, then spat into the vase. The mixture swirled harder.

'What now?' Moss asked.

But she knew. Hadn't Pa told her enough times as they sat around the fire? Hadn't she read it in his book? Now he'd push this mixture out. He'd send *healing* air back. But would anything change? She licked her lips and tasted the sweetness lingering. *That* was different already.

Pa carried the vase to the cave entrance. Beyond the cloth, the wind was racing-fierce, dragging Moss's hair over her eyes again. Pa pointed the vase opening towards where the storm clouds hovered, his clothing flapping in the wind.

'Change,' Pa whispered to it.

They watched the mixture swirl up out of the vase and hang in the air as a bright puff. It hummed and fizzed. Moss's eyes watered. She wanted to stick her tongue out to taste the air and keep it with her. But she also wanted to help Pa send it away. If that air went back to the Old World, the floods would go down. As she thought it, the orange mixture swirled and dived, moved towards the storm clouds.

'Take it,' Pa said. 'Heal the world with your pollen!'

And Moss felt a buzzing, bright, firefly spark inside her as the petal-air moved across the sea.

Fog

STEPHEN CONNOLLY

The fog had blighted the city for decades. It filled the streets, it invaded shops and houses. It slipped into theatres and halted the plays.

Worst of all the fog obscured the city from the first floor upwards: centuries of beautiful architecture invisible even at the height of summer.

Many blamed the fog on pollution from too many cars, more blamed the city's factories, others Global Warming and everybody blamed the government for doing nothing about it.

Unable to prevent the fog, the City Tourism Board learned to accommodate it, hiring guides to describe the city's invisible architecture to tourists. But this system had its own drawbacks. Most of the guides were students who spent so much time in the city's many bars that on some mornings they were in no fit state to describe anything to anybody. Also, they knew little more about the city's architecture than the tourists, so mistakes were frequent.

One August morning, a hungover student by the name of Carl stood beneath the city's late Renaissance Town Hall, his mind blank as to what he was supposed to be describing. He looked from the fog above to his clients – a flock of dull farmers – and back again.

Then he remembered a documentary he'd seen on TV, and having no other option, described to the tourists the Great Pyramid rising out of sight above their heads. The tourists were so impressed that as the tour continued,

Carl added other architectural wonders whenever he forgot what was actually above them.

Counting his tips at the end of the day, Carl realised he was on to something. That night, instead of carousing, he visited the university library for the first time in months for some serious research. Next day, faced with an even duller group of tourists, he ignored the official guidebook altogether and populated the heights of the city with the Seven Wonders of the Ancient World. The Town Hall again received the Great Pyramid, but the 19th-century post office gained the Hanging Gardens of Babylon and the modernist train station gained the Temple of Artemis.

Once again, the tour was a success and at its conclusion Carl's fellow guides were astonished to see his patrons showering him with cash. That night, over drinks in a favourite bar, Carl revealed all to his comrades. Some were furious but most saw the funny side, not to mention the financial one.

Next day, Carl's comrades followed his example and during their tours populated the city with the most fantastical of skylines. Many stuck to the Seven Wonders, but a few added other favourites, including the Taj Mahal, the Empire State Building, the Mosque of Hagia Sophia and even the Forth Rail Bridge.

The tourists returned home delighted by what they'd seen, or at least heard described. If any of them had doubts about the city's wonders, they kept them to themselves. Most sang the city's praises to their friends, encouraging them to plan visits of their own.

Visitor numbers mushroomed and all went well until inevitably questions were asked. Many tourists completed forms providing feedback about their holiday and officials grew suspicious when the same unlikely buildings started appearing in the paperwork.

The Tourism Board held an investigation and hauled in the guides for questioning. Carl quickly confessed, offering his resignation and the money he had accumulated. The Board read the riot act to all of the guides and the tours returned to truthful normality.

Naturally, visitor numbers plummeted and the city's hoteliers and restauranteurs complained: they had grown used to the city's new popularity. Business hadn't been so good in years and they were furious at the sudden drop in takings.

The Tourism Board reconsidered. Eventually the guides were summoned again and ordered to resume their 'alternate' architecture, with instructions to broaden their repertoire: a delegation of French businessmen was due on an official visit and it was felt only polite to include some familiar buildings for their enjoyment.

So all is now well in our city, despite the ever-present fog. Tourists enjoy a stimulating and informative holiday, Carl and his fellows are gainfully employed and the hospitality industry goes from strength to strength.

Even we ordinary citizens have begun imagining what lies above us: the fog has been with us for so long, who can say with any certainty what's actually up there? Other cities are restricted to a single, fixed skyline, but we enjoy as many as we are capable of imagining.

And the only worry is, what will we do should the fog ever lift?

damp change

SIÂN MELANGELL DAFYDD

She opens her purse to pay for bananas and out crawls a beetle. She blows it somewhere into the apple section while, over there, Matilda picks something up from the floor. 'Don't. Whatever it is, don't.' And the woman on the other side of the apples gives her fifty-three cents damp change. The smell of oyster water from the pavement too, and '*Ceci n'est pas un buffet!*' to the gulls or the tourists. A kid with a *trotinette* crashes into her ankle and a short woman with violently applied blue eyeliner takes offence on her behalf, questioning the youth, the open borders, politeness and God. *Ça va, ça va.* Matilda, leave it. She puts her change in her shopping and not her purse.

Where did the beetle come from?
She feels the world ought to stop a second to acknowledge this bug that crawled out of her money. It doesn't.

Matilda picks up that thing that she's studying in the market-gutter-water and returns with her left arm extended. The world, for her, is in her palm. Look.

Three Poems

JAMES DAVEY

Hand-puppets

I am ten, slouched on a kitchen chair,
staring through a television set

on which the presenter is talking to hand-puppets.
Sitting on the back step, Dad pulls a dead rabbit

from a plastic bag, calls me over. *Watch carefully*,
he says. He cuts a surgical incision in its belly,

spoons out its viscera with his fingers.
Intestines slip from its gut. I shiver.

A *delicacy*, says Dad, smacking his lips.
The carcass lolls over his hand – eyes enamel.

He splays it on the stone step, severs
its head, legs, presses down on his blade,

cracking the pelvis in two –
a sound like splitting wood.

He rips free the pelt, presents it to me.
I hold it in open hands.

When You Want it

Late night alcohol and cigarettes ... when you want it

Perform a U-turn when possible, says the woman
in my satnav – I call her Jane.
So I swing across the road
in one practised motion,
the sweep of my headlights
igniting the fine rain needling the pavement.
Bottles of Cab-Sav, cans of Carlsberg,
and a kaleidoscope of alcopops
rattle in the boot of my Fiat Panda
while Jane directs me to my next customer.
Drive three hundred yards, then turn left.
Only the restless and the homeless
wander the streets at this hour.
A girl collecting cardboard boxes outside Asda,
plastic bags wrapped around her shoes,
pulls up her hood and takes a swig
from a plastic bottle as I drive past.
At the next roundabout, take the second exit,
says Jane – and as she speaks
she appears in the passenger seat,
plump with her third child,
her hair cut shorter than normally – it suits.
She tells me the latest on the children
and her husband, Derek, an accountant
with a confident moustache,
describes their new house in Hampstead
with a gravel driveway and bay windows.
The baby is kicking; last week their cat
burned its tail in the toaster.
I can smell her perfume, citrus bloom.
The hairs rise on my arm.
In two hundred yards, turn right, she says.
You have reached your destination.

I pull into an unlit cul-de-sac,
park between a wheelless car,
propped up by four small pillars of bricks,
and a soiled mattress dumped by a fence.
A slice of light splits the darkness
as someone inches open their front door.
A sallow face peeks out from behind the chain.
I'm waved forward.
Perform a U-turn when possible, says Jane.

Morning Prayer

A deep-dream diver in gradual ascent:
I take myself in hand, carefully,
as if entrusted with a gold coin
or Hermes' final root of Moly.

I work a rhythm, an even stroke –
eyes clenched, breaths shallow;
I break the egg-blown surface of sleep
and re-enter the mortal world, *fatto a mano*.

The Midnight Bell

SARAH DRIVER

It's a frosty winter's day and the Goddess is making the waters of the sacred spring bubble and steam, like broth in a cauldron. My breath is a white cloud of mist.

I dodge past Drusus, the oyster seller, and almost drop my bundle of firewood in my haste to escape the staring gorgon—if I linger, his eyes could turn me to stone.

'*Aithne!*' Drusus yells at me but I just grin and walk faster, though I make sure not to run, because children have been known to slip and drown here.

Carefully, I tiptoe around the edge of the sea-beast mosaic and murmur a prayer to the mother for protection—no one steps on the beast if they want to avoid a curse. As I approach the healing baths, my ears are filled with laughter, shouts, curses and splashes. I step past the spits laden with roasting meat that drips juice on to the stones, the rich, smoky smell making my mouth water and my stomach grumble.

Suddenly a slave boy almost barrels into me and I slip on a splatter of garnet-red wine, but I stay upright.

'*Salve*, Aithne!' Felix calls.

'Watch it!' I tell him. 'I could've broken my neck!'

'Sorry. But listen. I've got to talk to you,' he whispers, grinning widely. 'You won't believe your ears!'

I won't believe *him*, more like. He's always telling strange tales from far-off lands. 'I'm working. Can't you see that?' I hurry on but Felix follows me. Ever since I stood up for him against that bully Armelle, he won't leave me alone, even though I'm a paid worker and an official citizen, and he isn't.

I dump the firewood at the mouth of the furnace and start piling logs in, to keep the fire's breath alive, which is fitting because my name means 'little fire'.

Felix keeps plucking at the sleeve of my green tunic. When I've finished, I turn to face him. 'What're you bothering me for? We'll get shouted at, or *worse*, if you don't stop messing about. Haven't you got soot to scrape or pots to scrub?'

'You won't care about getting in trouble when you see what I've found,' he replies, golden-brown eyes shining in his copper-skinned face. 'You've *got* to see it.'

I could swear by my freckles that he's lying. But the bug of curiosity has bitten deep into my skin—I can feel its sharp teeth. I sigh. 'All right. Where is it?'

'Meet me at midnight, in front of the temple steps.' Then, with a scrape of cloth against stone, he vanishes from sight.

Midnight? A chill runs through my blood. Mistress Enica is certain to sell me to the Emperor as a slave if she finds out I left the dormitory after dark. So I'll have to keep it a secret. I'm not sure I've ever had a secret before.

Only a thin silver moon guides me. I tiptoe from the sleeping quarters, throwing a black woollen cloak over my tunic and fastening it with a brooch. Tonight, it's easy to see why January is known as 'the doorway to the year', for the sky sweeps wide, dotted with so many bright stars that I feel as though I can see into forever. The lamps have been doused and an owl hoots from high in a tree above the temple courtyard. It's too dark to see the gorgon, but I know he watches me. A shiver tingles along my spine and I rub my arms against the icy chill.

Why have I left my cosy furs on such a bitter night, just because that great thump-foot Felix told me to? Some potent curse must have robbed me of my senses.

Suddenly an arm shoots out and grabs me. I swallow my scream when Felix's face appears, his teeth gleaming white in the moonlight.

'Think you're funny, do you?' I spit, snatching my arm away. 'You could lose me my job with the healers!'

'Just trust me for once.' Felix turns and hurries towards the network of healing baths. I follow, holding my hands out by my sides to keep from stumbling in the thick blanket of the dark. There's a faint smell of looming thunder, like the smoke when the coals are doused.

In the corner of the cold bathhouse, Felix taps a large slab of stone three times for luck and lifts it, to reveal a dark, dusty space. His mouth gapes. 'But it was right here! There must've been enough to buy a whole pound of silk, or a lion!'

'What are you talking about? You've wasted enough of my time. I'll be tired as death in the morning!'

Suddenly, the midnight bell strikes, clanging out over the stones. There's a rustle as a huge owl takes to the wing. It circles in the air three times, and zooms through the doorway. My head turns to follow its flight, but I cry out when I see a man standing before us, wearing a cloak of feathers. It's Priest Cassius, the haruspex, who reads the future from the innards of sacrificed animals! He's rarely seen outside the temple, where the likes of us are forbidden to go.

The haruspex drops a handful of silver coins into the hole beneath the loose stone, except now it's not empty; it's almost overflowing with hundreds of coins. Some of them bear the regal profile of the Emperor, but others show animals, or ships, or are so worn their surfaces are blank. The haruspex fixes us with cold blue eyes—they're worse than the gorgon's. I can feel my body beginning to freeze on the spot.

Felix grabs my arm. I'm so afraid that my limbs have locked in place. 'What are *you*?' I ask the haruspex, my voice shaky.

'A great priest does not answer to the likes of children,' he breathes, his voice bitter. 'Have you come to pay your dues, and save your fate?'

'What do you mean?' whispers Felix.

The haruspex begins to laugh; a deep, cracked rumble. 'Sometimes, animal sacrifices do not suffice to tell the future. They are not powerful enough to appease the gods.' His burning blue eyes switch between our faces. 'Sometimes, a child is required.'

'There's a pig of lead in the slave quarters, I can bring it to you ...' Felix garbles desperately.

'Lead?' The haruspex's eyes dance with mirth. 'You think that lead will be enough to spare your lives?' He darts closer. We back away, until we're pressed against the cold stone wall. 'It's precious silver I want, boy. Coin or paterae, it matters not. But if you can find none, you will be given to the gods, in order to divine the futures of others.'

He swirls his cloak of feathers and rushes through the darkness, a shadowy blur. An owl hoots, high overhead. Cassius's voice echoes into the darkness. *Bring me treasure before the morrow's midnight bell!* The pile of coins beneath the stone has gone.

'What are we going to do?' moans Felix. His face looks grey in the dim light.

'We've got to stop him,' I reply, teeth chattering, though whether it's from cold or fright I can't be sure.

'But how?'

'I don't know. I need some time to think.'

The sick have come to the baths seeking cures. I've spent the whole morning helping Mistress Enica care for the infirm and pox-ridden, even though I'm tired to the core of my bones.

The fires must be stoked, the Goddess must be appeased with offerings and fed with curses, and the sick need my help to ease their broken bodies into the bubbling waters. They cast votive offerings in the shapes of arms, legs, hearts, lungs, feet—whichever body part ails them—into the sacred spring, praying for cures. I scrub minerals into skin, rub ointments on to inflamed or blind eyes, and fasten amulets of jet around withered necks. Mistress Enica snaps her fingers for tinctures of eyebright, coltsfoot, nettle, hawthorn, marigold, and birch. The ripples of the water dance with the sunlight, making shadows play on the brightly painted frescoes.

I've barely had time to breathe, yet all I can think about is the hoard of buried treasure, claimed in exchange for life. What happened to those who couldn't pay?

A bony finger nudges me. 'Daydreaming again, are we? I'd have thought you'd learnt your lesson by now.' It's Armelle, her blue eyes glaring. 'There are fresh herbs to grind and ginger draughts that want heating. You'll never make it past the order of apprentice if you don't stop dithering. At this rate, *I'll* be chief healer whilst *you're* still fetching firewood!' She sticks out her tongue.

When she turns to leave, I pull out my imaginary bow and send an arrow made of air sailing into her back.

What if we sacrificed *her* to the haruspex, and stole his treasure whilst he was telling the future? The thought chills my blood. Even a bully doesn't deserve that fate—even the worst bully in the Empire. Silently, I curse Armelle with a plague of a thousand warts. As for the haruspex, I'll have to think of something else. But what?

I'm rushing across the temple courtyard when the idea flies into my head. The power of the gorgon must be greater at the chime of midnight—what if we were to hide the hoard before the eyes of the gorgon, and he could turn the haruspex to stone?

There must only be minutes before the midnight bell. I hurry over the frost-slippery courtyard, trying to brush away my doubts, but they cling to me like sticky cobwebs. I hope Luna, the moon goddess, is smiling on me tonight.

Suddenly, Armelle slips out of the shadows, a nasty sneer on her lips. 'Sneaking out after curfew? Mistress Enica will be most interested to learn of this.'

I pull my necklace from inside my clothes and rub my finger across the surface of the jet, to ward off Armelle's evil eye. 'Go away. You don't know how much danger waits here.'

Armelle snakes towards me, eyes glinting. 'The only danger will come from *me*, when I tell Mistresses Enica and Birkita, and the high priest, what you've been up to. So you'd better explain!'

I shake my head. 'I can't.'

'Then I'll tell, unless you give me your necklace. It will suit *me* far better.'

'But it was my mother's!' I cry.

'Too bad, little sneak.'

I sigh. 'All right. But you'll have to follow me and see for yourself. Unless you're scared?'

She frowns. 'I'll come. But any trouble and I'm going straight to the high priest.'

I nod. Quickly, we move down the silent corridor between the baths. Felix steps out of the shadows ahead. '*Salve!*' he whispers in greeting.

Armelle shrieks, but I clamp my hand over her mouth. 'Shhh!' I hiss.

When I take my hand away Armelle glowers like she's tasted something bitter. 'I don't associate with *slaves*.' She reaches out and flicks the slave symbol, sewn on to Felix's sleeve.

I cross my arms. 'As a healer, you should *associate* with whoever needs your help.' Armelle stays quiet, though I can feel her resentment.

We creep towards the cold bathhouse. But then a sudden movement flickers in the corner of my eye and I crouch behind a wall to watch, the others following me. The haruspex swishes through the night, wearing his feathered cloak. Why would he walk, when he could become an owl and fly? Then I glimpse what he's carrying and my heart gives a lurch—it's a wire cage, holding a white owl. Felix and I turn to stare at each other. 'Did you see that?' I breathe. What else has Cassius lied about?

'He's making for the *temple*,' whispers Felix.

'Come on. We've got to follow him.' I dart across the courtyard before Armelle can complain.

We inch up the temple steps, shielding our faces from the fearsome gorgon. Fear tries to snatch my breath but I keep going.

'You can't go in there!' Armelle's face is taut with fear.

I tiptoe into the temple.

Sulis Minerva is warmed by a single candle flame, and she's more beautiful than I could have imagined, but I avert my eyes from her as much as I can, to show respect. The haruspex's steps ring on the stone.

An elderly priest has fallen asleep whilst guarding the temple. The haruspex puts down his caged owl and reaches a hand into the priest's pocket. A silver coin gleams as he draws it out and drops it into his own money bag with a greedy smile.

Suddenly he turns and glares. Armelle stands frozen, next to an ornate pillar. 'What have we here? A spy!' He strides forward and grabs her. She must have snuck past me!

'Let go of her!' I shout, running at the haruspex. I kick his shin and he yells, releasing Armelle. 'Come on!' I tell her. We run from the temple and down the steps, Felix falling into step with us, Cassius on our heels.

He corners us at the sacred spring.

'You lied!' I pant, breathless from running. 'You're not sacrificing children—you just made us believe that to scare us away from the treasure!'

'So, the child learns the power of illusion. Of course I lied.' His voice is as slippery as a snake. 'Members of my religious order have been stealing from sleepers for centuries, to appease the gods. But now I'm going to claim the ancient hoard for my own, and *you* can't stop me—I'll see to it that you're silenced.' He takes a step towards me.

'Leave Aithne alone!' says Armelle. She shoves the haruspex. He stumbles back, and trips over the edge of the bubbling spring. He must have angered the Goddess, for the waters hiss and tumble, lapping hungrily at his thrashing arms. Before we can move, Cassius is swept beneath the churning water.

'We should split the hoard, in case raiders come,' I tell the others. 'And because the silver was stolen, we should use it to help people—like poor travellers with no money to pay for cures.' We fill leather pouches with handfuls of coins, murmuring words of protection. By the time we finish my numb fingertips are caked in dried blood.

We fill three smaller pouches with silver and each take one to hide, leaving eight to bury before first light. These we seal with prayers and earth, beneath a storage hut near the healers' dormitories. We stand in a circle and promise to guard our secret.

Armelle grins at me and Felix shyly. 'I'm sorry, Felix. I was stupid. I don't care that you're a slave. And I'm sorry I bullied you, Aithne. Friends?'

'Friends,' says Felix.

'Friends!' I echo. 'You saved my life, Armelle.' A shiver races through me. 'I'm frozen. Let's go back to bed.'

High in a tree, an owl hoots.

There is No Clock in the Cowshed
(The Suspense Fiction Module c. 1993–2012)

COLIN EDWARDS

It must, surely, have all begun with a little bit of theft: an idea I'd taken from Poe ... I feel sure that Edgar would've been quite happy with that ... but, certainly, Suspense achieved its MA apogee in and around the Cowshed at Newton Park. Once or thrice, it migrated to the Stables (or the Castle, appropriately enough), but it only became truly settled in the Cowshed. At the time, this housed all Postgraduate Studies, having pulled itself away from more bovine ruminations. From such soil and its Romantic fragrances (and a cunning renaming as *Sophia*), our Workshops slowly evolved down the years. Latterly, mixed with the painterly odours of Bath Academy of Art, I was to arrive at my very last, already fading, memories of the delightful – somewhat upgraded! – experiences of the decadent world of Suspense.

It had been a most singular journey: all the way from cattle to the Landed Aristocracy. I'll concentrate upon the former, if that's OK.

That little push that came from Poe – something to do with literature's Purloinings and associated Writer's Guilt – was an originating seed: it floated into our first Workshops like a wicked charm, with the deviousness of a naughty Poststructuralist's shape-shifting (grand one minute, the next only another cow in the room). I tell you, there were *presences* to reckon with – emanations not to be measured – beyond the retained warmth of the Cowshed chairs, purloined from an exiting group of MA students of Religious Studies!

(An unworldly bunch, to be sure, and short-lived too, to judge by the fates they were usually assigned at Final Exam Boards. But I like to feel that they contributed to that little, Newtonian *Space To Breathe* – or choke if unlucky – in our shared micro-world. Perhaps they've never really left).

How else to account for the energies – possibly ectoplasmic – and surely having little to do with my own performance as a kind of fraudulent impresario (*Blavatsky-Poe-Edwards*) – with his weekly, and weak, exhortations to the paying customers...?

So much of it all must still remain a Mystery – one obscurely related to the various versions we were to produce in class of the living and the dead (writers). It was a business both as simple and as complex as the passing about of white sheets of blotting paper, lightly moistened with the vague expectation that some wind-blown germs might find their way into the *Sophia* Hothouse.

Truth is, I was quite unconscious that, already, some unforeseen and larger stories had begun to germinate (another analogy might be the melancholy debates that are rumoured to happen on Richard Kerridge's Facebook page: they just steal inside and get on with it – without the Host (myself or poor Richard) needing to check up, to see how all our friends are getting on).

But this I will insist upon: never – no, not once – did I ask any one of the students to turn out a complete bloody novella!

However, by our third week of meeting – when we left Conrad's Marlow becalmed, adrift on a sandbank looking for useable materials (rivets?) – I should have harboured more doubts or presentiments. Now that we were all launched, it probably did behove *one of our number* to take a firm grip upon the tiller ... already, a good third of the students were wearing a happy, slightly drugged expression ... as if unaware that they were afloat upon a fast-moving current ... and the entire crew still quite oblivious to the fact that Cap'n Joseph Conrad meant business when he invited us into his *Heart of Darkness*!

By Week 5, more of our number were basking under the shade cast from the hidden glory that is the prose of Patricia Highsmith – the 'beautiful shadow' who finds comedy within the darkest of psychological sources. Pat would waver around the Cowshed rafters like a spirit let loose from Salem, ready to scold us if we failed to notice any of the 'best stuff' – for instance, how to make use of the smallest details of a day's events; or how to pace the *indirect free speech* (and it's pretty *free*) within the whirligig mind of a Charlie Bruno (Benefactor and 'Stranger on a Train') as it dreams itself across the full morning of a day that must end with an unpleasant strangling.

With what light-headedness we were all inveigled into the consciousness of that particular child / man, while romping about in Pat's *Metcalf Kingdom of Fun*!

'Perhaps it would be better for us not to know too much too quickly...'.

I think – I know – it was Jonathan who lobbed that particularly well-timed spanner into the Workshop (I even wrote it down!), as the rest of the class's pens all paused, in the strangely shocked silence.

Everybody was nodding sagely.

(I possibly attempted a smile – *even for the student who will purloin the weightiest and best lines!*)

Lawdy Law! ... when I think of the blissful sounds, in that Cowshed, of the eight scratching biros ... in the sounds of such silence ... I might as well have turned into the Buddha Himself: 99 parts Serenity, but with just that little-but-not-insignificant guilt-ingredient, which is often found to be so indispensable – hidden torment and unseen catalyst – to the functioning of suspense stories that actually *work*.

Now, when I think of all the Industry and the *expense* of the spirit-selves, murmuring on to the parchment ... the sounds, to me, of a kind of unbroken Trust ... well, I nearly fall *off my lotus-blossom* ... not even knowing which of my many shames has given me the shove.

A little too much eavesdropping over here, perchance? ... *Guilty. As Sin* ... But I'm only one in a long and distinguished line of very *unreliable* narrators, as you must already know.

Is it such a crime to experience vicarious (writer's) pleasure ... listening in to other people's Time Well Spent?

Like a Supreme Fiction of inhabiting Time *Collectively Well Spent?*

(Or something more to do with guilty pleasures being *shared*.)

What Bliss.

I see myself, momentarily, as The Fat / Buddha Controller, except I'm not terribly in control.

Dawn's looking at her watch.

Nobody leaves this Cowshed! ... at least, not in floods of tears. Preferably!

At least, not until I've given next week's *Writing Assignment*.

Pause while I reach for my scatter-gun of half-formed ideas as bags are urgently being retrieved from beneath our writing surfaces.

My word but those 3-hour Trips (dedicated to the Gods of Crime and Misadventure) could whizz past jolly *fast*.

Now Dawn's eyebrows express something curiously like impatience.

False Alarm! – we've forgotten to talk about last week's Assignment.

Moreover, I appear to be stuck on Week 6 (*phew! –* now I can think what the Assignment really is. Anyway, I'm thinking we all need a bit of a coffee-break …).

As the door clicks shut, I hear Dawn quizzing Jonathan about 'your novella'.

Novella…?!

A chill drops down into the proceedings with the heavy finesse of a redundant metaphor.

Jonathan and Dawn were a little too conspiratorial for my liking, as they had loped off to Caffeine City! …bum-twitch bum-twitch … *Sister Ray* and *Master Pat.…*

Now I'm the only living thing left in the Workshop.

'I wouldn't be so sure of that, Sweetheart.'

I'm letting that one pass.

There are the sounds of somebody choking on liquor and mistimed hilarity.

I shall simply refrain from returning callow one-liners back to the Master. Like our dear Queen thinly dreaming of unleashing the corgis on to Donald and Melania …

I unscrew my trusty hip-flask, trying to ignore the snorts of half-suppressed mirth and generalised titubancy from amongst the shadowy Cowshed corners. I know exactly what's going on there: that'll be Pat handing the baton across (in exchange, no doubt, for their own, shared hip-flask) to next week's high-minded Instigator of fictional Malice and Perversity.

No clocks needed for our Honoured Guests!

'Jeez. So what's he gonna serve up now. The dope.'

(Was that *ma belle ombre* (Pat) or Ray Chandler?? … as the years tick by, they've come to sound more and more like each other.)

'Tell me about it, Ray darling. The fast money says he'll go for the revved-up, high-octane Action Showdown. The one he's never gonna write himself. The dumb shmuck …'

But I know it's all become part of our timeless little ritual. Now I am just too happy …

For I think, by now, that I've knelt down here – in the Cowshed With No Clock – this little Workshop Isle – with a breed of happy misinterpreters of my weekly assignments – for a very long space – often outside of time itself

– and that I have drunk far too deeply in this place, and long, on the wine of its playfulness and sheer generosity of spirit.

I suppose that may be one of the more under-recognised things that can happen in the MA 'Context' modules: the Great Dead and living 'great' (writers) can metamorphose – generously! – into something which has a touch, or more, of fellowship. We have to find *ourselves in them* – even if we risk being taken for mildly boozy gatecrashers at the 'Acknowledged Legislators' Party. Once you've done (proper) kneeling time at the altar of Pat and Ray, you *do* know them, a little, for friends ... they've come to exist in a *Sophia* of kindly wits and sudden illuminations ... a place for risking the trial of one's very best efforts ... fully aware that one's best efforts in Workshop *shall*, when it is necessary, be extinguished, or rather – without malice – *revealed for what they really are* ...

Finally, one can only be grateful to every one of the people who gave precious time in order to prevent their friends from being lead, alone and blind, up the long garden paths of wordy misadventure ...

(*Ahem!*) ... And I'm raising my hip-flask to them all – the *wraiths* and fellow-disciples of the *risky roulette-game* that is Suspense – including the students belonging to my silverish days passed (in another titubant state) somewhere between 'Modernism and Postmodernism'. By then, we could fleet the time a little more carelessly, like plump Corsham epicures ... but in an Arcadia where Suspense Fiction would fail to share its own strange purplish strains of saccadic derangement – sadly – with the phosphorescent peacocks and a yet more brilliant shrubbery.

And even as I bathe in the memory of it – during a dull coffee-break – I find myself still pondering the question whether Creative Writing is making the world of Suspense more interesting, or just a tad blurrier ...? And I'm getting ready (never you fear, my colleagues!) for another eight biros to go *off* – one more time – in the Cowshed's declining light – with the blonde on the davenport pointing her silver-darted pen at my left leg artery ...

I never did like the jerky look in her eyes, but I do hope I will remember to thank her, sincerely, for that one last, shared act of theft.

from *The Ice Maiden*

INTRODUCTION

When we took the lid off the coffin, the body was lying in a block of ice. It was opaque and milky. We couldn't see what was in there. We took water from the nearby lake and heated it in huge drums and took cups from these drums to thaw the ice. It was a slow process. As the ice melted we began to understand the uniqueness of our discovery. You see, we thought we had found the burial place of a warrior.

It was the tattoos that changed our minds. The arms and legs were decorated with the most exquisite tattoos. They were visible on a close inspection. One, on the hand, a man chasing a reindeer. Possibly depicting a hunter. More reindeer were visible on the arms, their antlers branching into flowers. On one shoulder was the sun and on the other the moon and all linked together in an elaborate pattern. On the head of the body was a three-foot-long head-dress. We had never seen a warrior like this. Then the hair unthawed and we realised the body was a woman ...

N. Kulemzin, 'An account of the excavation of a Pazyryck burial', in L.G Suslov and V.A Anderson, eds., *Ancient Burials in Siberia* (Chicago, 1998) 45.

CHAPTER ONE

Listen to me. Listen to me. And I will tell you about the beginning. The mother reindeer came down from the north to the edge of the forest when all the earth was snow. She knelt down in the snow and gave birth to two children.

She gave birth to them. They drank her milk. They were her children.

Then as children do they quarrelled and the mother reindeer tossed them with her antlers up to the sky one to the east and one to the west. They became the sun and the moon and they are always trying to catch each other. Then she knelt down again and gave birth to two more children.

The first man and the first woman. They grew and the woman gave birth to more children, some went to the north to follow the reindeer, some went to the south to become our allies. Some went to the west to become the hut dwellers. Some to the east to become the traders but we stayed by the milky river and became the Horse People.

My father rode with the horsemen. His mare had the finest ornaments. His blade was the brightest. He rode with my brother. He was the firstborn. I was the second. I ran after the horses. My father laughed. My mother held me. She said you cannot go with the horsemen.

My mother sang to me. I slept by the fire. My grandmother held me. A grandmother's arms are strong with many years of carrying water. My grandmother sang also. She sang about the reindeer. She sang about the Raven. Before the beginning there was a void. And nothing lived there except the Raven.

She said this one is so quiet. She said this one is so thoughtful. I held my brother's knife. Longer than my arm. Heavier than a stone. The sun on the blade.

The fire in the blade. I could feel its fire but I was not a warrior.

I watched the fire and listened to the songs. The song of the warriors when they return from battle. The song of the great mother reindeer when she knelt on the snow. I saw my mother make the white coat for my father, the coat the chieftain wears. Made from the finest sheepskin, sewn through the dark nights of the winter. Her sharp needle pulled a red thread to make the patterns. Red as the blood when a sheep's throat is cut and it spurts into the bowl.

The smell of blood is strong and good. The white is like sweet ewe's milk. The chieftain's coat is blood and milk.

My mother washed the sheep's intestines and hung them in our tent. My grandmother cooked the blood and when it clotted she filled the intestines. She strung them in the cold air outside to dry them. This blood food keeps us through the winter. My people are people of blood. I love the smell of that cooking blood, so strong it fills our tent, so strong it makes my eyes water. I lie here and I long to smell that smell. I want to see my mother hanging up the intestines and my grandmother cooking the blood, the light of the fire on their faces.

This place I have woken to has no fire. It is like a tent but it is cold. The sides are hard and do not move in the wind. There is no wind. There is no outside. No grass or trees or water. It is all cold like the high hills on the mountain. But above the high hills there is sky. This place has no sky. There is light but there is no sun. There is darkness but there are no stars.

When it is light a woman in black sits by me. She does not look at me but she wants me for her own. I do not want this. I want to return. I have been disturbed from my sleep and I need someone to help me. Listen to me, I say but she does not listen.

Help me, I say but she looks at the cloths in her lap. I like it better when there is darkness. In the darkness I can travel. I can see people and hear their voices.

This land has many carriages and palaces. The people eat meat with fine silver. But they are hut dwellers with no fires and their horses run loose in the fields. This is not an honourable tribe. Listen to me, I say but no one is listening. Except a child once, a boy with brown eyes and a stick in his hand. He was in the grass by a small stream. He was trying to catch fish. I said, 'you cannot hit them, you have to spear them'. He looked up and I knew he could hear me. But a child cannot help me. There was an old woman who was dying. She was in a white palace with many other sick people. Her daughter was holding her hand. The old woman said, 'You are so sad, where is your mother?' and the daughter said, 'What are you saying? What do you mean?'

But the old woman looked at me with kindness. I remembered that look from my grandmother. I said, 'Rest now, soon you will be with your people,' and she said, 'thank you, I feel very happy.' And the daughter didn't know who her mother spoke to.

In the darkness there are so many people.

Listen to me. Listen to me. Who can hear me? Who can help me?

CHAPTER TWO

Every day the view from Claire's flat was different. This morning, as she stood by the balcony window she could see, across the rainy quayside, a man in yellow oilskins filling up a plastic jerrycan with water. His boat was a forty-foot Looe Lugger. It hadn't been there yesterday.

'Do you think he's come across from the Caribbean?' she said to Rob. She liked the idea of her view filled with people ending or beginning fantastic adventures.

'I can't see anyone else, perhaps he's done it single handed.' Just as she said that, a woman appeared on deck. She had hair flattened by the rain and she too was in yellow oilskins. The rain was beginning to slam down. It was March and still cold. Claire couldn't hear their conversation but by the way they were gesticulating she could tell they were arguing. The scene wasn't so interesting now. 'Perhaps, they've just come up from Plymouth,' she said and she turned into the room but Rob wasn't there. He was in the kitchen. A piece of toast in one hand and his mobile phone in the other.

'Yes, trains to London, are there any delays expected this morning?' he asked the unknown third person. 'London? Delays? This morning? Can you understand me?'

Claire poured herself a cup of coffee. Rob didn't usually stay over on Sunday nights. He was head of a research team in structural biology at Imperial College. One half of Claire wanted him gone. She wanted her week to start as it usually did, with her cycle ride up the docks and up Park Street. The other half wanted him there, in her flat, on this morning, every morning. Dark hair, brown eyes. His fleecy jacket and his combat trousers. He didn't look like a man going to work, he looked like a man going for a hike. The only thing he needed was a map. He didn't have one. He was looking through papers in his rucksack, eating the toast and still trying to get accurate information about the trains.

Claire wasn't even dressed yet. She didn't want to do that until he had gone. It wouldn't take her long though. She wore the same sort of stuff every day. Tee shirts and jeans. She never felt like an office worker.

Rob, at last, had finished phoning. He came and sat next to her at the table. 'It looks like the next train is cancelled. Can you believe it?' Claire could believe it, but she knew that Rob had little place in his life for cancellations.

He looked at his watch. 'The taxi should be here,' he said. What he didn't say, and what they both knew, was that he should have gone home last night. He phoned the taxi company. Claire squeezed his knee. He patted her hand. 'Taxi for 7 Brunel Buildings? On its way? Any minute? I do hope so.'

He had dark eyebrows and, when he was stressed, between them was a deep ridge. At night sometimes Claire put her finger there and stroked until the ridge disappeared. She liked it that he was dark and she was fair. Some couples looked like each other but they didn't. Rob, square shouldered, and straight backed; and her, lanky, sloping, long armed, white blonde. He called her 'The Viking', but she thought her face was too oval to be Scandinavian. Their characters were different too. He was resilient and solitary. She, sociable, argumentative.

The doorbell rang. Rob stood up and so did Claire. She was tall. They were almost the same height. 'I'll phone you,' they both said in unison and for the first time since yesterday Rob laughed. 'I'll phone you,' he said and he was gone.

Claire didn't get ready immediately. She wanted it to feel like her flat again. The rain pounded on the balcony windows. She could hear the people upstairs walking about. She washed up the breakfast things and opened the window in the bedroom. The air smelled of the sea and perhaps a smell of bacon from the harbour-side cafe. A radio was on in another flat. This was how her mornings usually began.

Dressed in black rain gear she unlocked her bicycle from the stand on the ground floor and swung herself on to it. It was a mountain bike and a fast one. She could get to work in twenty minutes if she pushed it. But she was slower today.

What did Rob say last night? 'Things have got to change, Claire.' 'Things' meant him in London and her in Bristol. They had been seeing each other for nine years, mostly at weekends and for holidays, but Rob's 'new' solution was that they should live together. It was not a new argument. It had dribbled across at least two years.

But Claire didn't want to leave Bristol. Quite simply she loved it.

She loved the boats tied up along the docks. The mess of them. Sailing boats: new ones, fibreglass and swanky; and old, crummy ones with peeling paint and patched sails; and occasionally a large schooner back from the Atlantic with a crew with sun-bleached hair and sun-wrinkled faces. The painted narrow boats and the yellow ferryboats, that took commuters to work and tourists round the docks, and the paddle steamer moored over the winter for repainting. She loved the harbour-side cafe and the chunky bacon sandwiches and the black-headed gulls that gobbled the leftovers, and the smell of the water, and even the mushrooming new offices and flats on the other side. The steel and concrete and glass reflecting the light. The view of the cathedral just visible down the avenue of new builds. She was pedalling faster now, the rain in her face. And her flat, she loved her flat. OK, it was new and featureless and the second bedroom was on the small side, but she loved it. She loved the view, from the windows in the bedroom and the sitting room, and the whoosh the shower made, and her tiny kitchen. And her white embossed bedspread from the market in Foix and the big black and white picture of a tree in Avebury that Rob had given her.

'It's a flat. It's a job. You'll find another one.' That's what Rob said but when she said, 'Well give up your job and move to Bristol then,' that's when the argument really started.

She was standing by the Arnolfini getting her breath back. She felt emotional and she didn't want to turn up to work like that. She wanted to shout at him like she had shouted last night. 'Why does it have to change? Why can't it stay the same?'

'Because I want to start a family,' said Rob.

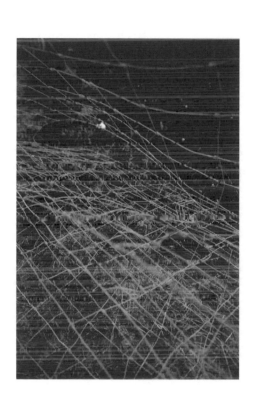

from *Imagined Sons*

CARRIE ETTER

A Birthmother's Catechism

How did you let him go?

With black ink and legalese

How did you let him go?

It'd be another year before I could vote

How did you let him go?

With altruism, tears, and self-loathing

How did you let him go?

A nurse brought pills for drying up breast milk

How did you let him go?

Who hangs a birdhouse from a sapling?

Imagined Sons 1: Fairy Tale

My son leans from the tower; his red pompadour, stiff with Aqua Net, resists the quick wind. When he sings, the notes hasten to the forest a mile south before they descend. I clamber on to my restless horse; she starts before I am secure. Almost too soon we reach the wood.

The notes are red. I pluck them like poppies.

Imagined Sons 15: The Courthouse

I sit in the last row. When I read the notice in the paper six weeks ago, I thought about taking up knitting, so I could busy my hands and eyes as needed. Instead I have become nondescript, the murky darkness of dishwater.

You arrive in a cheap suit and handcuffs. I am the surprise witness, an unforeseen alibi, another story about who you are and how you got here. Your father will swear me in.

Imagined Sons 26: The Pilot

Two hours into the Bristol-Newark flight, the seatbelt symbol lights up with a loud ding: turbulence. Moments after, a young man, barely of age, emerges from the cockpit in a navy suit and matching cap. He comes down the aisle, humming, surveying the rows to either side with a proprietary air as he passes. Passengers whisper to one another and point, and a squeal rises when the plane jolts, but his placid expression doesn't acknowledge it.

At my row he halts and asks with a smile, 'How ya doin', ma'am?'

I glance about, noting quizzical looks. 'I—I'm fine. Are you—the pilot?' I hear the woman next to me swallow hard as I say it.

His grin broadens. 'That would be worrying, wouldn't it? Your life in someone else's hands, someone not really grown up yet, you not able to do anything about it ...'

Softly I respond, 'You're not the pilot. You're too young to be the pilot.'

The plane shudders, and he turns, running back the way he came, becoming younger with each stride until he falls into the arms of a scowling woman, into the shape of an infant, swaddled in navy blue.

Imagined Sons 34: DJ

All right y'all driving home from work tonight, you've had a hard day and now we've got some songs to help you forget—but first, you'll forgive a man on his birthday one song for remembering. This goes out to, well, I don't know her name, but I'll say I was born in Peoria, Illinois, twenty years ago today. Here's Joni Mitchell, her music all done when she found her daughter, but such a legacy—here's 'Little Green' for you, you know who you are.

A Birthmother's Catechism

When will you let him go?

A man carves my name into granite with hammer and chisel

When will you let him go?

My grandmother's hair was never white

When will you let him go?

This door cannot be lifted off its hinges

When will you let him go?

Take two of my ribs to make a fire

When will you let him go?

It is time, Celan said, the stone made an effort to flower

How to Write an Award-Winning First Novel*
or at least, to be happier whilst trying

NATHAN FILER

On a rainy spring day in 2009, I shuffled into a lecture theatre at the University of Bristol to watch a presentation entitled 'Evidence-based Approaches to Positive Psychology'. I was deeply, deeply miserable.

Depression – somewhat ironically – was my bread and butter. I'd spent the last two years of my working life surrounded by filing cabinets in a cramped office, a short walk up the road from the lecture theatre. Here I helped to administer large trials – comparing side effects of antidepressants, the effectiveness of talking therapies, that sort of thing. It was good work, important work. The problem: I wasn't any good at it. My aptitude for statistics is woeful. I'm slow with databases and spreadsheets. My heart was elsewhere.

At home, hidden away in a cardboard box, were the first 20 pages of a novel that I'd been planning to write for years, only where was the time?

Then on that rainy spring day, slumped at my desk, composing a newsletter, I noticed an email arrive: it was a reminder that all were welcome to the lunchtime lecture, starting in 15 minutes. I reread the title. Evidence-based Approaches to Positive Psychology. These things tend to suffer from lofty verbosity. Translation: How To Be Happy.

I grabbed my coat.

The notes I made during the lecture remain pinned to the wall above my writing desk. They don't contain any insights on shaping a compelling plot. Nothing on characterisation or how to write convincing dialogue. There are no well-worn wisdoms on the importance of cutting adverbs. Writing a first novel demands far more than the words we place on the page. Here are my thoughts on how to do it, and moreover, for the experience to be a happier one.

HAVE SPECIFIC GOALS

The operative word here is 'specific'. My stack of pages hidden away, my hope to be a writer one day – were a start, but it was too vague.

It didn't bother me that I would often put aside my manuscript for a month, three months, six months at a time. Why should it? I'd write it eventually. The problem, the lecturer explained, is that when our goals aren't specific, it's too easy to convince ourselves that we're getting there when we're not. Then at the other end of the journey, we tend not to properly savour the attainment of ill-defined goals, because it is less certain that we've reached them.

Here's what I did. I replaced 'I want to be a writer' (something I'm still not convinced I've achieved) with 'I'll write something today'.

That's pretty specific.

The first evening, in a frenzy of positivity, I wrote a page. The next day I deleted it. But I also wrote a new paragraph. That went too. By the end of the week I'd written 2,000 words that would never make it into my novel, and I had also written a sentence that would become the opening line. It was there, waiting.

MAKE SURE YOUR GOALS ARE ACHIEVABLE

As my novel grew, as I found the voice of my central character and knew with greater certainty how his story would unfold – I set myself tougher goals.

Today I will fix that irksome issue with the chronology. This week I will complete chapter four. Next week I shall write to an agent, etc.

My vague desire to write a novel had now been replaced with the clear intent to write *this* novel, to tell this specific story. That felt great, because now it felt achievable.

All too often we set ourselves unachievable goals. Then we feel bad for failing (more on failure in a bit). Many writers set themselves word count targets, and for some this is helpful. I tried it a few times – setting out to write 1,000 words a day. That isn't so much, but I still struggled. I'm precise. I edit as I go along. My style isn't suited to generating work quickly. So I set myself an achievable goal instead. I told myself that it didn't matter if I only wrote ten words, or if I deleted 50. All I had to do was spend the time at my desk. A lot of time.

I couldn't quit my job, but I could write in the evenings. Two hours every evening, without fail. Five hours on a weekend. That was achievable. It worked for a while too, but writing can be hard and lonely and disheartening. I'd written to an agent, sent off 30 pages. Then the rejection letter arrived. I took that day off, took the week off. Stopped.

BE PREPARED TO FAIL ALONG THE WAY

I'm glad my lecture notes are pinned to my wall. It's obvious, I know, but we can all do with a reminder sometimes. 'The important thing,' the lecturer had explained, scanning the room before fixing her gaze on me. 'The important thing, is to see failures along the way for what they are. Setbacks in a longer journey. Not the end of the road.'

I wonder if there is a novelist alive who hasn't run into some kind of failure in their career. A rejection letter is a hiccup. Three rejection letters – that's three hiccups. What about 30?

I'd say if you get 30 rejection letters there's a chance that your novel isn't any good. That's not the same as you not being any good. However much of ourselves we pour into our writing, it's never the whole of us.

Besides, you're not trying to be a writer, remember? You're trying to write *this specific novel*. If it doesn't work out, consider writing another one. My debut – a book that won me a big prize and garnered much praise and attention – wasn't the first novel I had written. It's just the first one that got published.

Years before, I completed a children's book. It had a talking worm in it. That manuscript got a whole heap of rejections. But they weren't automated rejections. Not all of them, anyway. There was encouragement amongst them, kind words about the style. I was being told that it wasn't bad. The rejection letter for my 'second debut' went a step further: It's good. It's not for us. But it's good.

BASE YOUR AFFIRMATIONS ON FACT

Good isn't great. But good is good. Good might be good enough.

I think it's important to give ourselves a pep talk from time to time, a word of congratulations, a pat on the back. Writing is, on the whole, a solitary experience. We could be waiting a long time to hear praise from anyone else.

The key is to base our affirmations on fact. If you tell yourself you are the world's most remarkable storyteller, you've a long way to fall. But you can be good. That description you wrote earlier, capturing the precise moment when your character realises the truth – that was bloody good. It would stand up in any novel.

Savour these moments. It might be your private burden to suffer the anxieties of writing, but it's also your unique privilege to be first in line to enjoy what you create.

BE FLEXIBLE IN HOW YOU GET THERE

Nearly a 100 pages in, I hit a wall.

A first novel is a huge undertaking; we learn about ourselves as writers along the way. Sitting alone at my computer – even with the pep talks – was no longer working out. So I changed my approach and enrolled on the MA in Creative Writing at Bath Spa University. I didn't plan this at the outset, but that doesn't matter. The specific, achievable goal is what matters. I had committed to writing my novel; not to doing so without help.

For me, to be in a place with other writers sharing feedback and encouragement was very useful. Also useful was to be reminded that my novel wasn't the only one being written. I could contribute positively to other people's work. I could help other writers enjoy their successes. That felt good.

But Creative Writing courses bring their own challenges. When sharing early drafts with people, there's a danger of being buffeted around by conflicting advice.

TAKE RESPONSIBILITY

So remember, above all else, this is *your* novel.

If it's published then it will be your name on the cover. You can't write a book by committee.

That doesn't mean we should close our ears to all suggestions. If we share an early draft of a chapter with ten friends, and all ten come back saying that the scene with the meringue doesn't work, then probably it's worth reworking the scene with the meringue. But if only one person says it doesn't work

– well, your opinion counts too. I saw people who forgot this, who afforded other people's ideas a greater weight than their own.

I was fortunate. By the time I enrolled on the MA I had a clear sense of the story I wanted to tell, and this made it easier to be selective about the advice I took. If your reader fully understands what a scene is intended to achieve, and can explain why it's not achieving this – that's valuable advice. If they just don't have a taste for meringue, but you do – that's not so useful. Take responsibility. Keep the (delicious) meringue.

FOCUS ON THE STUFF YOU CAN CONTROL

If we're seeking representation from a literary agency, we can be sure to select agents who are accepting work in our genre; we can carefully read their submission guidelines and fastidiously adhere to them. These are the things we can control. What we can't control, is whether or not the agent chooses to represent us, and if our writing gets published.

If our novel does get published, we can't control how it's received or how well it sells. Heck – we probably won't even get a say on what the cover looks like. There is so much in the world of publishing that is beyond our influence.

Put it all aside.

Don't give another thought to writing a prize-winning first novel. Think instead about your next sentence, and you might just be on the way.

My novel is on the shelves and has been well received (better than the talking worm, anyway). But that doesn't mean it's all a breeze. I keep the notes from that lecture pinned to my wall and still use them.

Writing is hard and I falter often.

As for being a writer – I think that's always a work in progress.

When I received the request to write this essay I wasn't at all sure how to go about it or what I wanted to share. So I set myself a specific, achievable goal: 'Spend an hour at the keyboard'. Here's wishing you every success with your own writing, and more importantly, every happiness.

from *The Book of Astolat*

KYLIE FITZPATRICK

DECEMBER 1448

Elayne came to Grafton at night, huddled in furs. Mama said that she was the daughter of a baron and that she was to be schooled at Grafton. Elayne was only nine, the same age as Anthony, whereas Elizabeth was already eleven. She had decided that they would be like sisters. Elayne would come to the chapel with her every morning where, together, they would read prayers.

Anthony saw Elayne first because he was hiding from John and Richard, both younger and less canny, in a servant's cupboard at the front of the house. It was early in the evening and the children were still in the downstairs parlour reading and playing games. Anthony reported that the new arrival looked like a princess. He considered himself a poet.

'What else?' Elizabeth was irritated that he had seen Elayne first.

Anthony considered. 'She looks unhappy.'

'She will be cold and tired,' said Elizabeth. 'I wonder if they will let us see her this evening.'

In answer, the doors of the parlour opened and Elayne was ushered in by Mama. Jacquetta had offered to school Elayne because the Baron of Guildford's wife, who was Jacquetta's friend, had died two years before.

Anthony was right. She was thin as a needle and her skin seemed unnaturally pale; bone white. But with her sloping eyes and dense black hair Elayne could have been one of the princesses in Mama's tales. She wore a fur cape that reached to the floor, beneath which Elizabeth glimpsed scarlet silk. In the Wydeville house such rich cloth was only worn on occasions, and Elizabeth thought it a vulgar colour for a young girl. Being motherless, Elayne could not know such things. She would need to be advised.

Elayne's eyes darted around the room, taking in Mary and Anne on their brightly painted hobby horses, and Martha surrounded by wooden dolls. Lewis was attempting to teach Eleanor to play chess, though he was a poor player himself and she was far too young for a game of strategy. Lionel, who was only just walking, kept knocking the pieces from the board. Margaret, the baby, was sleeping in the arms of the nurse.

By the time Elayne's eyes rested on Elizabeth, she had given up on pretending to read. It was clear that Elayne was frightened but trying to appear composed, and exhausted but fighting it with all the strength in her narrow body. The intrepidness of this exotic arrival made Elizabeth fearful. Such a sliver of a person could surely not threaten her safe, sensible existence? And of course, she forgot sometimes that whatever Our Lord wanted must be offered up without question.

Jacquetta had her hand on Elayne's shoulder, but Mary and Ann were now circling around them on their wooden horses, pretending that they were knights about to capture their enemy. It was rare to see Mama in the great hall after supper, since evenings were her time for reading and writing in her library. The little ones were making the most of it. Jacquetta was laughing at her daughters, though her amusement was ungenuine and probably intended to soothe Elayne. It was not that Jacquetta of Luxembourg was without humour, or that she did not love her children, she just had limited patience for foolery before bedtime.

Elayne regarded the circling hobby horses warily.

Elizabeth marched over and took her hand. 'You can sleep in my bed tonight,' she said.

Jacquetta smiled and Elizabeth was rewarded. Pleasing Mama was almost as good as pleasing Our Lord, though the benefits were more immediate than having to wait a lifetime for recompense. Jacquetta divided her time and her attentions not only between her ten children, but also between her French and English estates. Mama was, Elizabeth had heard, an accomplished diplomat. She was not exactly sure what this was, but it sounded clever.

Elayne's hand was soft and warm, which surprised Elizabeth whose hands were always cold. How could anyone have warm hands in December?

The visitor allowed herself to be led to the fire, but Elizabeth's polite enquiries about her journey and remarks about the weather did not appear of interest to her.

Elizabeth was momentarily distracted by Lionel, who was always trying to eat ash from the hearth. By the time she turned back, Elayne had taken a book from the folds of her cape and was bent so low over it that there was no point in further attempts at conversation.

The hour until bedtime dragged. Elizabeth read the same passage of St Augustine over and over without understanding its meaning. Anthony tried to impress Elayne with some fledgling poetry he was writing in French, something to do with the Greek philosophers, that was unbearably dull. Elayne ignored him and, before he was even finished reciting, asked Elizabeth what she was reading. She lost interest immediately when Elizabeth showed her that it was Augustine's *City of God*.

When Anthony bravely resumed his recitation, Elayne stood up and walked slowly across to where Lewis and Eleanor were lying on a rug endeavouring to play chess. She crouched down and showed Lewis a move, which made Eleanor cry and complain that it wasn't fair. Elayne showed Eleanor the next move and the game was soon over.

Elayne hardly slept all night and, as a result, neither did Elizabeth, though she pretended for as long as she could. When the tossing and tangling of bedclothes became impossible to ignore, Elizabeth took Elayne's hand.

'What is it, dear?' she whispered.

Elayne was silent.

'You can tell me, I will be your friend.' Elizabeth was no longer certain of this, but it seemed a kind thing to say.

Elayne sighed. It was the sort of sigh that Jacquetta's steward issued when he was feeling burdened with the business of running the household.

'I am not very good at sleeping.'

'Is that all?'

'And I'm hungry.'

'Then we must feed you.'

Hand in hand, they tiptoed along the cold blackness of corridors where there were no prickets for candles on the walls, Elayne gripping Elizabeth's hand, and down the dark back stairs to the kitchens. Elizabeth woke the servant who was asleep on the floor and told her to fix some food.

They sat at the cook's table and ate cold game pie and drank cider. Elayne watched Elizabeth closely and she pretended not to notice.

'Why are you reading *City of God?*'

'You may call me Beth. Everyone does.'

'But why?'

'Because Augustine was wise.'

'What does he say?'

'That the church is a heavenly kingdom ruled by love.'

'A kingdom ruled by *love?*'

'Yes.'

Elayne ate the rest of her pie in silence and they returned to bed.

Elizabeth was almost asleep when Elayne turned to her, propped up on her elbow. 'How can a kingdom be ruled by love?'

'It is not intended to be taken literally,' Elizabeth said sleepily, because she had heard Brother Paul say the same thing to Anthony.

'What does literally mean?' Elayne asked.

'It means,' Elizabeth replied, unsure, 'that sometimes stories help us to understand things. Augustine says that the church was put on earth by Christ and we must all do as the priests say because they are like the disciples.'

'But how do you know that isn't just another story?'

Elizabeth had not considered the possibility and was, momentarily, thrown.

'Certain things are stories, but that isn't.'

'How do you know?'

'I will ask the priest.' It was only a matter of time before Elayne would ask her a question that she could not answer. 'What are you reading?'

'*The Book of Margery Kempe.*'

'Who is Margery Kempe?'

'A madwoman who went to Jerusalem.'

'Oh.'

'I will go there too one day.'

'On pilgrimage?'

'No! On a quest.'

'What will you quest for?'

'A story.'

'A *story?*'

'Yes. Eleanor of Aquitaine's crusaders stole a story from Jerusalem that came from the great library of Alexandria. Queen Eleanor gave the story to her court writer, Chretien de Troyes, and Chretien wrote the *Perceval.*'

The *Perceval*, Elizabeth knew, was the story of the Grail, one of the romances of King Arthur's knights, in which Perceval's quest took him into a land of enchantments. But Chretien de Troyes did not live long enough to finish writing his story, so the riddle that the knight Perceval must solve about the Grail remained unanswered. Elizabeth could not help but be taken with this idea, but she knew from her lessons that the library of Alexandria had been burnt to the ground by the Romans. 'But everything in the library was destroyed,' she whispered.

Elayne shook her head. 'Not everything. My Mama said that when Julius Caesar set fire to his own ships to frustrate Achilles, the monks knew that their library was in peril and rescued the most precious manuscripts and moved them to a temple in another part of the city.'

Elizabeth was entranced. 'But if the story was brought to Eleanor of Aquitaine by her crusaders, then it will not be in the Holy Land.'

'No, but if the Holy Land is where the story came from, then it must be a special place.'

'Have you read the *Perceval*?' Elizabeth asked.

'I am not permitted.' Elayne gave one of her heavy sighs. 'It is a romance and my father's priest says that romances are a pestilence sent by the devil to rot the female mind.'

Elizabeth had not known that a mind could rot. Mama had read to them from her romances about King Arthur and his knights, and it was their favourite game to pretend to be characters from the tales and to quest for the Grail, though none of them really knew what it was.

Elizabeth sensed that Elayne was preparing another question. She braced herself.

'So you think that priests know what God wants?'

'Of course. Don't you?'

'Why should I care what God wants when he has taken my mother?'

Elizabeth fell asleep thinking that she must ask the priest how to save Elayne from the fires of the damned.

from *Silence Dogood*

RICHARD FRANCIS

For most of my ten years at Bath Spa I had a shared office with my colleagues, in a prefabricated shed just behind the Newton Building (the upgrading to Corsham Court occurred as soon as I was safely out of the way.) There was a sign outside our hut that said DOG'S TOILET for the benefit of a blind student's guide dog which, it turned out, couldn't read anyway. We could, though, and did, working our way year after year through mounds of student pieces that, pleasingly, almost always improved (often dramatically) as they went along. And sometimes we discussed each other's books, because we wrote too. That was the whole point: the MA was, and is, a community of writers.

In the spirit of the workshops it's about time I brought a piece of my own work to the table. This is the opening of a recently finished historical novel, provisionally titled *Silence Dogood*. It deals with a real man, a Puritan preacher in colonial America called Cotton Mather, who was notorious in his time and since for his involvement in the Salem witch trials. My book begins in 1711, nearly twenty years after that terrible event. Mather's mind teemed with religious cruxes, superstitions and scientific insights; while his character was a strange mixture of hypocrisy, self-interest, pomposity and benevolence.

The book opens with a vision of angels but almost at once we find ourselves in a privy. The gamut of human experience is, as always, available, just as it was in the Creative Writing shed in Newton Park and now, no doubt, (accompanied by the screeching of peacocks) at Corsham Court.

CHAPTER ONE

Deep in his devotions Cotton Mather feels a call to the necessary house. Sighs. Shakes his wig. The prayer is directed upwards, his digestion, down. Even when he fasts, which is often, this contradiction occurs.

He raises himself up from his prone position on the study floor, moving his legs with care so as not to joggle the sphincter. Then a pause while he gathers himself. Then makes his way through attending angels, giving little bows as each in turn recedes from view with a blink of wings.

Beyond his study door, more earthbound beings make their presence felt. The substantial form of Goodwife Hodge, the wet-nurse, is seated on a chair near the top of the stairs and suckling baby Jerusha, who gasps and snuffles and smacks her little lips as Cotton tiptoes by, politely averting his gaze.

Then, going down the stairs, he has to squeeze past daughter Nibby who is on her way up. 'You should have waited, papa,' she tells him *en passant*, 'it's bad luck to pass on the stairs,' – and in a flurry of skirts and laughter continues on her way. He almost rebukes her – she is too old to indulge in superstition, even in joke – but doesn't, since it's her nature to be high-spirited and sparky, and in any case he must remain tightly bottled, so to speak.

At the kitchen table the heads of little Lizzie and littler Samuel are bent over a book (to their father's satisfaction Sam, who is only five, can already decipher some Latin); while consort Elizabeth is at the fireplace consulting with Jane, their housemaid, on the subject of eels, at least judging by a plate Jane is holding. Fish are of course a particularly Christian dish, though Cotton can't recall the Bible touching on eels as such, but he's not fond of them in winter when they smack of the sea's cold wetness. Eleven-year-old Nancy is sitting in the farthest corner of the room from the fire, as usual, sewing a cushion.

Everyone turns towards him as he hurries past, but he just raises a hand to indicate they should continue with their affairs.

Gusts of snow buffet him in the yard. The garden beyond is almost blanked out. There's a little drift against the house of office, stopping the door. He tugs at the latch but the snow is obstinate and he whimpers in frustration. It's the very smallness of the difficulty that flummoxes him, the way you can be thwarted by a sudden obstreperous detail. He lets his mind take refuge for a moment in larger perspectives:

Major Whalley's foot.

Those pirates condemned to hang.

Then, buoyed up by these thoughts, casts about for a tool.

On the rain barrel by the house is a piece of slate. Steps over, lifts it up, brushes away the snow that has settled on it. Pleased with this scraper he turns back towards the door, but just as he does so it opens, sweeping snow into an arc, and out steps Onesimus.

'Sorry, master. I hold it shut, for ...' Onesimus flutters his hands about his person, to suggest the need for decency even if he has no word for such a thing. He is blacker than ever against the whiteness of the afternoon. Cotton rubs the slate with his sleeve as if he wishes to clean it, then puts it back on the barrel. Onesimus concludes his miming by nodding awkwardly, then offers the door and steps away. Cotton takes his place in the small, pungent box. Black or white, we all make use of it. But each phenomenon in the world, whether thing or act, must have *two* uses.

In the darkness, breeches round his ankles, Cotton points a forefinger (twice) to stress this point. One material use, the other, spiritual. Thus, if you have long legs (Cotton does not) they should teach you to *run* to Christ. Or if you happen to be engaged in baking, *Lord, let a glorious Christ be the Bread of Life to us!*

But evacuation! What purpose can it serve, apart from the purpose it serves? (Cotton had a baby once, born without an anus, who died in three days.) It seems to be a function without any meaning beyond itself.

Cotton settles his posterior upon the O. Can this be the only action in life that makes no contribution to the grand narrative? A motion lacking all direction? Yet how many of one's days are spent performing it! Hours every week, many minutes in a day.

I will call these episodes Spots of Time, Cotton decides. He pictures wormholes in a book, down which certain words have slipped.

Perhaps because the air is so cold, his turd is like molten lead. He would gasp or cry except that Onesimus might still be in earshot, so mutters oh, oh instead. (He almost says Oh *Lord*, but stops short. It wouldn't be seemly to call on God from inside a Spot of Time.)

But then, at the very moment of release, a saving thought comes to him. Or rather, he realizes that his thoughts have been of a saving tendency all along. Has he been feeling humbled? Well then, it is right that a Christian should feel humbled. Bestial? It is appropriate that a Christian should feel abased. The very ignominy of the act is its use, and therefore its redemption. Loathsome circumstances contain a discipline of their own.

A little later, as he prepares his execution sermon (a sermon takes seven hours to write, two to deliver), his concentration is again disturbed. He hears his consort's voice, raised in reproach and, almost inevitably, the dread word *Creasy*.

Elizabeth isn't a reproachful woman, even with her stepchildren, as some second wives notoriously are, but young Creasy is a stepchild *par excellence*. (One of the condemned pirates is French, and Cotton must remind himself of the language. *Très bon, s'il vous plaît, it faut* have been spangling his speech and writing and thoughts all day long. He has Latin, Greek, Hebrew, German and French all secreted in various parts of his brain, like so many animals in stables waiting for their chance to gallop. He once taught himself Spanish in a month.)

Creasy is twelve, stocky, curly-haired, handsome and affectionate, but he has a strangely wayward nature. Abigail, his deceased mother, was a gentle, pious soul. Cotton himself is not gentle exactly, but is certainly pious: strenuous in his piety. But Creasy is wild, despite being named Increase after his grandfather, the greatest minister of his time – of this time too, for that matter, unless, Cotton wonders, unless he has now been superseded by his own son, Cotton himself. No, such a thought can't be entertained, especially if there is any chance it might be true, since greatness of this particular kind must be characterized by modesty, such being the paradox of achieved virtue.

He sighs, puts his quill on his desk, goes downstairs.

In the kitchen his son is sitting at the table, his face raised like a baby's while Elizabeth leans over him and washes it with a cloth, telling him off as she does so. Creasy's half-brother and half–sister, displaced from their studies, are standing nearby, watching with interest. Jane too, though when she sees Cotton she busies herself with her eels.

'Elizabeth!' cries Cotton, 'Surely he can wash himself if he's dirty!' (Here another example of the discipline of analogy pops into his head: as you scrub your face you can cleanse your soul of its dirt at the same time.)

Elizabeth jumps as if she has been caught in wrongdoing. Creasy jumps too, then looks sidelong at his father. Lizzie and Sam, having also jumped, also look sidelong at their father. Nancy, however, remains absorbed in her cushion.

'He's …' Elizabeth looks cautiously at the boy. It's strange how her rebuke has given way so promptly to a sort of conspiracy between them. Cotton feels unfairly excluded, as if it's *he* who has done something inappropriate or wrong. 'Bleeding,' she finally admits.

'Bleeding? Let me see.' Cotton steps forward, grasps his son's face and turns it to have a look.

'Bleeding,' little Lizzie repeats to Sam, as if she has had to translate the word for him, or at least pronounce it in a fellow-child's voice, and her brother nods enthusiastically, repeating the word under his breath.

Creasy's squeezed cheeks make his mouth pout like a toddler's on the verge of tears. Suddenly Cotton feels on the verge of tears himself. He loves this troublesome boy so much, despite all his faults. Or rather, he is forced to admit, to some extent *because* of them. This is a puzzling and worrying admission. God loves us but hates our sins, and you ought to love your son with a love as like God's as possible. In his thoughts he can make that distinction, but in his fatherly heart he loves Creasy exactly how he is.

Creasy whimpers. His upper lip is not merely pouting – it is swollen, and there is a cut to one side of his mouth. Also he is developing a black eye.

'And what happened to you?' Cotton asks.

'Nothing.'

'I see.'

Cotton remembers certain scuffs and bruises he himself received in his childhood. When he was just a small boy at school, no more than eight years old, he began a project to show his fellows the error of their ways and bring them to a greater understanding of religion, but was rewarded for these efforts by sneering remarks and blows. On one occasion he was beaten to the ground and had to return home weeping to his parents. To his amazement his father, instead of sympathizing, seemed very glad to hear of these persecutions.

For years Cotton puzzled over his mysterious reaction. Increase Mather is a man who must be analysed and interpreted. He's not one to give anything away. His face can shut in your face like a door. Finally Cotton realized that the only possible explanation was that Increase must have felt proud his son was willing to suffer for his faith. No other explanation could make sense of the evidence.

Even when Cotton was at Harvard – he was admitted at just eleven years of age – a similar thing happened. He tried to encourage the other scholars, all older than him, of course, to pray, and was spat at for his pains (and once, in the yard, fiercely elbowed). The hostility became so great he had to withdraw and be educated at home for the remainder of his freshman year.

He developed a stammer in his childhood and has often wondered since if this was caused by a fear that the world would fling any good and improving words straight back at him. But, sadly, crusading zeal is not likely to be the cause of Creasy's woes.

'This nothing you talk of, it must have been equipped with a strong set of fists.'

As sometimes happens with his rhetorical strokes, Cotton's sarcasm suddenly develops a metaphorical density, and in his mind's eye he sees a terrible black figure, a solid nothingness, advancing toward his boy through falling snow and beating him into submission. It is an image of atheism or apostasy and once or twice it has confronted Cotton himself. On one occasion he tried to describe the experience in his journal, teetered on the very brink: *I am assaulted with solicitations to look upon the whole Christian religion as – I dare not mention what!*

Dark things occur, permission is given for evil to reign, the ways of God are so strange that anyone might think that He isn't, that He doesn't …

I cried unto the Lord for the quenching of those fiery darts, for preservation from that blasphemy that would be the unpardonable sin.

'I was fighting with some boys,' Creasy finally admits.

'And what were you fighting about?'

'Just fighting.'

'There's only one cause worth fighting for, and the way to fight for it is to suffer, not trade blows.' Cotton stares at Creasy while he says this, and then transfers his gaze to Lizzie and Sam to include them in this lesson (and in hopes of curbing their obvious glee at Creasy's exploits). He gives a quick sidelong glance to Nancy in order to transfer a morsel of the lesson to her but she is still peering down at her cushion.

'He *has* suffered,' Elizabeth puts in.

'But not for the right, *malheureusement*.' He ruffles his boy's hair as he says this to mitigate the triumphant sting of French.

The outcome is that while Cotton continues with his execution sermon, his battered boy sits in a corner with a Bible, tasked with tracking down in its abundance of pages a useful reference to *peacemakers*.

from *The Staymaker*

SALLY GANDER

'*a corset is a lie, a falsehood, a fiction, but for us,
this fiction is better than reality.*'
— Eugene Chapus, 1862

CHAPTER ONE

The woman stood out on the pavement beyond the shop window, her stark white hair hanging loose down her back and shimmering in the winter sun. She had no bag, no coat, and wore only jeans and a sweater even though the temperature was icy cold. There was something about the way she stood, arms hanging by her side and fingers loosely curled that stopped Gabriel's breath as he waited for her to move on or cross the road, anything so she didn't look so cold and alone. He felt a strange suspension of time as the traffic surged up the road, shoppers and workers brisk and ready to start their day, but this woman and himself held silent and motionless with only a pane of glass between them.

He'd been looking at the scarlet dress on the mannequin in the bay window. There was a gap in the chiffon of the skirt where a bead had dropped and he searched the floor now, moving a step or two so the light would find it, wondering if it was a loose stitch or a mistake when he'd made the dress two years previously, Sarah in the early stages of her illness and his work something he still cared about. That seemed like a distant memory now, a distant life, parcelled away so tight it was almost as though it didn't belong to him.

He felt the dull tug of a job that needed doing and went into the studio at the back of the shop where the coffee pot gurgled in the small corner kitchen. He turned off the gas ring, fetched a needle and thread and the box of beads, and returned to the dress expecting the woman outside to be gone, but no, she was still there, surely growing colder with every passing minute.

He leaned forward to find the gap of light again, the lip of his own corset pressing into his chest but his concentration was caught by the wisps of white hair rising and falling beyond the window. He imagined a frost had gathered around her overnight which would crumble away when she did finally move, the tender shoot of her body budding too early, vulnerable without warmth, without shelter. She could die out there, he thought.

The needle stabbed his thumb and a pearl of blood oozed out. He took a tissue from the box on his desk and pressed it against the wound, opening the top drawer and pushing away the pile of bills to find the box of plasters, wrapping three long strips around his thumb.

The woman seemed to be looking at the church opposite with a paint-peeled sign that declared *Jesus knows your sins and he will save you*. Was this what she was looking at? He wanted her to turn around so he could see her smile but he sensed there would be no smile, her bearing suggesting something closer to despair. He focused on the shallowness of his breath, allowed a narrow surge of adrenaline beneath the rigid steel boning, his laces tight and comforting.

Out in the road the queue of traffic moved on and the woman's shoulders straightened, her fingers curling into loose fists, her head turning a fraction to the right and he sensed she was stepping out into the road but the movement was so fluid and ethereal that he felt mesmerized into a kind of sleepy unreality so that by the time he realized what was happening it was too late, the clamor of an engine, the rush and squeal of pneumatic brakes, the bus hitting her and she was thrown, her body curved in a graceful arc, white hair fanning out like a snowflake with one arm extended to break her fall. Her movement had all the elegance of a ballet dancer and he understood with a shock that he had witnessed a choreography of intent. She lay now in a crumpled heap, the bus stopped a few feet away from her, but slowly she sat herself up and he could see a looseness in her limbs, a sad resignation in the tilt of her head that told him she wasn't seriously hurt, a man rushing to her side and obscuring his view.

He left the needle and thread on his desk and went outside. Already there were more people helping her to her feet, the bus driver pitching out of his seat, wrestling with the door mechanism and shouting with a rage that brought spit flying from his lips, his passengers peering through the windows, hesitant and shocked.

'Didn't you bloody see me?' The bus driver stamped down the steps and stood over her, hands on fat hips. 'What were you bloody doing? What? Are you stupid, is that it?'

The man helped her to her feet, her eyes a stark blue that were framed by pale lashes, lips purple with cold, a bloody graze blooming on her forehead. When she looked at Gabriel his grief for Sarah surged up and he remembered all too clearly the brutality of his longing, his inability to keep it safe within the confines of his body and he had to press it back down into the chambers of his heart, dragging his eyes away to break the spell.

'I've got a bus full of passengers,' the driver yelled. 'What about them, hey?'

The crowd of people began to disperse once they realized the woman was alright and it was only Gabriel, the bus driver and the man that remained.

'I've got a timetable to keep. I can't just—'

'You should go,' Gabriel said, helping the man guide her on to the pavement, 'if that's the choice, you should keep driving your bus.'

'You go on, mate,' the man said. 'We can make sure she's alright.'

The driver opened his mouth to speak but thought better of it and went back to his passengers, complaining to them as he climbed back into his seat.

'Bring her inside,' Gabriel said. 'She needs to sit for a while.'

The bus moved off behind them and they went into the shop, sat her on the sofa. The man squeezed her arms, her shoulders, 'Are you hurt?' he asked. 'Do you have any pain?' When he reached the woman's hands he hesitated, a soft 'Oh' escaping his lips as the woman looked up at him and he pulled his hands away, frowning. 'I need to go,' he muttered, looking at Gabriel. 'I'm on my way to work.'

'I'll look after her,' Gabriel said. 'She can stay here for a rest, I'll make sure she's all right.'

He nodded, glancing back at the woman with a wary expression and Gabriel was desperate for him to leave now, an intruder in their private space. But still he hesitated. Gabriel had always been good at interpreting what people needed, from years of working in an intimate space with his clients he knew that the smallest gesture, the subtlest of eye contact was sometimes all that was needed to give the necessary reassurance; so now he touched the man on his elbow, smiled with complete understanding of his uncertainty, and said, 'Of course, I'll look after her.'

The man nodded again and turned away, went through the door without looking back.

The telephone rang and the woman pulled back into her seat, withdrawing into herself. He went to the desk and picked up the receiver, *'Greene and Knightley,'* he said, quiet and impatient, not his usual telephone manner. 'How may I help you?'

It was Tobias, a regular customer who was due for a fitting that morning. He was having troubles with his lover and he wanted to postpone. Gabriel tried to listen, to engage, but the woman drew his eye, not by anything she did but just by being there, existing in that room, milk pale and delicate.

Tobias was telling him that his lover wanted to leave, to travel, to *live life*, he said, *but isn't he living his life with me?*

She doesn't belong here, Gabriel thought, not in this shop or this city, not even this country. He imagined her coming from a forgotten time when living just meant surviving, finding food, hiding from the enemy, seeking out what little warmth and comfort the landscape had to offer.

What should I do Gabriel? What?

He tried to place her age but couldn't. She could be in her early twenties but the wisdom and expression in her features suggested someone older, someone with experience and knowledge only gleaned from a full past life.

She raised a hand to her forehead, touched the edge of the graze, ran her finger over its raw centre without a flinch and Gabriel realized there was silence down the telephone line, an aching space.

'Come in today, Tobias,' he said, 'it will help you to think, and I'll listen if you want to talk.' Tobias agreed and finally hung up; Gabriel replaced the receiver.

The woman looked at him cautiously and again he was reminded of Sarah, those final few days when she could only ever look at him sideways, as though she was turning more and more towards the darkness that was drawing her in. His heartbeat thudded through his torso with a surge of pain, the blood expanding deep within his ribs and pressing against the bones of his corset with a power to tear fabric and pull apart laces. He was giddy, his vision turning hazy so he was only vaguely aware of the woman pressing her hands against her chest and gradually his pulse slowed, like the winding down of a march, and he found himself gazing into those pale pupils feeling utterly exposed, his pain at losing Sarah like a label pinned to his lapel.

She began to shiver and he said, 'I'll make some tea, it's so cold today.'

He thought she might leave and run into the road again so he gestured for her to follow him through to the back of the shop; the suggestion of a smile crossed her lips.

Once they were in the studio he felt a wave of embarrassment, the clean lines of the shop a stark contrast to the cluttered messiness of the cutting room, a messiness that was clearly winning over Jude's occasional cleaning. He saw the room as this woman must see it: the cutting table in the centre with its mess of tangled calico, frayed ends and knotted cotton, bolts of fabric stacked in the space beneath it; the sewing machine on the table beside the window surrounded by paraphernalia, scissors of varying sizes, cotton reels, pin cushions; rolls of steel boning propped against the wall. The chair stood at an angle as though someone had just left it, and only now did he see its peeling blue paint, the fabric seat torn with yellowing foam bulging out like flesh. There were books stacked on shelves; several free-standing mood boards with haphazardly pinned sketches, sample fabric and lace; another table with the sound system, its CD drawer open like a tongue; and beside it stood a mannequin wearing a calico toile, the nude fabric exacerbating his sense of exposure.

He realized he'd grown sloppy, the calm order of the shop a clear deceit, and just to compound his sense of vulnerability she walked around the cutting table, her finger trailing across its smooth surface and its fine layer of calico dust, moving on to the screen that separated the cutting room from the fitting area, her fingers tracing the delicately painted roses, muted shades of reds, golds and greens, Red Admiral butterflies resting on variegated leaves, ladybirds crawling amongst the thorns, the colours chipped and faded with age.

She swayed slightly, reaching for the edge of the screen to steady herself and he rushed to hold her up, her lips now as white as her skin which was clammy and cold to the touch, and for a brief moment he supported her whole weight until she righted herself again and looked up at him with a gasp, her eyes darkening with fatigue.

'When did you last eat?' Gabriel asked.

She closed her eyes and leaned into him, her full weight light as a bird.

'You should lie down,' he said, 'there's an empty room upstairs. You can rest, have some food.' He thought she would pull away and look at him with suspicion, but she nodded, opening her eyes to follow the floor and concentrate on keeping upright.

He led her beyond the screen and through the fitting area, catching a glimpse of their reflection in the full-length mirror on the opposite wall and the waist-cincher on its stand, waiting for the warmth of Tobias to make it real. How odd they looked, her white skin and white hair so delicate she could drift away, stark against his dark hair and charcoal-grey suit that concealed his solid armour.

He pulled back the heavy curtain in the corner and helped her up the stairs, hoping they wouldn't meet Jude coming down as he was all too aware how intimidating her appearance was, and worse if she was in a dark mood. When they reached the corridor, Jude was coming out of her room and he had the strange sense that she was drawn out by his thoughts. She looked fierce with her shaved head and a map of piercings across her face, a glimpse of tattoos beneath her sleeves.

She stopped, her easy glare shifting from him to the woman.

'Jude,' he said, 'this young lady needs a rest, she'll be in the spare room for a while.'

'What's the deal?'

'She had an accident. Not badly injured I think, just a little shaken.'

They looked at each other and Jude said, 'Don't fuck him around.'

'Jude,' he said quietly, 'I'll be downstairs shortly.' She nodded once and carried on down the corridor, her footsteps hard against the bare floorboards.

The bedroom was sparely furnished except for a single metal-framed bed and bedside table, a chest of drawers in the corner, and a metal rail on wheels with several crooked hangers.

He sat her on the bed. She looked small and lost in the open space of the room. 'Jude works with me,' he said, 'she's strong-minded but she's generous too. A wandering soul, I think.'

She looked up at the postcards on the wall. There were a hundred, maybe more, a jumbled patchwork of places and people.

'People often stay here,' he said. 'It's an open house. People need somewhere they can stop. Just to breathe. To breathe and to think.'

He knew she wouldn't lie down until he was gone so he went back to the door, his hand resting on the handle, wondering if Jude had stayed in the studio or was tumbling out into the city to find an outlet for her restless energy.

'Rest,' he said. 'I'm expecting a customer but I'll come back soon with some food for you.'

He closed the door and walked down the corridor, trembling as he realized he understood something of this woman's soul even though she hadn't said a single word.

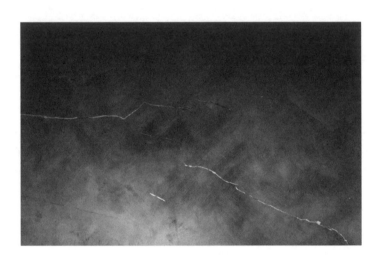

The Sigh of the Moon

SAM GAYTON

At the waist of the world in the middle months, the heat in the city of Arbesque comes close to a fever. The sun glares down on the streets like an infernal blazing eye, and never once does it blink behind a cloud, not until the day boils down to dusk.

Then night comes, and the heat-sick city cools at last. Cold blue stars spread across the sky's brow like beads of sweat, and the wind they call the *Seluna-maquat* – the Sigh of the Moon – blows in from the west, bringing with it the smells of jasmine, and lemon trees, and July storms.

They say to stand in Arbesque, and feel the *Seluna-maquat* tingle on your goosebump-skin, is to know true happiness.

One year – the Year of the Fainting Stars – when the middle months came to the waist of the world, the *Seluna-maquat* did not blow.

The sweet Sigh of the Moon came not to Arbesque.

Now the dusk brought as much torment as the dawn. No one could sleep. Without the cool wind, even the thinnest cotton sheet felt stifling as a feathered quilt. Children thrashed in their beds, listening to the groans of the houses and the cries of the tomcats.

It grew hotter, and hotter, and hotter still.

In the first of the middle months, the paint peeled and flaked from the dome of the Sultan's palace like a sunburned head. And still, the *Seluna-maquat* did not blow.

The second of the middle months came. Shallow, sticky pools of molten glass appeared out amongst the dunes. The desert sand itself was melting. And still the *Seluna-maquat* did not blow.

In the last of the middle months, an old beggar of Arbesque called Koshai lay in his gutter. Looking up, he saw two stars faint in the night sky.

Down they fell into the city below, and the first of them fell right on the very spot where the old beggar had sat ever since he could remember.

Clunk!

It dropped into the wooden bowl Koshai held out for passers-by to fill up with little brown coins, and there it lay – dull, and grey, and round, and no different from the cobbles Koshai had slept on all his life.

The old beggar stared at the fallen star with amazement. He wondered if the night was tricking him with a mirage, like the day often did. Now the wind had gone, it could certainly be so. Perhaps his old eyes had decided to add to his misfortunes by finally failing …

Yet when he reached out his shaking hand, Koshai's fingers touched the star in his begging bowl, and he knew then that it was real.

Koshai picked the star up and held it to his wrinkled face. Now he could see that it was not like a cobble at all. It was a glassy orb, completely smooth and wonderfully cool. The old beggar had never seen ice, not in all his long life, but he had heard of such a thing, and with the cold star in his numb hand Koshai thought to himself: *this must be how ice feels to hold.*

At the centre of the star there was a tiny, twinkling glow. The glow was smaller than a fleck of dust, but – so Koshai thought – more beautiful than the royal diamond the Sultan wore in a ring upon his finger.

The old beggar had never seen a snowflake either, but staring at the cold twinkling at the star's heart Koshai thought to himself: *this must be what it is like to catch a flake of snow.*

As Koshai stared in wonder, the twinkling light grew brighter, and in his ears he was astonished to hear someone speak.

'What happened? What happened? Oh, whatever was that?'

It was the star.

'You fainted from the sky,' answered Koshai, speaking softly into his palm.

The star turned pink at the old beggar's words. 'Fainted?' it asked in a small voice. 'You mean I fell from my place? The shame! Yes, I see – the other stars are laughing at me.'

Koshai craned his neck upwards. 'I don't hear anything.'

'Of course you can't *hear* them!' said the star crossly. It was now the colour of a candle-flame. 'Stars speak the language of light, which cannot be heard, but can only be seen. Look – do you see how they twinkle?'

'Yes,' said Koshai.

'That is their laughter,' said the star, dimming to a dull purple as if it wished to hide.

'Don't be sad,' said Koshai. 'I am glad you came down here to talk to me.'

'And where have I fallen, exactly?' asked the star. 'And who are you?'

'You are in my palm. And I am Koshai, a poor beggar. Tell me, star, do you have a name?'

The star glowed brighter in his hand. 'I am Betelgeuse,' it said.

Koshai smiled, though it hurt his cracked lips. 'Salaam, Betelgeuse. Welcome to Arbesque.'

'Arbesque?' said Betelgeuse, and tremored to green.

'That's right,' said Koshai gently. 'The city at the waist of the world.'

'I should like to know why I left my place in the sky to come here,' huffed the star.

'It must be the heat,' said Koshai. 'Usually, the nights are cooler, but this year the *Seluna-marquat* has stopped blowing, and there is nothing to cool the blazing of the sun –'

It was as if Koshai had lit the fuse of a firework. Betelgeuse bloomed into a kaleidoscope of panicked colours, leapt from his palm, and fell back down again into the gutter.

Koshai picked the star back up.

'The sun!' said Betelgeuse in terror. 'Oh, please not the terrible sun! We stars must hide from *him*! If I am not back in the sky by dawn, the sun will melt me away to nothing! Won't you help me, Koshai? Won't you put me back in my place in the night sky?'

Koshai did not know what to say. He was just a poor beggar. Nobody had ever asked for his help before.

'I am sorry, Betelgeuse,' he said at last. 'I do not think I am tall enough to put you back in the sky.'

'You do not have to be tall!' said the star in his palm. 'If you might but give the sweat from your brow, then I might twinkle brightly again. That would be a start.'

Koshai wiped his forehead with his free hand, and looking down he saw bright beads of sweat on his wrist. Catching Betelgeuse's light, they shone the same colour as the star.

'Gladly should I give my sweat to you, Betelgeuse,' Koshai began. But then he hesitated. A sly thought slid into his mind, as silent and as poisonous as a viper. Before he could stop himself, he added: 'Yes, gladly would I give my sweat to you. But then I would have nothing to keep me cool when dawn comes.'

'Give me your sweat, and I shall give you one wish in return,' Betelgeuse offered. 'For we stars can grant such things to those that do us kindness.'

'Very well,' said Koshai, trying to hide his excitement. And even as he gave Betelgeuse the sweat from his brow, the poisonous thought in his mind raised its green scaled head, and fixed Koshai with its hypnotic stare.

'Would you like anything else?' he asked.

'Next I will need your spit,' said Betelgeuse, who was twinkling fiercely now. 'So that when I hit the roof of the sky, I will stick in place and not fall down to earth again.'

'Gladly will I give you my spit,' said Koshai craftily. 'In return for another wish, of course. For if I give you my spit, my mouth will ever after be terribly dry.'

'Of course, of course, another wish,' said Betelgeuse, who thought only of being back in its constellation by dawn, so that it might escape the glare of the sun.

'It is a deal, then,' said Koshai, and he spat on the back of the star, so that Betelgeuse would stick to the sky. 'Is that all that you need?'

'Give me but one sigh from your lungs,' said Betelgeuse. 'Then I will make myself light enough for one sigh to blow me all the way back to my spot in the heavens.'

'Gladly,' said Koshai greedily. 'Only, I must have a third wish from you, Betelgeuse. For I am so old that every breath might be my last, and so each is precious to me now.'

'Three wishes,' confirmed Betelgeuse. 'Now sigh, please, and I shall grant them.'

Koshai breathed in deep, and out. Like a feather Betelgeuse, the star, drifted from his palm, up into the gleaming sky.

'Oh! Oh! Oh!' said Betelgeuse the star, as it rose slowly up. Already it was the height of the city lanterns that lit the street.

'Thank you, Koshai the beggar. And as promised, I shall grant you three wishes. But you must tell me quick what they are, for soon I will be back in the sky, and unable to hear you, unless you can speak the language of light!'

Of course, Koshai could not, and so he spoke his first wish very quickly and very carefully, for he knew from listening to stories as a child that wishes must be worded just so, or they are liable to go wrong.

'I should like my Luck to visit me at last, Betelgeuse. Nothing has ever gone right for me, from the moment I was born to the instant you fell into my bowl, but now that will change. That is my first wish!'

'Granted,' said Betelgeuse, still rising. And to the wonder of Koshai, from the alley to his left came a beautiful black cat, with eyes as round and gold as coins. It padded silently up to Koshai and sat by his feet, purring.

It was his Luck, come to him at last after a life of begging and misfortune.

Koshai wanted to dance with joy, but he knew he could not celebrate yet, for Betelgeuse was now as high as the red-tiled roofs of the houses, and still rising.

'For my second wish,' he yelled to the star, 'I should like to hold my Youth again. For I am very old, and I have almost forgotten what it was like to be young.'

'Granted,' said Betelgeuse. The star's voice was very faint.

Now Koshai looked around, and down on to his old, stooped shoulder there swooped a tiny bird with feathers blue as sapphire. To his amazement, as the bird touched him, Koshai found his bones no longer aching; his chest no longer wheezing; his skin no longer sagging. His heart began to beat louder and faster, until it was like a drum in his chest.

It was just as he had wished – his Youth had come back to him.

Koshai wanted very much to run to the city's well, and look down into the water far below, for he knew that he would see not the face of an old beggar, but a young boy – a young boy with all the Luck in the world.

Yet now the star was just a sparkling speck above him, and Koshai still had one more wish to make, if Betelgeuse could hear it.

'THIS IS MY FINAL WISH,' he called, cupping his hands and yelling hard enough to wake the Sultan in his palace, 'I WISH TO HOLD MY OWN SOUL.'

Koshai's voice echoed up into the sky, and then there was silence.

He waited, straining his ears for the star's reply.

Finally, echoing down from the heavens, Betelgeuse's faint voice came.

'Granted, Koshai ... And should you see my friend, who fell and fainted too, please show them the same kindness you showed me.'

Koshai did not reply, but looked down into his hand to see what was there. For a moment, in the darkness, it looked like nothing at all.

Then his Soul fluttered, and Koshai gasped. It was a butterfly – with beautiful wings that whirled and swirled with patterns and colour, never staying the same.

How changed Koshai was! Now he had his Luck, his Youth, and his Soul. So long as he kept them close and held on to them tight, he would never grow old, or die, or become a poor beggar again. Such was the power of the wishes he had made.

But far from making him happy, Koshai now felt troubled. What if something happened to any of the creatures around him? What if his Soul fluttered away, or his Youth flew south for the winter, or his Luck found a new owner?

Koshai, who had spent his whole life with nothing, holding out his wooden bowl for anything, now found he held everything, and the thought of losing it all was almost more than he could bear.

And in his mind, the poisonous viper that had slithered there and made its nest raised its head.

And with its flickering tongue, told Koshai what to do.

He acted at once: first he caught his butterfly Soul, and dangled it in front of the blue bird.

Snap! With one gulp, Koshai's Soul disappeared down the beak of his Youth. Pressing his ear to the bird's tiny chest, Koshai heard the butterfly wings fluttering around in panic.

'Now my Soul can never leave me,' he cried in triumph. 'As for my Youth ...'

Trapping the frantic bird in his hands, Koshai offered it to his golden-eyed Luck.

Gulp! Koshai's Youth was swallowed whole too. Now the butterfly was inside the belly of the bird, inside belly of the cat. Koshai picked the silky black creature up in his arms and stroked its head softly, until it fell into a deep purring sleep.

Now Koshai's Soul and Youth were trapped safely inside his Luck. And yet strangely he felt no better than he did before. His face was flushed, his breath came heavy, and his mouth tasted of nothing but dust.

'It is just the sweat, the spit, and the sigh that I gave to Betelgeuse,' Koshai told himself. 'In but a few moments, all those things will come back to me.'

He waited patiently, and come back they did. Yet the strange anxiousness did not leave. If anything, it worsened.

And suddenly, Koshai knew what it was.

'I did not ask Betelgeuse for *Happiness*!' he cried, slapping his forehead. 'I have everything but that! Oh, what a fool you are, Koshai!'

Yet all was not lost. For he had seen *two* stars fall down to Arbesque, and Betelgeuse was but the first. If he could but find the other, he might ask to hold his Happiness ...

At once, and still with his sleeping Luck in his arms, Koshai set off to search the city's midnight streets.

He no longer hobbled or wheezed as he walked. Merchants who had once shooed him away from their pyramids of pomegranates and dates now nodded to him and murmured *Salaam*. The beggars he had spent his whole life beside – Abed and Yasir and the swaddled leper who swore he was rightful king of Jaffa – none of them recognised Koshai. They raised their bowls up to him and muttered their piteous sounds.

Koshai walked past them all. He strode through dusty plazas, past dried-out fountains, under palm fronds that were dry and brown like the pages of old books. The moonlight lay upon the streets like a nurse's cool hand on some fevered forehead. Koshai kept a hold tight on the golden-eyed cat in his arms. The creature squirmed in his grip, but he did not let it go. He could not. In his heart, the strange unhappiness spread through him like a sickness, and Koshai – who had known thirst and hunger, who had known old age and misfortune – had never felt any misery to match it.

'Oh, where is that second star I saw?' he whimpered. 'I must find it, I must have its wishes.'

And he felt the green serpent, whose name was Greed, stir within him.

Perhaps Koshai would have searched Arbesque forever, until he grew old and bent-backed again; and perhaps if that had happened this story might have held a moral at its centre, as a plaza holds a fountain; and the moral might have gushed forth sparkling lessons such as: 'Careful what you wish for', or 'Happiness comes to those who give'.

But Koshai held his Luck, did he not? And so, in no time at all, he found himself stumbling by happy accident down a dark alleyway, where, shining bright as the diamond in the Sultan's ring, a second star lay weakly on the sand.

Koshai bent down and picked it up. This star was plump and purple as a fig.

'Salaam, star,' he said craftily. 'Do you need help?'

'Help?' exclaimed the star. 'Help?! How presumptuous! How preposterous! The great Rigel needs no help! Help, indeed!'

Koshai frowned. Rigel was a much more pompous star than Betelgeuse. Wishes would have to be wheedled out of him.

'Very well, Rigel,' Koshai said. 'I shall leave you here to sunbathe –'

In his hand, Rigel darkened to the colour of a week-old bruise.

'Sunbathe?' it cried. 'Sunbathe? What sort of fool are you? Whoever heard of a sunbathing star? I am ... I am simply here *moon*bathing. That is why I fainted – ahem, I mean fell – pardon me, *descended* down to this ... this place where I am.'

Koshai shrugged. 'Of course. I am but an ignorant beggar. It is just that this is Arbesque's sunniest spot, and we are but minutes from sunrise. So I shall leave you to finish your moonbathing and get back to your spot in the sky.'

Watching the star's colour craftily, Koshai leaned down, as if to place Rigel back in the dust.

'Leave me?' spluttered the star. 'Leave? How rude! I have not yet given you permission!'

Koshai bowed deeply so that Rigel would not see his smile. 'How right you are. And it would be rudeness too if I did not help you back up to the heavens after your moonbathing.'

The star made a little sniffing sound. 'Yes,' it said. 'Quite so.'

Koshai was trembling with anticipation now. Inside him, his Greed hissed, as if it could taste the wishes with its forked and flickering tongue. He was gripping his Luck so tight under his arm, the cat began to wriggle and squirm.

'Perhaps you would like the sweat from my brow, the spittle from lips, and a sigh from my lungs?' Koshai asked Rigel.

Rigel turned pink. A deep gong sound came from the star's core. 'Spittle?' it shrieked. 'Sweat? How disgusting! No, that will not do at all. Tie me to a firework. That would be more fitting.'

Koshai scowled. 'Firework? Star, I have but sweat and spittle and my own breath. That will be quite enough to send you on your way.'

'A bird, then. Preferably a dove.'

Koshai had a bird, but it was the blue bird of his life, and he was not giving it away. He began to feel angry. Within him, Greed bared its fangs, and hot poison dripped through the beggar and sizzled.

Before Rigel said any more, Koshai acted.

Lick!

Drip!

Huff!

In a few seconds it was done. The star in his hand spluttered.

'Outrageous!' it cried. 'Outrageous!'

'It is done now,' snapped Koshai. 'See how you rise up? Now give me my wishes, quick!'

Rigel flashed so cold and so bright that Koshai was dazzled. 'I shall do no such thing!' it bellowed as it rose. 'You are a rude and nasty creature, and I shall never go moonbathing here again!'

Koshai's face twisted in rage. He lunged up with both hands to yank the rising star back down. Rigel would be his hostage until he gave Koshai the wishes he deserved!

It wasn't until both his hands clapped themselves around Rigel that Koshai realised he had dropped his Luck.

With a yowl, the golden-eyed cat fell to the ground with a thump. It gave one shuddering jerk, and Koshai's Youth flew from its mouth on blue wings. At the same time, the butterfly of Koshai's Soul emerged from the startled, gawping bird.

Before Koshai could gather them up again, the bird had vanished into the sky, the butterfly had flittered over a wall, and the cat had darted beneath his feet and away.

Koshai was old again.

And mortal.

And unlucky.

'Ah, this night!' he wheezed, his voice as ancient as the dust beneath his feet. 'I have held it all, and lost it all, and been unhappy all the while! And what it more, it is all the fault of my Greed!'

And reaching within himself, Koshai drew the viper of his Greed out from its hateful nest, and cast it from him forevermore.

Old and hunched, Koshai stood in the almost dawn with a star in his hand.

'Who are you?' it asked him querulously. 'Have you rescued me from that terrible young man?'

Koshai did not know what to say. Of course, Rigel recognised him no longer, for he was old again, and the Greed that had filled him with its poison was gone.

'You should be getting back to your place in the heavens, star,' he said simply. 'Sunrise comes any moment.'

'Indeed!' Rigel said. 'Do you have a firework, perchance? Or a bird? I should like a dove best of all.'

'Alas no,' said Koshai. 'I have none of these things.'

Rigel flushed pink with embarrassment. 'I see,' it said. 'That is a shame, for … for I cannot get to where I must go. Not on my own.'

And the star looked so sorrowful that Koshai's heart was filled with Pity, which is a far gentler creature than Greed, and he found himself saying: 'Why not ask the wind? Perhaps it can blow you back to the sky.'

At once, Rigel sparkled bright. 'Your suggestion is splendid!' it said. 'The wind! I did not know she travelled down here as well!'

'She does,' said Koshai. 'Though she has not visited Arbesque for many a month …'

'Why, that is no problem,' Rigel declared. 'We stars speak the language of light, you know, and we sparkle over half the world. She is surely blowing somewhere, is she not? I will ask my friend Betelgeuse to find her.'

At once, Rigel twinkled, and above him, in the constellation Koshai called the Huntress, Betelegeuse shone back.

'Here!' Rigel said with a chortle. 'Here she comes. Oh, I am indebted to you, my friend. Will you hold me up as she passes?'

Koshai raised up his thin arms, and on his bare skin he felt the faintest tickling.

Like a breath against his skin.

Like a sigh.

Cool as moonlight.

And it was then that, finally, the *Seluna-maquat* blew in from the desert to flutter the dust from the market awnings, to soothe the children thrashing in their sleep, and silence the howling tomcats of Arbesque.

'My thanks!' said Rigel as the sigh of the moon carried the star aloft. 'You have helped me, friend! I should be glad to offer you a wish?'

But Koshai, the old and unlucky beggar, did not hear him. His eyes were closed and his Soul was still. A smile was on his lips, and would be forevermore. They say to stand in Arbesque, and feel the *Seluna-maquat* tingle on your goosebump-skin, is to know true happiness.

On Starting Your Book, and Finding Your Reader: a Proposal

MAGGIE GEE

1

Starting your book – I know, that's hard. A new project: at Bath Spa we call it a 'Manuscript Proposal', the brief, hopeful statement of intent that writers submit about their unwritten book – let's say, for argument today, a piece of creative non-fiction, since that's what I've just been teaching. Maybe the idea of a proposal catches the element of falling in love that you need with a new project – will you marry me and live alongside me for months and maybe years and right to the end, however bitter-sweet? The end of your arc: where the curve of the narrative, you hope, will touch ground, some time in the future, in the real world of readers.

2

What the idea of a proposal doesn't catch is the loneliness and risk that all creative acts involve. Yes, Creative Writing courses offer the (mostly supportive, sometimes competitive) company of other writers and, in our case, the help of your own dedicated manuscript tutor who is at your side from the start to the finish of the project. The promise is simple and important: where you go, I will go with you.

But the truth is, we can never be there when it counts most, at the moments when the book is actually struggling into being. Because everyone writes alone, and though writing is read as though it were a continuous unfurling, the truth is it has to start somewhere, the truth is it will start and stop many times along the way, and the very beginning is when a writer is loneliest of all.

To all my fellow writers just setting out along a newly stretched tightrope in the early morning mist, one step, then another step, shoulders a little tense (relax them), eyes on the future – good luck! You will need it. Going out over the void of the unwritten is never going to be easy.

But there hanging in the mid-distance in front of you, glowing, multicoloured, too tiny to decode, is the image of the perfect book you are going to write. Nothing has happened to spoil it yet. It is the jewelled dream of the book. It is what keeps all writers inching forward: one day we will get there.

Wait a moment, though, what are we doing, exactly?

And you, you in particular. Why are you here?

3

Why are you writing something down in the first place, spending too long at the computer, missing the fun other people are having? Why have you abandoned dog, home, garden, lover, family, job, sleep, to do this odd and painful thing? Your friends, your partner, your parents, may be puzzled, suspicious, respectful, proud, and anxious: what if you are deluded? Why are you paying good money, with no guarantee of a pot of gold at the end? Why are you undaunted now you are here, as tutor after tutor points out how difficult the market is, how rare success?

What you are beginning is, in fact, not a simple stating of something, a mere unfolding of a mental plan. No, you are drafting a message, and the message is one you have to write, one you are impelled to write.

And the message is going to someone. If it were not so, the book could stay inside your head, and you could avoid all that struggle, the locked muscles, the snowdrifts of drafts, the nerves before workshopping; the mysteriously obtuse tutors (they don't like it), the occasional brilliantly perceptive tutor (she loves it!); all the rigours of feedback, the multicoloured, maddened cat's cradles of suggested 'track changes' edits, every single one, at first, an affront to the purity of your intent. (Though tomorrow, if you're like me dealing with edits, you may accept most of them.)

If a book were not a message to someone else, it need never be effort-fully hauled into the light. But the message must be read. If you are writing non-fiction, you want to tell people something new about the world, some-thing you alone have seen and lived from this particular angle. You want another human being to see it that way, to realise what you have realised.

Yes, the first thing you need is a reader.

4

One way I can gauge how important readers are to me is my mental computa-tion of how many books I have written. I would say I've written 14 books with another almost ready to go. Yet in addition to the 14 on the shelf, there are another two large, hefty hardbacks objects on the shelf that have my name on. They are my master's and doctoral theses, and I never consider them to be books. Why not? Because they have both had only four documented readers – in each case my supervisors and my two examiners. So to me, evidently, it is readers who complete a book, readers who bring the writing into a shared world of discussion, shared emotion, recognition.

Starting to write may be hard, but finding the reader is harder. Creative writing courses offer something very important: interested and committed 'initial readers'. By that I mean 'readers who read a work in progress'. Your manuscript tutor is paid to read, to encourage and advise; your workshop cohort is motivated to read by mutual self-interest – if they read you and offer constructive feedback, you will do the same for them.

But 'initial readers' are not the same as the ideal reader you will need at the end of your endeavour. The ideal reader does not read to critique or to praise; they do not read provisionally, half immersed. The ideal reader, once hooked, sinks into your work and becomes part of it for the duration.

The ideal reader does not know you beforehand.

The ideal reader pays.

5

I nearly called this piece 'hailing your reader' – as in grabbing a black taxi out of the loud, indifferent, traffic-thronged streets of London. In a bookshop hundreds of books are all looking to attract that one reader who just walked through the door, ready to make an impulse buy.

Snaring a reader happens in two stages. Books in codex form – i.e. not parchment scrolls or wax tablets but layers of sequential pages – are characterised by being closed and having covers. In this they differ from the touchscreen digital content with which they are competing; the printed book has elements of privacy and distance that recall its origins as a high status object meant for ecclesiastical, royal or moneyed elites. So the first challenge for the book in this democratic age is to convert the barrier of its cover into bait for the passing reader, who must be lured into stopping and opening it. The excellence of current book cover design, particularly in non-fiction, an area that is harder to sell than fiction, is evidence of how seriously publishers take this challenge. Covers are ingenious, aesthetically pleasing, exciting, hot or cool as the book requires. The designers are doing their very best to pull readers towards our pile of copies.

Let's pretend that our reader has paused and picked up the book. Now he or she is reading that all-important first paragraph, that crucial first page. Have we got it right? Will we catch their attention, will they read on and eventually take the book to the till because they can't bear not to read the rest of it? Sometimes everything depends on the beginning.

6

Fiction is famous for show-stopping beginnings. Charles Dickens's *David Copperfield* heads its first chapter 'I am born', and continues 'Whether I shall turn out to be the hero of my own life, or whether that station will be held by anybody else, these pages must show.' Angela Carter starts *Heroes and Villains* at a cracking pace with 'Marianne had sharp, cold eyes and she was spiteful but her father loved her.' And here's Peter Carey, mystifying and intriguing the reader in *Bliss* with 'Harry Joy was to die three times, but it was his first death which was to have the greatest effect on him, and it is this first death which we shall now witness.'

When a reader picks up a novel, effectively there are just two parties in the relationship which begins, the reader and the writer, because the reader knows that the world he is entering is wholly made up by the writer. These fictional beginnings all say to the reader, in one way or another, 'Hey, I am going to entertain you – stick around and be dazzled and amused.'

When a reader crosses the threshold of a non-fiction book a different relationship is starting, involving three parties – the writer, the reader, and the real world, a world in which the reader also lives, and about which she or he has knowledge, opinions, and beliefs. Fortunately readers also have gaps in their knowledge they are curious to fill. Today's reader needs to be convinced that this particular writer – you or I – is the right person to do that job.

Looking at the beginnings of non-fiction books, I am fascinated by how much they have changed over the two millennia since Roman historian Cornelius Tacitus wrote his history *Germania*, in AD 97-99. Which begins like this, briskly impersonal and full of imperial certainty: the external world is simply there.

> Germany as a whole is separated from the Gauls and from Ractians and Pennonians by the rivers Rhine and Danube: from the Sarmatians and Dacians by mutual misgivings or mountains: the rest of it is surrounded by the ocean, which enfolds wide peninsulas and islands of vast expanse ... The Rhine, rising from the inaccessible and precipitous crest of the Ractian Alps, after turning west for a reach of some length is lost in the North Sea.

Whereas this is the beginning of Carole Shelby Carnes's intriguing 2014 social history of a town in the American South, *A Street in a Town Remembered: a Memoir of Shelby, Mississipi (1852-2010)*:

> I have always had difficulty with directions apart from up and down. Right, left, north, south were matters that have made me pause for reflection ...

Our contemporary historian begins with a confession of fallibility about where things are and a willingness to share her 'reflection' with the reader – and that's more than a geographical demurral, since the American Civil War and the fallout of north-south conflict and racial fault-lines are central to her history.

In the tripartite relationship between reader, world and writer; first-century AD Tacitus takes his reader for granted and simply addresses himself with magisterial certainty to the world; whereas twenty-first-century Carole Shelby Carnes admits she has no claims to omnipotent knowledge, confides her flaws to the reader, and effectively asks him or her to humour her and like her.' 'I'm ready to talk,' she seems to say. 'Come with me.' This book, like so many other contemporary works of creative non-fiction, is the story of a quest for understanding rather than a simple imparting of knowledge acquired. The relationship between writer and reader is now in the foreground.

This technique is equally an acknowledgement of the window frame through which both will be looking. Albert Einstein drew the world's attention to the importance of 'the man at the railway carriage-window', in other words the specific reference point from which objects or events are seen. Once you acknowledge that the point of view of the observer changes what is observed, introducing the writer-observer to the reader becomes essential.

Here's another example of a non-fiction beginning where everything rests on the compact between the writer and his audience, Colin Grant's brilliant 2016 book about epilepsy, *A Smell of Burning*.

'Are you epileptic?' Almost everyone asked this when I told them that I was writing a book about epilepsy. I would like to have said 'yes' to see where the conversation went. On some level, answering 'no' felt like a betrayal. When they followed up with the question, 'Why are you writing about it?' I would describe this scenario.

A man writhes on the ground. His arms slap and snap about him. His legs kick out at some invisible enemy ... A strange guttural sound comes from his throat and his mouth froths with foam. Your journey to work is abruptly interrupted by the sight of him. Perhaps the man is drunk ... You move on. Of course you do.

'That man,' I would say to the people who asked about the book, 'is my brother, Christopher.'

This is the special point of view from which the book is written, then: that of a brother, and, we find as the book progresses, a bereaved brother. 'Trust me, reader', this beginning seems to say. 'I have been there.' There's another interesting tactic in these paragraphs where Grant is wooing his new reader, and that is the use of 'You' – 'Your journey to work is abruptly interrupted' – to implicate and involve the reader personally in the story he is telling.

Claudia Rankine's extraordinary and controversial, semi-poetic non-fiction book about race in America, *Citizen: An American Lyric*, addresses the reader as 'You' from the very start, but differently to Grant. I think she does it as a way of making the 'You' of the reader, who might be black or white, one and the same as the black 'I' who is telling the book and feeling the pain. She starts like this:

When you are alone and too tired even to turn on any of your devices, you let yourself linger in a past stacked among your pillows. Usually you are nestled under blankets and the house is empty. Sometimes the moon is missing and beyond the windows the low, grey ceiling

seems approachable ... you fall back into that which gets reconstructed as metaphor.

The route is often associative. You smell good. You are twelve
attending Sts Philip and James School on White Plains Road and the
girl sitting in the seat behind asks you to lean to the right during
exams so she can copy what you have written ... The girl is Catholic
with waist-length brown hair ... You never really speak except for
the time she makes her request and later when she tells you you
smell good and have features more like a white person. You assume
she thinks she is thanking you for letting her cheat and feels better
cheating from an almost white person.

How does this work? I think it is a very intimate beginning. The reader
is actually asked into bed with the writer, to share her pillow. And then the
reader has to share the awkwardness and shame of the long-haired schoolgirl
who accidentally insults the writer, aged twelve, by showing she thinks 'looking like a white person' is something admirable.

7

Some of this relates to what I was teaching a week or so ago at Stockholm
University as part of their creative linkup with Bath Spa, which made me
think about non-fiction, and about readers, and beginnings, in ways that
were new for me. (One good thing about teaching is that you have to keep
refreshing your knowledge and your approach, partly because new reading
matter and new ideas come in all the time from students.)

But how does the reader's experience of beginnings relate to my own
writing process, and to yours? What happens to the reader on the first page
is not the same as the process of beginning to write, and beginning to write
again, that the writer undergoes. And yet we need some of the same fresh-
ness, the same energy, some of which can only be drawn from reading. It's
one of the questions we ask at interview: what do you read?

Like most writers, the more I have written, the more I have learned there
is more than one way to get going. Bath Spa's teacher-writers will all have
completely different techniques, which we will all press upon you with equal
conviction. You will find your own, or you have already found it, and then
over the course of your life as a writer, you will find others.

The cautious tightrope artist's walk that I described in the second section of this piece is not always true to my experience of starting novels. When

I am writing fiction I alternate between paralysis and absolute rashness. After weeks or months or years of procrastination or 'research', followed by a few jittery days of unnecessary self-grooming and making foolish purchases online, one morning I will sit down with my notebooks or at the computer and suddenly rush out headlong across the void, trying to go so fast in my first draft that I do not have time to fall off. I will use 'word count' in a blunt and brutal way to keep going: x thousand words a day (that is not a Roman '10', relax, it is 'x' for a variable number of thousands, less now than when I was younger and did not make a connection between spending too many hours at the computer and RSI or 'repetitive strain injury', the writer's nemesis, which likes to hover in the wings. But I mostly ignore it! Surely I will just ABOUT beat it to the end of the book. DO NOT TRY THIS AT HOME.)

After the minimal number of weeks or months I will plunge panting on to the far end of the rope, without much idea of what appalling carnage I have left behind me. Then it's time, after a pause to recover, to find out what I wrote. And to edit. And re-edit. And re-edit again.

Oh, but I nearly forgot my best tip, my 'Favourite Tip', which I will now insert into the text for free: write the end first. Yes, how to begin, paradoxically: start with the end.

I do actually do this when I am writing novels. If I write the ending, just a few pages, maybe just a single page or single paragraph, it helps me to believe that eventually there will be an end to this labour, and that I will reach it.

But non-fiction – that's a very different matter. And we are seeing more of it here at Bath Spa. There is more memoir: there is more bio-fiction – that interesting, problematic genre of narrative where real people come back to life in books that are somewhere between fact and fiction.

8

Just over half-a-dozen years ago I decided to take a break from fiction and write my life – which would only be interesting to the reader, it seemed to me, because of what it had in common with other lives. It would be boring if I just told my life from A to Z. Instead I thought, why am I writing it? I am writing it to understand my short life on this planet. Out there must be thousands of other human beings doing just the same thing, and probably asking just the same questions as me. And so I made a list of questions, and structured the book according to my list, setting out my questions at the very beginning and then trying to answer each one in turn by thinking through what I had learned in my life – in a way, thinking it through alongside the reader.

The research did matter, though. I have living brothers and cousins; I had to try to get my facts straight. The things you are most sure you remember may be the things you get most wrong. At last I sorted out how old I was when the Berlin wall went up and during the Cuban missile crisis, events which seeded in me the horror of war that emerges in all my fiction. Closer to home, I found that photographs, maps and plans helped me most. Drawing a map of the houses and gardens where we lived, and then, within those, drawing a plan of each room, helped me remember so many incidents. Once I had the fireplace and the table, I remembered the cups and saucers on the table and the events around the fireplace – how we dried ourselves around the fire in the lounge after washing our hair or ourselves in the kitchen sink, for example. Colours of things returned, location of windows brought back a memory of the views they revealed.

And yet the biggest challenge was getting a reader to look through the window with me. That was the hardest thing. My non-fiction book was not a race through a story but a jigsaw of thought and images whose ordering and re-ordering took longer than anything else. And how to begin? How to find my reader?

After many false starts and moments of despair I began *My Animal Life* with what I might call a 'coo-er' fact, an 'amazing fact' that at the same time binds in the reader with me, the writer.

I am alive at the time of writing this. And so are you. For nearly four billion years of life on earth, neither of us existed: we were a blank. For the next few billion years before the sun burns up the earth, our bodies will be bones under the ground, or ash, asleep ... we are between two states of non-being, two endless nights. Unprepared, we are thrust on stage. The light is on, the eye open. Life!

I am reminding the impulse buyer, the reader pausing just for a split second in his or her ramble round the bookshop one Saturday morning, that this brief electric moment of contact between us as he or she riffles through my first pages is just a metaphor for something much deeper we hold in common. That we are suspended in the same brief stretch of time in the enormity of history and pre-history, and that my book has things to say – in the ear of this reader, this particular reader who I desire – about what we share.

Something remarkable happens every year at Corsham Court when the new cohort of MA writers arrive, hurrying past the mad black frozen sea of topiary to one side. Now they are entering the heavy blue door of our wing of the beautiful, pale stone house that the lucky peacocks flash erratically across. Soon, safe inside the door, dozens of new myths begin feeling their way into being, just as the books of the tutors have done. They gather like mist on the lawns, they propose themselves in spectral form in December, but by the following spring they are rooted like young trees, almost inevitable, becoming part of the world.

Books, like trees, must begin somewhere. At our best, what we do in the shelter of the Court is help them to grow: upwards and outwards, towards the happy end, towards the reader.

Writing Through the Thinning

EMMA GEEN

My first term at Corsham Court was spent searching for Narnia. The estate, with its air of waiting history, had no right not to be guarding some secret magic or portal to another world; so I fumbled at the back of ancient cupboards, up twisting flights of stairs, face first into ha-has and down dead-end passages of foliage; in this way covering every available inch of the building and grounds. My hunt was finally rewarded with the discovery of an iron key, the heft of which fit snugly into the palm of my hand but no lock I could ever find. I laid it back to rest in the cupboard where it had been waiting, along with the ladybird stirrings of a dormant childhood excitement.

Adventure has a long history of letting me down. As a lonely country child subsisting on a diet of fantasy, spells would come over me in which I felt that if I was only to rush to the end of the lane or the duck-house at the bottom of our garden then my call to adventure would be waiting. A conviction that would only be disabused by standing, barefooted from the urgency, in the chill mud as our indifferent ducks nattered around me. I'd return to the house haunted by the feeling that my life had been stillborn.

Disappointment bred desolation and, at last, I shared the despair with my father who told me that I would just have to find the real magic in the world. To my young ears, it felt a cold consolation but, with time, I grew up, or at least older, and became a writer.

Adventure is not random, it arises in certain situations. One of the most common in fantasy fiction is called the 'Thinning'. This trope describes a world in decline, where heroes are called upon to restore their lessening reality as magic fades and the land sickens, often to the point of becoming a parody of itself.

I write this piece at such a time. Magic is draining from the world at a terrifying rate. Though such spells have their own knowing, the names we have given them are Po'o-uli, Beysehir Bleak, Bubal Hartebeest, Marquesan Swamphen, Pyrenean Ibex, Chinese Paddlefish, Yangtze River Dolphin and others too numerous to list. These magics have passed from the world forever but others under threat include empathy, inclusion and the embrace of diversity. Not to mention that, in the scrabbling of the right to 'make American great again' and establish 'Empire 2.0', the West is steadily crumpling into parody.

You need only put an ear to ground to hear the low thunder of bedrock that announces that the gods that have ruled over the Western world in recent centuries are dying, suffocated by their own excesses. Fascism is crawling out from under the bed and into positions of power. Climate scientists are uncertain what course the collapse of ecosystems will follow but can promise that portents are disastrous and may even spell the extinction of all life on Earth. Capitalism and consumerism, raptly, inevitably, proceed to eat along the length of their own tails; for, when humanity grows blind to everything beyond itself, nothing else is left to devour.

Faced with such Thinning, it can be hard to see recourse to anything beyond despair or apathy. Scratch the tissue-thin ideologies that rule our lives and nihilism rears its head from beneath the surface of all things like some Lovecraftian horror. In comparison to such malignant forces, the lives of individuals seem to pale to an insignificance bordering on comic. It's almost amusing to appreciate that never in any of the dystopian tracts of recent years did anyone ever imagine that the overwhelming response to pending apocalypse would be a profound 'meh'. Yet, when the narratives that underlie our personal life stories quake and shatter, emotional denial should be of no surprise.

Creators of fiction are no more immune to the wailing and gnashing of teeth than anyone else and in recent months many writers have seen their horror at the headlines lead to a thinning of their daily word counts. Set against the reach of recent events it's hard to resist the idea that our scribblings count less than ever. Few writers have achieved the enlightened state of divorcing their care from their own success, myself least of all, and yet, at the same time, it becomes increasingly apparent how little reviews and prizes and book sales really count. When dwarfed against the numbing vastness of the Thinning, none of us appear to matter in and of ourselves. But perhaps, in some small way, our words can. It would be a mistake to wait for Gandalf to carve symbols into our doors or a watery lady to thrust swords into our hands but in the murder of an MP by a right-wing terrorist, or the unmarked starvation of yet another a polar bear, or an unnaturally warm January, the Thinning whispers that the hour of our call to adventure is finally at hand.

For when the gods are dying, we must birth new ones. When magic fades, we weavers of the imagination must reverse the tide. And when people on the precipice fall into apathy, the arts must teach us how to dance, clear-eyed, at the edge of the world.

To say that it behoves writers to hold back such uncannily colossal forces of destruction is a responsibility large enough to be crippling and none of us can expect to engineer any great turning on our own. Yet there is a sense by which just doing what writers do is a beginning in itself.

If we follow the ideas that drive the current Thinning back to their roots we eventually find ourselves in the Enlightenment with its new understanding of the self. The notion of selfhood originated, of course, much earlier but it was this era that took identity and rendered it increasingly discrete. Though the emancipation of women and colonized people lagged behind, Western man increasingly understood himself as separate from body, nature and his fellow humans. This turn of thinking was positive in many regards, giving us advanced philosophies of bodily autonomy, human rights and secular democracy, yet the increasing emphasis on the self also carried the threat of an inward turn that could blind us to the ways in which the self is ontologically dependent on that which lies outside its boundaries. New distances between people, both figurative and literal, began to splinter through society and it was in large part the need to bridge these gaps that saw a new aesthetic and moral technology explode in popularity. Its name? The novel.

With its fascination towards the passionate inner lives of characters, the novel embraced new notions of selfhood while simultaneously closing the gaps they entailed by inviting readers to temporarily dissolve their individuality into the concerns of others. These small acts of literary magic were, arguably, what was later to be referred to by George Elliot as the 'sympathetic imagination', as 'a mode of amplifying and extending contact with our fellow men beyond the bounds of our personal lot'.[1] In this way she, and other writers, aimed to gift the reader the power to better 'imagine and to feel the pains and joys of those who differ from themselves'.[2] The novel, in other words, became a key technology for empathy.

To put it another way, I believe that the spell writers can weave against the Thinning is to remind people what it is to love. Any reader well-versed in fantasy may well cringe at the tired trope in which love is revealed to be the power behind magic, yet this cynicism is misplaced when one of the most troubling aspects of dominant Western ideology is that it has blinded us to love's very nature. Not only have we been misled into thinking of it as primarily Eros; but Capitalism has consistently sold us the misconception that love is an act of seizing hold of another as a possession and that this, in turn, is best achieved through commodity driven self-actualization. In short, that love is an act of buying and owning.

Iris Murdoch offers a truer definition when she writes that 'love is the extremely difficult realisation that something other than oneself is real'.[3] Little wonder then that it has been perverted and dismissed as a serious force for change when it is the exact antithesis of an era defined by the pursuit of self-interest and the atomisation of people. For love is what happens when we resist the urge to seize the other for our needs and instead open ourselves to the possibility of the other entering and changing us. Love, I would argue, is that same creature as being lost in a good book.

Somewhere in Corsham Court, a key that has no lock lies in an old cupboard alongside an upturned stapler and a piece of blank paper. It feels fitting that I never found where to put it because the doors we writers must now desperately work to open are not those of wood but those into the minds of others. For if we can succeed in prising open the insular self, then these cracks may yet be enough for magic to seep back into the world.

Alphabetical alchemists, ink illusionists, enchanters of the page, all you minor hedge-witches, our time is now.

---

[1] G. Eliot 'The Natural History of German Life', *Westminster Review*, (1856) 55.

[2] E. George, 'To Charles Bray' in G. Haight, ed., *The George Eliot Letters Vol. 3*, (New Haven, 1954) 110–11.

[3] I. Murdoch, 'The Sublime and the Good', *Chicago Review*, 13 / 3 (1959) 51.

Going Out

GIANCARLO GEMIN

Jenny smiles at me. 'We're not saying "no", but Mr and Mrs Carter, and me, are just a bit worried.'

'I been in the town loads,' I say.

'But not on your own,' says Mrs Carter.

'I know which bus,' I say. 'I know where to get off. I know where to get it to come back.'

Jenny's smile goes sort of stiff and she looks at Mrs Carter.

'I'm sure he'll be fine,' says Mr Carter, standing at the sink. Mrs Carter doesn't even look at him and I don't think she's happy about him saying that.

'That mean I can go?'

Mrs Carter looks at Jenny who gives this tiny nod.

They go on about the mobile phone and calling regularly and Mrs Carter gives me a twenty-pound note, which is a result. So I'm putting my coat on and I suddenly feel scared. I want to turn round and say, '*You made me scared now! I was fine before you went on and on …*'

They say goodbye and I'm outside and the door clunks behind me. I try not to look back, but by the time I reach the corner of the street I can't stop myself – there's Mrs Carter watching from the window.

If they hadn't made such a thing about it I'd be OK, you know? As soon as I see the bus my heart's thumping, and when the bus stops the doors hiss open like a warning.

I sit in a seat and let out my breath. I wonder if the other passengers can tell it's my first time out on my own, but they stare out the windows or down at their phones.

I wish the journey is longer as the bus comes into the centre. I stand up. The hiss of the doors warn me again before I step on to the pavement. The weird thing is when I came into town before with Mr or Mrs Carter I never noticed the noise, but now it's like ten times as loud and ten times as many people.

I feel stiff as I walk, like I need to concentrate to make my legs work, and I realise I haven't thought about where I want to go, or what I'm going to do. I remember the indoor market – I like that place, but I'm going in the wrong direction. I don't want to turn around. You can't stand out – know what I mean? I stop at a shop window just to pretend I'm looking at stuff. I walk the other way and check to see if anyone's noticed.

The noises change as I go into the indoor market, like I'm in a big room. Everything seems brighter than when I'd been before, and even the smell of food and stuff is stronger.

I stop at the pet store. There's loads of cages of birds screeching, while the hamsters and mice sleep – furballs in the straw. In another cage, there's a black and white kitten. It has blue eyes, and it gazes up at me, meowing, but I can't actually hear it because of all the noise. It must be thinking, *where AM I?* I feel like I'm going to start crying.

'Sweet. Isn't it?'

I turn and the man's looking down at me.

'Why's it on its own?' I ask.

'It's the last one – sold the others.'

I wonder who would buy a kitten and leave one behind.

'D'you want it?'

'No.'

I walk away. It's funny, but seeing that cat makes me forget I'm on my own for the first time. The cat's face stays on my mind, until I hear my name called out.

Two girls are standing, looking at me. I don't recognise them at first, 'til I realise it's cos they're not in school uniform.

'Where you off?' she asks – don't know her name. Maybe they've been sent to check on me, know what I mean?

I shrug my shoulders. 'In town on my own,' I say. 'Mrs Carter …'

'Who?'

'She's …' I feel all hot. I like the girl next to the gobby one – she's not smirking, just looking at me.

'Taking us for lunch then?'

I can't tell if the gobby one's joking or not. 'No,' I say. 'Gotta go.'

I look up at the roof of the market, like that's where I got to go.

'See you then.'

They turn and go, the gobby one giggling. The one I like looks back.

I walk and walk. I'm enjoying being on my own now – no one can tell me what to do or where to go. I can't remember feeling that before. I don't feel scared. I think Mrs Carter and Jenny believe there are bad people everywhere, but I haven't seen any.

I'm hungry now and I go by this cafe. It looks nice inside. So I go in.

You probably think this is silly, but when I push open the door I expect everyone to stop talking and look at me, but it doesn't happen.

I go to a table and sit down. Mrs Carter and Jenny would say I should have a sandwich but I see this cake in a glass cabinet just as a woman comes up.

'Yes, love? What can I get you?'

I point at the cake. 'What's that?'

'Victoria sponge.'

'I want that and a hot chocolate.'

'Do you?'

'Yeah,' I say. She looks at me funny and says, 'Please would be nice.'

She turns and shouts, 'One hot chocolate. One Vic sponge. No Ps and Qs.' I don't like her.

When you go in a cafe on your own you've got nothing to do until they bring you the stuff. So you got to pretend you got something to do, see. I move things around on the table to fill some seconds. I'm warm and think about taking off my coat, but I don't want people to look at me.

I pretend I'm really interested in what's going outside the cafe, then this weird thing happens – I feel completely alone. I mean I know I *am* alone, but I'm thinking I'm not here any more. Invisible. Mr and Mrs Carter's house doesn't exist. I've got nowhere *to* go. It's silly, but if you want to you can frighten yourself just by thinking. I can feel my panic getting worse and worse, then my phone rings.

It's Mrs Carter – her picture comes up on the screen, like she'd heard me thinking. I look at her face.

'You gonna answer that, love?' the waitress asks.

'Hello.'

'He-llo. How you getting on?'

'Fine.'

'Where are you?'

'Cafe.'

'Oh lovely. Having lunch?'

'Yeah.'

The waitress brings the cake and hot chocolate.

'What you having?'

'A sandwich,' I say and glance at the waitress.

'Well, I'll see you soon, then. D'you think …'

'Bye.' I hang up and glance around. I feel bad, but I don't like talking on phones.

There's a fork with the cake but I pick it up and bite a lump out of it. It's lovely.

The cafe door crashes open.

A massive, red-faced woman comes in. 'God above,' she says and drops her big shopping bags by the table next to me. 'Don't know why I come in on Saturdays,' she says. She grunts and moans as she struggles to remove her overcoat. She doesn't care people are looking.

'Oh Meg,' she says to the waitress. 'I'm shattered.' She looks across at me and asks, 'What you got there, love?'

'Hot chocolate, Eileen, with a slice of Vic sponge,' the waitress tells her to save me the effort.

'That's it. That's what I'll have. I'm too bushed to bother deciding different.' She sits down. 'Torture. Absolute torture. People banging into me like a rugby match.' Just when I go to look away she looks right at me and asks, 'How is it, love?'

Don't like people speaking to me or calling me love, but I can't ignore her. 'Nice,' I say.

'There's nothing like a piece of cake and a hot drink when you've been knocking about town for a morning.' It's like someone's paid her to speak to me. I pick up the mug of hot chocolate and take a gulp so I don't have to talk, but the drink is scalding hot. It burns as it goes down my throat. I screw up my face it hurts so much.

'Oh, take it easy love,' she says and turns to the waitress. 'Meg, Meg! Give him a glass of water, quick! He's burned his mouth on your hot chocolate.'

Everyone's looking at me like I been hit by a car, but my main worry is getting the water quick enough to stop the molten chocolate dissolving my stomach. I grab the glass off the waitress and take a gulp.

'Boys,' says the waitress, 'always rushing.'

'Better?' the woman asks.

'Yes. Thanks.'

Her order arrives and we're both eating cake and sipping our hot chocolates together. I was embarrassed at first, but now, in a way, I like it.

When I get up to go she smiles and says goodbye. I manage the 'Goodbye', but not the smile.

I feel good back on the bus, though my feet ache. I hold the box tightly on my lap. I text Mrs Carter to say I'm on my way back, and she texts back, *Well done. Sausage and chips for dinner.* It's my favourite.

When I get off the bus it's getting dark and the street lamps are coming on. I see Mr and Mrs Carter's house. The lights are on and it looks warm. I feel my throat tighten, like when I saw the kitten. I see Mrs Carter at the window, as if she's been there the whole day waiting for me. I wave at her and she waves back. I feel relieved and worried at the same time. I just hope they don't make me take it back – Mrs Carter did tell me she liked cats.

A Lexicon for New Times

ELIANE GLASER

Elite (n.; adj.)
1. Financial and corporate power (obsolete)
2. Those who have a university degree; academics, journalists and experts. See also Liberal elite
3. Those who believe in equality
4. **The Left**

Intellectual (n.)
Person with cosmopolitan / aloof demeanour. See also **Elite; Sneer;
'Out of touch'**; Jew
Antonym: **The people**

Elite media (n.)
Comfortably-off influential progressive opinion-formers (obsolete)
Antonym: The actually dominant right-wing press

Global elite (n.) (oxymoron)
1. Persons who support multiculturalism, cosmopolitan values and the free movement of people
2. Goldman Sachs

Anti-globalisation (n.)

1. Of Naomi Klein: opposition to the free movement of capital (nearly obsolete)
2. Of Donald Trump: opposition to the free movement of labour

Expert (n.)

1. A person who by virtue of their experience, training or education knows more about their area than others
2. A person who is powerful; who sneers

Sneer (v.)

To be an academic, a journalist or an expert

Right, the (n.) (obsolete)

See Centre-Right; **The people**

Hard-Left (adj.)

See **The Left**

Left, the (n.) (obsolete)

Conservative (adj.)

Radical reformer

Reform (v.)

Privatise

Revolution (n.)

1. Overthrow of government (obscure)
2. Consolidation of right-wing governmental power by reference to **The will of the people**

Will of the people, the (n.)

1. Theresa May
2. Paul Nuttall
3. The *Daily Mail*
4. Dictatorship

People, the (n.)
See The Centre-Right; Native Britons; The real America
Antonyms: Those who wanted to remain in the European Union;
academics, journalists, experts

Populism (n.)
1. Of **The Left**: a strategic opposition to the financial and corporate
   takeover of the political system (obsolete)
2. Of **The Right**: The people's opposition to political elites who
   favour immigrants
3. Goldman Sachs

Nazism (n.)
Right-wing populist opposition to immigrants who are themselves
elite (Jews)

Racism (n.)
1. Prejudice towards ethnic groups less advantaged than your own
   (obsolete)
2. Prejudice towards ethnic groups perceived to be more advantaged
   than your own
3. Displaced anger about economic injustice

Economic crash, the (n.)
See **The big state**

EU, the (n.) (oxymoron)
1. Technocratic neoliberal bank-driven entity that prioritises the
   preservation of the Euro over the livelihoods and democratic
   autonomy of citizens of Southern European countries
2. Entity that protects citizen and worker rights
3. Immigrants
4. Lofty, unaccountable political elites who trump national sovereignty

Brexit (n.)
Brexit

Parliament (n.)
1. Institution in which competing class interests are represented (obsolete)
2. Lofty, unaccountable political elites who trump the sovereignty of **The people**

Democracy (n.)
1. Representation of **The people** by elected MPs (obsolete)
2. Rule by **The people**

Politician (n.)
Elected representative (obsolete)
See also Judges
Antonym: **The people**

State, the (n.)
1. Entity designed to distribute resources efficiently and equitably and support the vulnerable (obsolete)
2. Meddling, paternalistic officials who think they know what's best for ordinary people

Big state, the (n.)
See **The state**

Authority (n.)
See **The state**; Government; **Politician**; **Expert**

Power (n.)
See **Marxist critique**

Marxist critique (n.) (obsolete)

'Out of touch' (adj.)
1. Person who lives in a city
2. Intellectual

Gatekeeper (n.)
Editor at a newspaper or magazine or at a publishing house; artistic director of a theatre company; Artists and Repertoire department

of a record company; person who upholds the values of truth or beauty
(nearly obsolete)

Avant garde (n.)
See **Elite**

Culture (n.)
See **Popular culture**

Popular culture (n.)
The market

Public service broadcasting (n.)
1. Challenging, high-quality output designed to protect the public
   interest from market pressure (obsolete)
2. Broadcasting that serves the public

Public (n., adj.)
1. The common good (obsolete)
2. The market; private

Wisdom of the crowd, the (n.)
The prerogative of global technology corporations to appropriate and
simultaneously destroy the cultural heritage of humanity. See also
Horizontalism

Horizontalism (n.)
The vertically-integrated business models of global technology
corporations

Curator (n.)
1. A paid professional who filters culture for quality and presents the
   best of what has been made, thought or written to the public for their
   enjoyment and enlightenment (obsolete)
2. A person; a bot; an algorithm

Critic (n.)
A paid, professionally-trained arbiter of quality (obsolete)
See TripAdvisor; Quality Assurance

Amateur (n.)

1. As good as a professional, but not elite
2. Worker who does not sleep

Village Bay

The cliffs of the stacks rose up before us, so huge, more than a thousand feet high, they blocked out the last rays of the setting sun. It was like sailing towards a mountain. Dark, terrifying walls of cliff, crusted white with the stinking bird poo called *guano*. The smell was enough to make me sick.

And then, totally out of the blue, the boat rocked wildly and we dropped deep down into the trough of a huge wave.

The force threw Mara forward. She grabbed the mast just in time. She yelled my name.

I didn't know what to do. The boat was totally out of my control. It seemed to rise up, up, up to the crest of the wave. Any minute and we'd crash down again and capsize. I held on to the tiller with all my strength. My brain became mush.

Mara scrambled to the stern to help. She loosened my grip on the rope for the mainsail and let it out so it wasn't so tightly stretched, but that made it even harder to steer. Her face was drained of colour, her hair wet, plastered to her face from the spray.

Each dip down, down, down was terrible, like we were going down to the bottom of the ocean. Each time it felt like we must surely tip over. We were taking on water, too. Mara's dog Django slid from one side of the boat to the other until Mara grabbed him and held him tight between her knees.

Relentless, one wave and the next and the next took us and pitched us deep down, and then we rose higher and higher, and each time it felt impossible we'd survive.

The sun had long gone. The sky was navy dark, like the sea. We would drown, in darkness, in the terrible ocean, and no one would ever even find our bodies ...

It seemed to go on like that for hours.

It was nearly dark. The boat crested another wave, slightly smaller than the ones before, and as we dipped and rolled down the other side, through the spume and spray, I glimpsed something other than ocean.

Ahead of us was the curve of a bay, and a sloping beach.

Mara saw it too.

The waves rolling in got smaller.

We limped into the shelter of the bay, the land either side stretched out like arms to protect us from the full force of the sea.

Mara baled out the water we'd taken on board.

I tightened the sails again. The boat steadied. We could hear each other speak, again.

Mara shook her head. 'Extraordinary. I've never been in seas like that.'

'I'm shaking,' I said. 'My legs are like jelly.'

'You were magnificent,' Mara said. 'We're almost there.'

Her words made a warm glow in my belly.

She kept on baling. I stayed at the helm. And so it was that I, Jamie Robert Mackinnon, sailed *Stardust* into Village Bay, St Kilda.

My finest hour.

'Those massive waves? That was *swell*,' Mara said. 'Since you asked. Waves that come from a storm hundreds or thousands of miles away. When there's a big empty stretch of ocean with no land in the way they just keep rolling on, uninterrupted. We were lucky not to capsize.'

'Lucky? It was a blimmin' miracle,' I said.

'Let down both sails. We'll row from here,'

I did what she said on autopilot, too tired to think.

The sails fell in a jumbled heap on the deck. She went forward to untangle the ropes and roll up the sails. I moved to the middle, to untie the oars. My legs ached from sitting for so long: hours of being hunched up, freezing cold and wet and terrified. I could barely feel my fingers.

'The tide's high.' Mara peered through the gloom. 'Is that the jetty? Over there, at the far edge of the bay?'

It was hard to see anything in the dark.

'I'm so cold and wet and tired –' I began.

'Just row,' she said. 'Don't waste energy on moaning.'

The wooden oars hurt my palms. The sail ropes and salt had rubbed the skin into blisters. *I can't do this*, I wanted to say, but I didn't.

Very, slowly, one oar each, we rowed across the bay.

Even at this time of night, white sea birds rose and circled the cliffs. The air stank of fish and old, rank seaweed: the smell of rot and damp and death.

'Stop,' Mara said.

We rested the oars. It was suddenly quiet. Water dripped from the blades; the boat rocked gently. I heard the wash of water against something solid. I turned and saw the stone hulk of the old jetty, rusted iron rings for mooring, and steps leading down to the water.

We'd made it.

'We'll tie her up here, just for tonight, so we can get on land,' Mara said. 'But she'll smash against the wall if the waves get up. Put the fenders out.'

We stowed the oars under the seats, fixed the fenders along the side of the boat. Mara went up the steps first, with one bag of stuff, and tied the painter to the mooring ring.

I brought the other bag. Standing up, climbing from the boat to the stone steps, it all felt extraordinary. To feel dry land – well, a wet step, but solid, fixed – was amazing.

But I was shaking all over. Frozen. Too sleepy, almost, to stand.

Mara helped me up the last step on to the jetty.

She waited. She was searching behind me, peering down into the boat in the darkness.

'What?' I asked.

'Where's Django?' Her voice was full of panic.

'I – I don't know. Django?' I called down.

We waited.

I dumped the bag and went back down the steps.

Even in the dark I could see the boat was empty. There was no sign of him at all.

Mara sobbed. Terrible, raw, uncontrolled sobs that went on and on. I thought she'd never stop. I was scared I'd start too.

When had I last seen Django? In the swell, he'd definitely still been there: Mara had held on to him. After that? When we got the oars and started rowing? Had he still been crouched under the seat? Probably, but I couldn't be totally sure.

Perhaps he'd been so desperate to get off the boat he'd jumped as soon as we got near enough to the shore. But surely we'd have heard him? And Django hated water, hated swimming ... Had he leapt up the steps before us? In which case, why wasn't he waiting at the top?

Mara called and called his name into the dark.

We listened for an answering bark. We strained our eyes, peering out into the bay. I imagined him paddling to shore, running along the sand, shaking his wet fur ...

But there was nothing. Only the total darkness of an uninhabited island, where there were no lights at all.

The mournful cries of a thousand sea birds,

the slap of water against the stone jetty,

the suck and draw of waves reaching the shore.

Above us stretched the dark sky, no moon, a scattering of stars.

'Come on,' I said at last. 'We have to find a place to sleep.'

'No,' Mara said. 'I'm going back to look for him.'

'Oh – no – Mara! Not now, in the dark ...'

'You go on,' she said. 'I'll find you later.'

I didn't even argue. I let her climb back down those steps, untie the rope, set the oars.

I was too tired to think straight. All I wanted was to lie down on land that was dry and didn't rock and sway

and to sleep

and sleep

and sleep.

The Ghost Works

PHILIP GROSS

As if cranking up the word machine was not enough,
keeping our toolkits tidy: tweezer, wrench and what
that sprocket's for, God knows ... The thing *we* know
is that there's something more: unaccountable, true
and sudden, that shiver of warmth (keep it between
ourselves) on the skin: you've been touched by a ghost

of the new. Or is this just a brush with cliché: *ghost
in the machine?* No. We live littoral lives, close enough
the shoreline of the said-before to walk between
tides, browsing flotsam, parched weed-wrack, whatever's the buzz of the day for the flies ... and true-
life treasure – *Look, mum, emerald!* (The kids know

it's wave-ground glass. It's only you, you know-
all adult, who's fooled, as if you never guessed
that it's the light, the play of it, that's true.)
Ghosts were always a figure of speech. Enough
said, they fade. And we're left accounting for what
won't be counted, what slips through the space between:

creation. At work in the narrowing seam, between
words, between hear- and -say, it's hard to know,
as the Age of Compliance sets in, just what's
been lost. (Consider the Valleys, slopes grassed
over, bland as mission statements. Is it enough
to hide the slag beneath? How green is true?)

Ghosts, zombies, vampires – what rings true
through the old tropes is young lives caught between
inside and outside, life and mechanism, true enough
for the times. As for that shy-spooky thing I know
as Me: a spiderweb of neurones shivers in a gust
and glints ... until one day a thread snaps, and what

will I be? Can't say. Hand me the thingumajig, the what-
d'you-ma-call-it (yes, we know Unknowing by its true
names here), tools for the workshop. The what-ifs, ghost
writers all, lean from the shadows. The lit space between
is living. Us. The work-in-progress. *What do you know?*
says the evaluation form. Tick the box for *Enough*

as if you'd ever cease from asking what's between
the lines, how true is true. As if there's any way to know
except to be engrossed, or any such thing as enough.

Not Much of a Ghost Story

TESSA HADLEY

This isn't much of a ghost story, but it's probably as close as I'll ever get to writing one. I'm not really that kind of writer. I teach part-time in a Creative Writing department in the west of England, and no doubt some of my female colleagues would be more happily at home than I am with the supernatural. I'd say my novels, two so far, were more like mind-puzzles: disguised as urban dystopian thrillers, whose playfulness perhaps isn't always obvious. Our university setting is conducive to more romantic flights. For complicated reasons to do with the plight of the landowning aristocracy after the war, casting around for local institutions to take on the expense of their inherited property, all our postgraduate teaching takes place in a stately pile with an Elizabethan front, Georgian picture gallery and Victorian back quarters. The rather poignantly faded rooms downstairs are even open to the public – in the summer, on certain afternoons – and there are a few paintings worth seeing, among them a Fra Lippo Lippi and a Sofonisba Anguissola.

I share an office at the very top of the house, tucked in under the angles of the roof above the third storey. The ceilings slant abruptly and it's prone to flies; an electric device on the windowsill emits a blue light and sizzles the tiny corpses. Sometimes in an ungainly burst of flight one of the peacocks makes it up this high, then stands with his tail fanned on the stone parapet outside the window, turning it this way and that for vacancy to admire, while the wind blows the fan like a sail and sends the peacock staggering on its silly feet, clawed like high heels. At the top of the short staircase leading from the third storey corridor up to this room there's a landing lined with bookshelves, and, beyond that, a further set of utilitarian wooden steps leading up to a door which opens on to the leads. One afternoon this last spring when I was alone in the office with the door open, waiting to see a student about a problem they were having in my Suspense module, I wandered out and up these last steps without any particular plan, except for passing time, and found to my surprise that the key was in the lock of the door at the top, which it had never been before. So, I opened the door and stepped out on to the roof.

It was beautiful up there: I say so and I'm not easily moved to rapture by exterior things. I'd been chilly in the office but out on the roof the sun was hot. I could see all around me, in a complete circle in all directions and for what seemed like miles, though it probably wasn't. The gardens and the park beyond were by Capability Brown – whose park *didn't* he design? – and by combining accidents of nature with tricks of landscaping he'd contrived to blur its edges so that even now you couldn't see an end to it, nor any signs either of encroaching modernity; not even giveaway telegraph poles, let alone the nearby industrial estate or MOD barracks or the motorway. It really was, for an illusory moment, as if past and present lay open to each other and you could move between them blissfully, without effort. The light had the bleached brilliance and tenderness of early spring: the world was starting up all over again, and seemed scoured clean of all the accretions of past mistakes. The grey and beige of winter trees and grasses glowed mauve with fecundity, bursting with readiness for regrowth; the roof-lead under my feet gleamed like pale, old silver; light flashing between the trees from the lake seemed a signal.

Far below me young man in a dark greatcoat – presumably a student, though not the one that I was waiting for, taller and with longer dark hair curling on his shoulders – was walking away from the house towards the ha-ha, stepping carefully so as not to crush the early aconites and crocuses, which grow in swathes among the roots, and great dipping, twisting limbs of the venerable horse-chestnuts; in places these limbs have grown down to the earth as if from their extreme heaviness, resting on it before striving up again. The whole thing – spring, the lovely day, my vantage point – went to my head, I felt quite dizzy from some unaccustomed sensation. It was not happiness exactly; it was more like power, possibility, an exaggerated sense of my capacity. I believed for a moment – against my better judgement of course – that I could do anything. There was so much I knew, and saw, and understood; how could I fail to translate this into some great illuminating art, some achievement to astonish the world and make it see me?

Then I heard voices from the landing outside the office, at the bottom of the stair which led up on to the roof. My student had arrived, or rather two of them together; they'd seen through the open door of the office that it was empty, and they were talking about me, not knowing I was close at hand above them and could hear everything clearly. – Are you looking for X ...? one of them said, a girl.

I'd better keep my name out of this.

– He hasn't turned up. I'm not surprised, she said. And then they agreed that I was always so distant, and negative about everybody's work, and that they didn't seem to be able to do anything to please me. – He's so prescriptive, said the other one. – As if he thinks that he's got all the answers.

Apparently they both wanted to change to a different group. I was sorry because I rather liked the young man, and didn't think he was without talent. Did they really imagine that being nice to people had anything to do with good writing? But some of my female colleagues run their workshops more like therapy sessions, as if their primary responsibility was to be encouraging. It was an awkward situation. If I went down now, they'd realise I must have been listening close at hand. I hesitated, and then I'd left it too late to move. And the whole time I was standing there, eavesdropping involuntarily, I was also watching that dark-haired student making his way between the trees in the garden far below; his coat was flapping open and I somehow knew that his hands in his pockets were balled in fists, in anger. An explanation seemed to fly into my mind from nowhere, leaving no room for doubt. I thought, ah, so he's not a student. He's the tutor. He's the tutor and the boys he has to teach abuse him and have no interest in learning. Why should they learn? They will inherit wealth and privilege whether they know anything or not.

We have tutors on our Creative Writing courses – personal tutors and manuscript tutors – but I was quite clear that wasn't what I meant. What I meant was that he was a tutor in the nineteenth-century sense, suffering because he had been hired to teach the stupid sons of the family whose home was the great house beneath me. And that he was actually in the nineteenth century. I really don't know where this conviction came from. It was so odd, to watch him walking there, head bent, stumbling over the tree roots, and believe I was actually watching something happening in another time. And yet it was easy too, as if I'd simply found myself inside a novel which was from a different era but nonetheless entirely comprehensible to me. It's precisely through novel reading, of course, that we find the customs and categories of other ages so transparently comprehensible.

The tutor knows, I thought, that he's ten times cleverer and better informed than anyone else in the household, and yet that it doesn't mean anything because no one else knows it, they're oblivious to his intelligence because of his shabby clothes and poverty and awkwardness. And he's heading away from the house because he wants to go to the extreme edge of the place where he's confined, to put as much distance as possible between himself and the boys who torture him. You can believe, dear reader, of course, if you like, that I was just feeling sorry for myself because I wanted to be more popular with the students, and that the whole thing was simply an association of ideas. In any case, I skulked miserably up there on the roof while my students waited for me on the landing, and the young man in the grounds below arrived at the ha-ha, the sunken boundary, then followed it round on the inside until the wall of the kitchen garden blocked him from my sight. All my exhilaration in the spring day was spoiled. Eventually when the students gave up on me and left, I crept downstairs and emailed them both an apology, saying I'd been stuck in traffic. But this story really isn't about me.

I saw the tutor twice more after this. I had locked the roof door behind me when I came down and left the key in the lock, and the following week when I climbed the steps again – wanting to escape after an interminably dull meeting, in which student complaints that I was too 'judgemental' had come up – the key was still there, and so I turned it and went out. It was another lovely day like George Herbert's, 'so calm, so fair, so bright,/ The bridal of the earth and sky', and spring was farther advanced; the hoary old boughs of the horse chestnuts had shaken out new leaves of the palest green, as soft as cloth. And there was the tutor below me, making his way again in his long greatcoat through the trees, away from the house towards the ha-ha. My heart leaped up when I caught sight of him. I both believed I was seeing someone alive in another time and didn't believe it. It occurred to me that to fit in with novelistic convention this tutor ought to be in love with the lady of the house and mother of his charges: the only woman of his class he saw from day to day, even if she was ignorant and silly. After all, he would have a young man's needs and urges. But I also knew that if he was in love this was only a plot distraction. His real suffering was because time was passing and he hadn't achieved anything, he couldn't; because he was shut up here, obliged to earn his living, away from the great world. As I watched him until he was out of sight I grieved with him.

And the third time I saw him ... The third time was awful. The weather had changed, temperatures had dropped abruptly and the paths were littered with tender, young leaves smashed down in fits of driving rain. Between the fits a sleety grey mist wrapped close around the house, and all its brave perspectives contracted to this suffocating damp. Things were going badly in my marriage – oh, I hadn't mentioned I was married, had I? Well, things were going badly with my wife. I shouldn't have gone out on the roof; but I wanted to know what it was like out there in all weathers, not only when the sun shone. And when I stepped out on to the leads I saw the tutor at once, hurrying far down below with a purposefulness I hadn't observed in him before, hair slicked close with wet, hands clenched in his pockets as if he were hanging on to something, head bowed and shoulders hunched against the same drifting, sleety onslaught which was beating down on me.

He wasn't headed in the usual direction, towards the ha-ha. I saw that he was making for the bathhouse, a queer little place standing alone in the grounds, built in a muddle of different styles: gothic mixed up with classical. Behind an arched facade there's a stone plunge pool, and behind that there are openings to either side – which these days have fluorescent tape across them, warning it isn't safe to go any further. If you ignore the warning and step over the tape, as I did when I was first exploring the campus, you find yourself on a curving cramped stone stairway, smelly and thwarted and dark, obstructed with rubble, leading to a poky upper room spattered with bird droppings. The place is only for show apart from the bath itself, it only has any meaning seen from the outside. Watching the tutor hurrying in that direction, I was filled with foreboding. By the way, there is no factual historical basis for any of this. I never found out that there was any actual nineteenth-century tutor corresponding to my imagining, nor any unpleasant story attached to the bathhouse. My foreboding was only an intuition – a writer's intuition perhaps, though it's not the kind of thing I'd use in one of my own novels, it's too obvious. Nonetheless in that moment of watching I was quite sure. The tutor was gripping his razor in his pocket, and was going to cut his throat in the bathhouse.

And as if I'd forgotten this was only a story inside my head, and that I couldn't possibly in reality pass across into some imagined era in the past, I came stumbling in uncharacteristic haste down the wooden stair from the roof, then down three further flights to the ground floor, ran out of the door at the front of the house in all that horrible weather and around to the back – as though a life depended on it. I don't know whether anyone was watching, gloating because for once the famously imperturbable and opinionated

X was making an awful fool of himself. It must have taken me five minutes at the most to arrive at the bathhouse, and by that time I was horribly winded; gasping for breath with pain like a band across my chest. I'm not in good physical condition. Of course, there was nothing there. The stone bath was only heaped with a sodden detritus of twigs and sweet wrappers and last year's dead leaves; when I pushed past the warning tapes and searched on the steps and in the upper room they were only unspeakably dank in the murky light, stinking of mould and rot, piled up with filth in the corners. Yet I was filled with the bitter sensations of futility and loss.

There is a coda to my non-ghost story. I couldn't end it there, could I? Not for the purposes of this uplifting commemorative anthology. My ending is a tribute to progress, albeit perhaps always partial and provisional. I'm not a suffering tutor in the nineteenth century. Teaching Creative Writing to postgraduates is much more rewarding. I'm very lucky. I returned upstairs and fetched the key from the door which led out on to the roof, then handed it in to the admin staff, suggesting it shouldn't be left in the lock, it wasn't safe for anyone to go out there. Still dishevelled and disordered from my flight in the rain, I bought myself a consoling cup of tea in the student cafe and, not wanting to be alone, drank it for once sitting down among the students. I even spoke to them, and listened to them too. That seemed to go down well.

Back and Forth, or Home

SABRIN HASBUN

When we opened the door, the smell of mould sucked us in.

Everything was exactly the same.

Wait. How did we arrive here? The car, the car door, the small gate, the scruffy garden, the roses, the first door, the white door, the fresh hallway. The second door, our door. Now.

I needed a minute to retrace the short distance from the car to that moment when we had been sucked in by the smell of the mould of our own house.

Our own house. It was exactly the same, everything in the same place. Just mould and dust and time had done their job. As if someone had always lived there, but had remained seated on the sofa, immobile, while mould, dust, and time did their job.

Our own house. In that moment I didn't even know if I could call that space my house. I hadn't lived there for the last twelve years and, before that, I hadn't ever lived there for more than a few months a year.

Our own house.

So why do I recognise the position of every object? The black chairs around the glass table, the Japanese paper window between the entrance and the living room, the broken glass of the left door, and from the right door, I can already imagine all the objects of the kitchen: the cups, the fridge, the old gas stove, the smell of toasted bread. If I focus my eyes I can also see the movements of my brothers, my father, my mother impressed in the grooves of the air since the last time we were here all together, in December 1999.

The smell of the mould brought me back to the present moment. That house was not mine. No more. I was just a guest of the objects we left behind: I recognised them, but they didn't recognise me. The last time they saw me I was a little girl of ten, short enough to sleep in the sofas my father built and to leave the big bed to my older brothers. Now I had to make the bed for myself and sleep alone in the room we once fought for.

The veranda, my favourite room, was now totally unusable. The mould there took it all and it was impossible to open the door without being forced back by the smell.

Many of the things in the kitchen refused to work: the oven, the sink, the window. The flames, more convincingly cooperative, released a strong smell of gas reminding us of our desertion.

I looked at my mother.

For me, after all, this was more a home of my imagination, something I thought about as a summer childhood playground. More an idea of belonging, a box of small little memories: eating on the carpet in the living room, the shade of the living room when my mother closed the curtains to let me sleep during the first hours of the afternoon, the shadow of the lemon tree on the kitchen balcony, the kitchen balcony transformed into a swimming pool during the hottest days of July.

But for my mother, this house had been her real, actual home for ten years. A home that she had never expected to leave. Her first home in her new chosen country; a house that helped her not to feel homesick. The living room was the place where she used to host friends: musicians, writers, all avid smokers, filling the space with sounds, words and smoke. The kitchen where she learnt how to prepare Arabic dishes, the balcony that she filled with water to let us play during the hottest days of July.

I looked at my mother. She looked at the objects as the objects looked back at us. She didn't want to recognise them. Since the first step we again took into this house after twelve years, she immediately saw a deeper difference in the objects. As if they were not just covered by dust and mould, but somehow shaped by them. Shaped into something that she refused to recognise.

She stopped for a while, looked around her, and then moved on to the kitchen.

She opened all the cupboards, touched all the cups, the plates, the forks, the knives, the spoons, the blue glasses, the pans, my baby bottle, the sugar jar. She touched the sugar jar a bit longer, opened it and then closed the cupboard again.

'I will never come back again.'

She knew it. She knew it not only because she and my father has decided to sell the house. She knew it in a more inescapable way. And she was not just speaking of our house: she was speaking about Palestine. The detachment she felt for the objects of her house was the same detachment she started feeling a few days later for the entire town. Ramallah was no more Ramallah: it was just a town with an unmanageable urban expansion which was scratching away all she remembered.

Our house, once at the edge of the town, a step closer to the countryside than to the city, surrounded by fields and hills, was now a small point folding under the weight of the huge buildings around, the new residential area, a shopping mall, a lemon tree covered in sick lemons.

I don't know if her detachment started with the house and then took over the entire town, or if it was the town which took over the house. But at some point, our home and Ramallah melted into each other and became for her a hostile lump in which she could no longer find her place. Her chosen place. They refused to recognise each other.

'I love these plates, I want to take them with me!'

'Don't be ridiculous, we can't put them in the suitcase.'

'We can find another way.'

'No, we can't.'

My mother refused to help me in my desperate desire to take all the objects of our Palestinian house to Italy. Not all, some of them. The blue plates, the blue glasses, the blue vases, my old toys, the blankets, some random objects that I wanted to keep. But my mother looked at them as if they had already gone. She kept on ransacking the wardrobe in my brothers' room. She went in, opened the shutters, ransacked a bit, took out a box, ransacked the box, whispered something, changed her expression, changed her expression again, changed her expression once more, quickly closed the box, quickly put the box in its place in the wardrobe, quickly closed the wardrobe.

She did this over and over again during those days, while I kept on going back and forth among the rooms, trying to fit the objects I wanted into the only suitcase I had. She ignored me and I ignored her; I in my stubborn desire to keep hold of everything, she in her desire to let everything go.

I didn't care about what she was doing and she didn't care about what I was doing; I went back and forth between the rooms, she did her stuff and then went back to my brothers' wardrobe.

'Mamma, look what I found here, in this chest'

'I know what you found there, we can't take them to Italy'

'But all these ...'

'We can't bring all those books back to Italy.'

She said no, but she nevertheless came in the living room with me, to look at the books I had found in the chest. Books had always been her weak point. She started taking them out without looking at them, as if to find as fast as possible the bottom of the trunk and close the matter. But then her eyes started to linger on them a bit longer, to look at the titles, her hands began to touch the pages with more delicacy, her nose paused to detect their smell. She started to leaf through them, finding inside the pages the remains of a bookmark made from a bill, a piece of paper scribbled by my brothers, a birthday card from Italy, a photo.

Each book released for her not just the words and stories she used to find inside it, but also the stories she herself put inside: the stories of the moments when she was reading those books, twelve years ago, twenty years ago, thirty years ago. Some food for the house, my brothers drawing for her while she was cooking, her mother missing her on her birthday, a kiss between her and my father.

Those books reconnected her to her life in our house, to the life she had chosen for herself when she was in her twenties. Finally something she recognised; she recognised them and they recognised her. They gave to each other their stories.

'We can find a place for them in my suitcase,' she eventually deliberated.

When I went back less than two years later, my father hadn't yet sold the house, but we both refused to stay there for our two weeks in Ramallah. There was too much mould there, and dust, and too many objects. We rented a room in one of the new hotels in the area instead, and went to the house just for a few hours, to see if there was anything else we wanted to bring back to Italy.

Now I could understand my mother: those objects were a presence of an absence.

I went to the kitchen, opened all the cupboards, touched all the cups, the plates, the forks, the knives, the spoons, the blue glasses, the pans. My baby bottle and the sugar jar weren't there.

'Babbo, where are the baby bottle and the sugar jar?'

'Your mother brought them to Italy last time, don't you remember?'

At the time I hadn't even noticed it; I was so wrapped up in my urge to carry everything off.

The blue plates, the blue glasses, the blue vases, everything was in their place, as always, but they were no longer the same objects. I didn't recognise them and they didn't recognise me. They no longer gave me back my child-hood fantasies. The imagination of my summer playground. They just kept on reminding me that my mother didn't want them. I looked at them with her same detachment.

'Do you want to keep them?' my father asked.

'No. Mamma didn't want them.'

I strolled around the house, going back and forth between the rooms, trying to find something my mother would have wanted, something that could help me to find her once more. But I couldn't find anything. Nothing in the kitchen, nothing in the bathroom, nothing in her bedroom, nothing in my brothers' bedroom.

Wait.   My   brothers'   bedroom.   The   wardrobe.   The   box.

I ran again into my brothers' bedroom, went to the wardrobe, opened the shutters, ransacked a bit, found the box, took out the box, opened it. I changed my expression, changed my expression again, and changed my expression once more. The box was full of letters. My mother's letters. The letters she wrote to my father during the first years she went back to Italy with us, and my father remained here to work. The box was full of her words. Her stories.

The stories of those moments when she was writing those letters, twelve years ago, twenty years ago, thirty years ago. Some food for the house, my brothers drawing for her while she was cooking, what she did on her birth-day, a missed kiss between her and my father.

Those letters reconnected me to her life, to the life she had chosen, to the life she had lived in that house, far from that house, back and forth between two countries.

She was right. She had never had the time to come back to Palestine. She knew it. But now I found her again there, in our house in Ramallah, in a box full of letters full of her words.

Four Poems

MATT HAW

Fen Raft Spider

So she's back, dipping two toes
where minnows & the other
gelid fishies gub on thin water
like so many mouth breathers.

Now hiding in a skin of air,
submerged, she's mirror'd
in the plane she passes through.
To surface, the image must

collapse on itself, leave her
dry, clinging to a rush float.
It's like not even water can
stand to touch her, can abide

her arse hairs, her caviar eyes.
You squeamish cunt. To Boudicca
she's the living striated fen light
who was away but now she's back –

Omen of calamitous tribes,
the redeployment of garrisons,
Boars & bears & wolves says Boudicca,
                                        oh my.

The Urban Regeneration of Her Tribal Lands

Along the old branch line, she wrinkles
her nose at wafts of anaerobic rot.

Fly agarics thrust, syphilitic through
the mulch. Panties hang on hawthorn

like something flayed. The overgrowth
affords glimpses of potholed cul-de-sacs,

caved-in trampolines, the milk-
eyed stare of bathroom windows.

There's the iron ribbonry of council
commissioned sculpture to consider,

lit nightly by thin, uneven LED light.
The piss-head's hotspot, a ruined

signal box draped in a ghillie suit
of fern & ivy where she puts an ear

to heaped rubble. *Through the insect
tombs* says Boudicca, *I can hear down*

to the ocean floor, past the din of industry,
years shovelling steam, centuries

of creaking tumbrels, to where the last
living tribesman of the east reanimates,

heaves himself from the fen
& goes in search of skewered meat.

A Vision for the Topographical Future of East Anglia

In quick-dry raiments, ecologist
soldiers patrol concrete levees.
The wind slaps jade North Sea
over the tide barrier. Out in

the shimmering, amphibious
trawlers sift sandbars for bivalves.
Inland, the salt marsh goes on
for miles of sea grass & sampha.

At dawn, Boudicca punts her raft
back to the stilt houses, a Celtic
knot of eels in a bucket,
her breakfast. She is tan, cinnamon

freckled with fishing everyday
in brackish sun, how she lives
since the rewilding of the east.
When the tide sits low

the dunes island like beached
bull seals. On still days, water
clears & she looks down
on submerged bungalows,

the ruins of churches, hatchbacks
crusted with barnacles. Sometimes
They come with their masks & cuffs
but don't trouble her much.

She rules her omega-3 rich
regency, eating congregations
of fry & crustaceans fat from
burrowing for corpses in the silt.

For the Other John,

stell blaimes gahd
bud et's osterity
rekt unuther
generayshun, Hal.
Rampunt beestees
uhbrord en dailite,

shuck & eskaypt
tygers, Prasutugus
messin', przoomed
eetun, alung wiv
menee uhthers gnown
boi ther prufeshuns:

pohits und hors.
Sumwere en thu fenn
iz uh ded rhoot hollo
full of steinkin bones,
crakked jor
uv discuntinyood

Albyon amung 'em,
wer culaborators
bough wiv oyl'd
smylz. Et'sall supher
on, wun morr dai,
wun morr. *aye no.*

Little Birds

JULIE HAYMAN

They sit you in the winged armchair facing the window, ignoring your flapping hands and wet cheeks. They put your walking stick within reach and cover your knees with the patchwork quilt. 'Here you go, Mrs Merrick,' they say, tucking you in. 'Here's your quilt; your son brought it so you won't get cold. He didn't mean to make you upset; he's gone now. You know, your son – Patrick?'

You don't know anyone called Patrick and have never seen this quilt before. Your hands flap. The two women exchange looks you can't interpret. The black one is the kinder of the two; she holds one of your agitated hands between hers to still it, then pulls a paper tissue from her sleeve and wipes your cheeks dry with slow, careful strokes. 'You be all right now, my love,' she says, her broad face inches from yours, and you're not sure if it's a prediction or a command. 'You sit and look at the little birds in the yard.' The women saunter away, their shoes squeaking on the linoleum.

There are no birds. There's a tangled hedge outside the window, its branches grey as tungsten. A straggly tree with papery bark stands leafless against a day pale as milk in water. Words flutter in your head: *brambles, silver birch, white sky* and your mouth tries to capture them, but the words take flight and are gone. You smooth the quilt under your hands, fingertips touching the fabrics like braille. *Silk*, you think, *linen, cotton, rayon*; but a moment later these words too are gone.

Someone is groaning on the other side of the room. You crane your head to look but can't see past the wings of the armchair. The groaning turns to screeching. 'Come along, Mr Dodd,' says the white woman, squeaking across the linoleum to the screecher, 'I've got your pills. Swallow them down for me.' A hand slaps the Styrofoam cup away and pills skitter across the floor. 'Doreen, come and give me a hand with Mr Dodd,' calls the white woman, her voice strained. The black woman comes in – you recognise her heavy sigh – and three pairs of feet stumble and trip out of the door.

There is no movement in the room, and none outside. Your hands, gnarled as ginger roots, tremble on the quilt. You know they are your hands because they wear your rings, the ones with Chinese characters engraved on them. You can't recall what these characters mean; perhaps happiness or good luck or wealth. You can't recall whether you've ever experienced these things, whether your life was happy or sad, or how your hands became so knuckled, so clawed. You have no idea how much you may have forgotten, only that thoughts, words, memories fly high out of reach.

Your hands find a loose thread in the quilt and pull. Stitches pop open, one by one, along the side of a turquoise-green hexagon. The turquoise-green hexagon is one of six which form a quilt-flower, the centre of which is a piece of red gingham. A memory alights, unbidden: you are five years old, hanging up a red gingham PE bag on the peg outside the classroom. Someone pushes past and the iron peg stabs your forehead. Blood beads your red gingham PE bag, your white blouse. You open your mouth and howl …

Someone is howling now, like a dog. It bring you out of your reverie.

'Now then, Mr Carter, stop that.' It's the white woman's voice. 'No need for it. Doreen: your help, please. Mr Carter's shit his pants again.'

A smell wafts across the room, scratching in your throat and making you gag. You lift the quilt to your nose, to block the stench. The hexagon near your eyes shows a pattern of dahlias and daisies, green and yellow on a white background, and you think these flowers would brighten the grey and white things outside your window. *Brambles and silver birch and white sky*, you think. *Dahlias and daisies. Dahlias and daisies.* You believe that if you keep repeating these words, they will not flee, you will keep them in your mind's cage. *Dahlias and daisies and brambles, silver birch and white sky …*

The curtains in your marital bedroom were made of linen with a design of green and yellow daisies and dahlias. You watched the flowers sway in the breeze from the open window that first night as Clive dug inside you and planted Patrick there. Patrick was born safe and well, but you had the curtains taken down after Simon came out a few years later with a hole in his heart. And after the stillborn twins – each the size of a pigeon, the weight of a bag of sugar – you cut up the curtains. Why must you remember that? You tear at the quilted flowers, pull the stitches apart with your hands, with your teeth, biting through the memories of Clive and Patrick and Simon and the twins, tearing up the dahlias and daisies. *Dahlias and daisies*: and what were the other words you wanted to keep in your mind-cage? *Brambles* was one, but the others have escaped.

Now you need a wee. You wonder how to attract the attention of the black woman. You know she has a name but it soars somewhere beyond your reach. 'Hello?' you call weakly. No one responds. A man clears his throat in a chair behind yours and switches on the television. The sounds of a cricket commentary smother your calls. You try to lift the quilt off your knees, to grab your walking stick, to find someone to help you, but the quilt is too heavy. You pull out more of the stitches, ripping the hexagonal flowers apart, casting aside neatly scissored plates of rosebuds on chequered grounds, white anchors on blue seas, lime and pink and khaki geometrics. They flutter to the floor and you think: this was my mother's spring dress that she grew too small for and I too big; this came from Patrick's pyjamas, the ones he hated because he thought the print too childish; this was our cushion material in the house by the sea.

Your wee is trickling out now, warming your pants and thighs and the seat beneath you. How will you tell this to the white woman and the black woman? The tangled hedge outside waves at you in a sudden breeze and you think: *brambles*. You wipe yourself with the quilt, wetting the design of Laura Ashley's white sprigs on a petrol-blue background, drying yourself with the print of a jolly red teapot with golden spout that came from your beach skirt, the skirt you tore up when Clive finally announced he was leaving. You rip at these hexagons and the seams come apart easily. The teapot floats silently to your feet.

'Cup of tea?' The Asian tea-lady wheels the urn on the trolley towards you. She looks with dull eyes at the quilt unravelling over your knees. 'Want a cup of tea or not?'

When you don't reply, she wheels the trolley away. You hear the teacups chiming, the spoons chattering like teeth. Your drawers are wet and cold and sticky and beginning to itch, and you stink. You look at the hexagons in your hands and around your feet and can't remember why they're there or what, if anything, you were about to do. There are scraps of 1950s cotton material showing two cartoon girls, one dressed in red playing a flute, one dressed in green playing a cello: you and Sissy at your music lessons, before Sissy caught rheumatic fever and went to the sanatorium and never came back. You tear this memory apart and tears drip off your nose and chin. You keep tearing, hands and teeth, until red and green, orange and brown, yellow and purple scraps litter your lap and your armchair, and there is nothing left to remind you of anything except *brambles and silver birch and white sky*.

The light outside has turned imperceptibly from milky white to bath-water grey. Shadows creep along the colourless grass. Soon the white woman or the black one will come and snap on lamps, bring in supper, close the curtains, and words like *brambles*, *silver birch*, *white sky* will disappear.

Squeaking feet make their way across the linoleum in the fading light. The black woman looks at the patchwork scraps piled on the floor and strewn across your legs.

'Oh, what a shame,' she says, 'Mrs Merrick! Destroying that beautiful quilt that took you years to make. Your son will be disappointed. Your whole life went into that, and it's all torn apart.' She picks up some scraps which flutter in her grasp like broken wings.

Your hands flap. You look past her and suddenly there is a multitude of linnets and sparrows, song thrushes and wrens, robins and ravens flapping about in the brambles. You fling your walking stick at the window and thousands of little birds fly away.

et Cie, SA

PHILIP HENSHER

On the opposite side of the road is a new office building occupied by an Italian shipping company. This is in Geneva, where we live. The district is a residential one, quiet and salubrious; the streets are lined with cedar trees, beech, lime and maple. Respectable widows walk their dogs: in fur coats between November and March, in bright raincoats the rest of the year. Our concierge has a dog called Praline, a splash of beige hair with a pink extrusion of tongue at its centre. We wonder whether Praline is allowed to exercise with anyone but the dogs of the other concierges. There is an English park with winding paths, a lawn, an arboretum and a collection of gymnastic equipment in wood and metal, for the passing fitness enthusiast. Two famous film stars live nearby, in retirement. There are few office buildings.

The Italian shipping office is an opulent one. We have a good view, a hundred yards away, from our flat on the sixth floor. The walls are of tinted glass, giving the building a greenish, aquarium look, and the front of the building is shielded by a bank of curving steel poles, a curved glass wall. At ten thirty each night, a timer makes the steel shutters of the building descend, one by one, from the top left-hand corner to the bottom right-hand corner, a technological performance that no one from the company is there to see, but which all our neighbours, we think, enjoy. At the front of our building are two cherry trees, a magnolia and a loquat, dark and glossy, bearing fruit like lit festive bulbs in spring. Their building has a stone forecourt, and, behind, a garden: squares of neat trimmed hedges, knee-high, with lollipop bay trees at each corner, surrounding teak decking. Here the smokers of the shipping company stand and smoke: the men of the shipping company.

You notice the men of the shipping company in the street. They are dressed in a particular way. Their suits are blue, a shade more brilliant than is conventional, and close-fitted. The bottom hems of their jackets flare out like peplums as they walk; their trousers are close about thigh and calf. When the weather is warm, they carry their jackets on a hooked finger over the back of their shoulders; when it is bright, they wear sunglasses. Their shoes are brown, often to the point of orange; a decision that was once unconventional, to wear bright brown shoes with a bright blue suit, but they all do so now. Or nearly all.

The painter is lucky in the practice of his art. His subject is everywhere, unencumbered by the requirements of significance. A painter, at a loss, may set up his easel, take out his sketchbook and sit wherever he happens to sit. He may just depict what happens to be in front of him. If you look at Goya's sketchbooks, they are full of figures glimpsed in the street. Some of Lucian Freud's, or Stanley Spencer's, most haunting images are of what happens to be seen if you look out of the window. They don't need to plan; they don't need to dig for importance.

Sometimes you see a man walking the streets near here, in Geneva, and it does not occur to you that he might be attached to the shipping company with its wall of glass eighty metres high, its exquisitely detailed model of a cargo vessel underneath the eight-metre maple in a pot in the lobby. His hair may be rumpled; he may be overweight; his suit may be black and baggy and shapeless. His face is unhappy and lined, though he is still young. He has made some dreadful mistake, you can see in the way his elbows hug his side. And then he turns into the garden of the shipping company. The tight-suited smokers of the company watch him approach. When he is close enough they turn away without greeting him. He goes into the building of his employer, ready for an afternoon of being bullied and snubbed, ready to suppress the possibility of tears.

We are fascinated by the prize-winning life of the building, but the importance of its events is inverted for us. From our flat, we cannot see inside the building by day, when it performs its function; it is usually darker than the street, and most of what we see is reflection. But in the evening, the building is still lit, and the nearly empty rooms shine out in the blue twilight. We watch the four cleaners go from floor to floor, doing what every cleaner always does. The shipping brokers have gone home, but a man follows one cleaner in her work. He often sits on a desk. You can see him talking to her, moving on when she moves on. She does not seem to respond. Perhaps he is her supervisor, moving with her from one perfect, sinister room to another, disposing of the day's confusion. When he does not talk, his head moves, following her around the CEO's office, which faces our flat, following her around the shipping brokers' room, two floors beneath.

As it happens, though I describe myself as a writer, I haven't written anything for over a year, since finishing a novel. Like a painter, I decide to exercise those muscles of writing by looking outwards, seeing what may be seen. It is banal when you first look. It happens everywhere. But banality is a category that dissolves under the gaze. Like Flaubert in *Bouvard and Pécuchet*, every writer discovers that banality, once looked upon squarely, becomes unique, full of significance, sometimes touching, often tender. The things that are done every day by everybody. A shipping company, where everybody, bar two or three, dresses the same. There was probably no need to specify anything about the way brokers should dress; most people just understood.

When people come to visit us, they always remark on the same thing: they always point out that our near neighbour is Sophia Loren. She lives in contented retirement with an entourage of elderly homosexuals, to take her to the opera or out to dinner. We know, we say, and we believe that she takes her exercise in the English garden every morning, but we've never seen her. Sometimes outrage follows this, as if we had lived in a city for ten years without taking the trouble to see its famous museum. More often speculation about how old Miss Loren must be takes place; quite often we indicate the apartment of our other celebrity, a famous French actor, which was burnt out after an extravagant New Year's Eve party held by his son went wrong. Indoor fireworks, we believe.

Once a woman lawyer arrived and said something quite different: she said that she had no idea that we lived opposite the shipping company. She would not, she said with exaggeration, have accepted our invitation to lunch if she had known this was the case. She had worked there for eighteen months. It was the most horrible experience of her life, and she still, ten years later, had nightmares about it. We were amused, but she would not be drawn further. When we sat down, she asked quite seriously if she could change her place. She did not like to sit with her back to the window. She would prefer to be able, at all times, to see the shipping company, its wall of green glass, its air of a complex and decisive life run according to its own inexcusable rules.

Miss Em

TANIA HERSHMAN

They ask Miss Em to wait outside. It is because you're wearing blue, they say, and it's true, she put a great deal of effort into her outfit, her trademark brooches, one on either side. More aquamarine, thinks Miss Em as she watches everyone else troop in, as she sits and wonders whether tomorrow, if she chooses red, or pink, a greener shade, this time the doors will open to her, this time she will squeeze into the back row, although she knows it upsets them, throws their balance, undermines the hormonal harmony, her tendencies. A sigh is stuck inside her throat, as she sees the doors, once again, shut, and blue she sits, her fingers playing with her brooches, listening to the murmurs she is denied from within.

The Marionettist of Mírové Square

JASON HEWITT

Some years ago, before the Russians, when the land we are standing on was once Bohemia and this town was to some Aussig an der Elbe and to others something older; and if you imagine that beneath our feet now there were cobbles, and that if you glanced past the stone column of St Anthony and through the melee of busy market stalls, then there, just there, in front of the building with the shuttered windows that later, during the *Protektorat*, had been a *Gasthaus*, you might see him, for he would be there – the marionettist of Mírové Square.

Each day, on a small stage marked out with chalk, the dusty particles of which the pigeons would pick at, he would sit on an old oil canister with his trilby hat upturned on the ground, and, holding the control bars of a marionette and playing a harmonica strapped to his head, the white-haired marionettist would make the puppet boy dance. The boy's wooden feet in wooden clogs would lightly clack on the paving, his little shorts would rise and fall as his legs lifted and dropped with the strings, his varnished hands would swivel and wave, and the hair – that some people said was real – would gently lift in the breeze.

Each day the marionettist would be there, and each day the boy would dance. And between the dances the man would rest on the canister with the marionette perched on his knee, both heads turning in tandem at this and at that, like sparrows playing in the gutter or wheeling up over the mountain peaks of buildings like arrowheads through the sky. Then, as the clock in its tower struck six, the old man would collect his trilby, emptying out the three coins that he had put in himself that morning; he would hoist the canister by its strap on to his back, and by the echo of the sixth chime, he would be setting off down the side of the square, walking the marionette beside him so that his wooden feet in wooden clogs lightly click-clacked over the cobbles.

No one much thought about him. No one could quite remember when he had arrived or where he had come from. All they knew was that he kept a narrow shop down a narrow alley that no one but him ever had need to venture down. His name was known only to himself; and he did not care to share it.

This, for many years, was how it was. The two of them would be there on market days when you might see them through the throng of stalls; or on other quieter days, when the square was empty but for a couple of school boys, the bells on their bicycles tinkling as they bounced over the cobbles, or an old man, pipe in mouth, dragging a squatting dog across the pavement, or a gaggle of women bustling through, or – after the German tanks had arrived and the atmosphere was thick and twisted – perhaps there would be just a group of soldiers puffing on cigarettes and kicking a rotting cabbage around, until all its leaves lay like crumpled skin around the square.

That was how he came across her. You might know the date.

For many years Jews had lived there peacefully – the families of Weinman and Petschek, after all, had made the town what it was – but on that frosty November morning those few Jews who hadn't already fled to Prague were pushed and cajoled out of their houses and bustled into the square. Many gathered to see them go, as they were shoved into line and forced on to trucks, some crying, others stone-faced, some with small suitcases that would later be taken from them, others with nothing held but the hand of a child.

The crowd jostled.

There were jeers and shouts.

No one took much notice of the old man and his puppet watching from across the square. Nor did they pay particular attention to Otmar Petschek, the Jewish mining manager, who, holding his daughter's hand, bent down and whispered something to her, then glanced across to an old abandoned cart and, past that, a narrow alley.

Then as if on cue a scuffle broke out – all eyes suddenly on a woman who tried to pull free from a soldier's grip – and in that moment, as the butt of a gun struck her down and all eyes were on her – *was she dead?* – no one saw Petschek signal with his head for the girl to dart across the cobbles to hide behind the cart's wheel and then disappear into the alley. Only the old marionettist from his spot could see her, crouched down in that slit of darkness, nothing but the nub of her nose protruding like the smallest stub of wood.

The trucks left.

The Jews were gone.

The satisfied crowd dispersed.

Nothing about Mírové Square was any different again but for a new silhouette in an alley, a shadow that all afternoon did not move and that the marionettist watched through the corner of his eye. Only when the clock struck six, the November sun dissolving and the square deserted again, did he walk the marionette across the cobbles to the entrance of the alley. He leant the wooden boy in so that the little girl hiding within the darkness could see his painted smile; and then, carefully guided by the old man's strings, the wooden boy reached in and offered her his little wooden hand.

I probably don't need to tell you that little Eliška went home with the man and his puppet. The times were different then – a winter was coming, so dark and malevolent, that for many years any act of kindness, no matter how small or selfish, had to be grabbed and kept close to your chest. This was how Eliška ended up at the shop, how there the old marionettist led her up the narrow throat of a stairwell to a child-sized bedroom with a child-sized bed.

'This is Pavol's room normally,' he said in a voice that splintered and creaked. 'But Pavol can stay with me.'

The next day she went to the square with the old man and his puppet, and the next day and the day that followed. She grew fond of him, fond of them both; and as the days passed the thin-painted smile across the marionette's face seemed to grow wider and wider. He would dance and jig, his patched shorts lifting, his glass eyes glinting in the sun, and the hair that some people said was real blowing across his face. Sometimes when little Eliška watched him she could no longer see the strings or the man. Sometimes, she thought, the marionette boy was dancing all on his own.

Each night the marionettist worked, chiselling. He sat at a battered table in his workshop in a dusty cave of candlelight. She would watch him working the wood: carving out a leg or an arm, oh-so-delicately sanding it, then protecting it with licks of varnish, or sewing clothes from old scraps, and fixing the hooks and strings. His own hands were as gnarled as bark but the fingers worked with such dexterity, joints bending, tendons pulling, the open and close of finger and thumb. Only occasionally did he stop to circle a shoulder; every dried joint within him ground like in a pestle and mortar.

Some Sundays, when the weather was fine, they would tramp up to the forests, walking the puppet boy with them; and there, beneath the trees overlooking the town, he would tell her ancient stories like that of the Jezinka who stole people's eyes, or that if you press your ear to a piece of wood you can hear if it is silent and good for the taking, or the slow crawl of rot through its grain, the crackling chomp of woodworm.

'Can you make a marionette out of any wood?' Eliška asked the old man.

'Of course,' he said. 'Although some are easier to use than others. Limewood is best. It's light and easily worked with a chisel but it does not easily splinter. You should choose the wood based on the puppet. Every tree has a spirit, you know, like every person. My job is to find a match.'

'If I was a puppet,' Eliška announced with a smile, 'I'd want to be made from mahogany.'

She was only joking but he took it seriously.

'No, no,' he said, tutting. 'No. Far too dark. You want a good strong oak or ash for a pale skin like yours, or maybe even pine, although, of course pine dents and, no, you don't want that. Perhaps some day I will make one though, just like you.' He gave the girl a knowing wink. 'And then you can choose for yourself.'

They walked on, Eliška kicking the pinecones and their feet crunching through the needles. The old man carried the marionette like a child, the boy's arms and strings draped over his shoulder, the head resting against his neck.

'Why don't you have any children?' she asked.

'I did once,' he told her, but said no more than that.

Night after night the old man worked, chiselling, chiselling, chiselling and blowing the wood dust away. No one ever came into the shop but that didn't much matter. Besides, they were never there. Each morning they would walk the marionette into the square and the old man would make him dance, while Eliška wandered about with his trilby hat and the three coins that he put in there every morning and took out every night.

Until one day that is, when a woman they had not seen before suddenly stopped and stared at them. She stood, hesitating, a dozen or so yards away from where the old man sat on his canister, the marionette on his knee. She held a shawl tight around her; her hand clutching the wool was thin and her face pale and expressionless but for her eyes that were locked on the boy.

She took a step closer. And then another.

Like so.

Until her eyes widened, her gaze still firmly fixed on the puppet.

'Could I ...?' she asked, her voice like paper. 'I'm sorry but ... Please forgive my impertinence, but, could I, could I hold him, please – just for a moment?' She pointed. 'Could I hold him, please?'

The man said nothing then nodded. He ushered her over, getting up from his canister seat and signalling the woman to sit. Then, stood behind her with all the strings pulled taut, he sat the boy gently down on her lap, the wooden bones of his thighs upon hers, his calves and jointed ankles and feet tilted and dangling below. The woman took the puppet's hand in hers and held it, its varnished palm and jointed fingers, and it was little Eliška that saw it first – the woman's eyes starting to pool.

The next day when the marionettist opened the shop she was there and had been for an hour.

'Please,' she said, handing him a photograph – a faded black and white image of a child in shorts, braces and a shirt. The marionettist stared at the picture and at the woman stood on his doorstep, her shawl still clutched around her and her knuckles tight to her skin.

He had no idea how to say no so in the end he asked: 'How tall?'

'About so high,' she said, showing him with her hand, just there. 'Quite small. Not very tall for his age at all.'

They did not go to Mírové Square that day. Instead they worked all morning, all afternoon and night, the photograph of the child leant against a jam jar in which the old man kept his brushes, the light from the candles when it grew dark flickering across the boy's creased and faded face. The marionettist fashioned clothes for him from the scraps he had and a few bits and pieces from Pavol's wardrobe. And when it was done the next morning and the woman returned, he told Eliška to wait with her at the front of the shop while he brought the wooden boy out from the back. Standing behind him, the old marionettist carefully guided him out, pulling the strings and working the limbs so that when the woman saw the puppet she did not see the man behind him at all. All she saw was a small hand nervously appear from around the door frame, and then a face and the rest of the head, and then, as he stepped fully into the light, the strings disappeared in the sun altogether, and there was just a hand with a cross held over his head and his movements a little jerky, his wooden feet gently click-clacking across the floor.

The woman's eyes stared with wonder. 'My Viktor,' she said.

The next day there were two more women and the day after that a queue; each with a photograph clutched in their hand; each with a son, a daughter, a grandchild that was lost to them; taken, they said, by the war.

They did not go to Mírové Square any more. But, instead, they worked every day and half of the night, Eliška in charge of fashioning the clothes, sharpening the tools and updating their orders. They charged fifty pfennigs. The old man said 'I'd rather Czechoslovak korun' but in those days trying to pay in korun wouldn't even buy you a slap.

Week after week their business flourished and morning after morning when the old man opened the shop he would find himself faced with a queue.

They each clutched a photograph, their faces pale but hopeful.

'My little Otma.'

'My little Hana.'

'My little Walter.'

'My little Moe.'

And then one morning the marionettist sent Eliška out across the square to buy new cotton, but Eliška did not return. It was gone midday before he had noticed, and another hour before he finally decided to close the shop with a sign in the window that said 'Closed for lunch'. Then putting on his trilby and walking the marionette boy with him he went out looking for her, down the narrow alley, into the street, across the square, up and down other streets and other alleyways.

'Eliška,' he shouted.

'Eliška,' he called.

'She was here,' Mrs Holmerova at the haberdashery said. 'A little girl of so high. I sold her three spools.'

'She has probably got lost,' the marionettist said, tutting, because he had not wanted to cause her worry. 'I am sure I will find her. You know what these girls are like. Good day.'

And Mrs Holmerova nodded.

But he did not find her. They searched and searched, walking the streets until in the square the market stalls had been packed away and the clock struck six and people hurried. No one helped him. No one dared to look at him. Nobody told the marionettist what they had seen that day. And when the square at last was empty and full of shadows they stood by the stone column of St Anthony amongst the soldiers' cigarette butts and the cabbage scraps.

'Eliška,' he called. His voice splintered. But neither the old man nor the marionette boy could see her anywhere.

The next day there was just a lone woman standing there when he unlocked the door. She was young with scraggy hair tied in a knot and thumbprints of eczema pressed down her neck. She looked up at him on the step, as they always did, and pulled her hand from her pocket. 'Sir,' she said, offering up the photograph. 'My daughter,' she started to explain. 'Agáta. She is –'

'No.'

She paused, uncertain.

'But –'

'Sorry,' the marionettist said, quite firm now, 'but no.'

The woman stalled again, her mouth trying to formulate words that were not there and her eyes, already raw around the edges, now started to fill.

'But … everyone said …' she begged him. 'I have walked all the way from Teplice. Do you not understand? It has taken a whole day to get to you. Please, will you just – Please –'

She tried to push the photograph into his hand anyway, and he caught a glimpse of a girl with untidy plaits.

'The Germans took her,' she said. 'To a camp.'

'I'm sorry,' he said.

'To Terezín.'

She held out the photograph again, her face now crumpled and desperate. 'Will you not at least look at her? Please!'

'No,' he said, and then, 'I'm sorry. I don't make them any more.'

Now, as you walk through the town's narrow streets you might still see one, through a window perhaps, tucked in a bed, or propped at a dinner table; or perhaps even being walked across the square by an elderly mother, their little wooden clogs clipping the flagstones, or held, hanging, against a chest, a wooden face glancing at you over a shoulder and their wooden legs limp and dangling.

Who made them has most likely been forgotten. No one knew his name or thought to ask; he no longer comes to Mírové Square. But look hard enough and you might still see me, walking unnoticed through the narrow streets or turning off down an alley to a closed and dusty shop. And, sometimes, on the edge of a forest overlooking the town, surrounded by limes and ash and birch, I sit on an old bench with her and Pavol. I rest one hand of hers on my lap, the other I take in my palm. And I hold it.

I hold it.

I hold it until the wood warms and softens, and I feel her with me, her fingers slowly taking hold of mine.

I feel the gentle squeeze of her hand.

Proof

BEATRICE HITCHMAN

Hush over the green village; hush hanging over the summer. You on the bicycle, your brother Rémy trotting at your side along the road; you not slowing down for him. Him on the edge of crying because you won't.

You grip the handlebars, swerve a little; pass Mme Dufour, who is in her front garden, billowing out her white sheets and clipping them to the line; and you say hello, but hardly look at her. Mme Dufour says: *Bonjour, Juliette*, with that little purse of the lips; Rémy, now with an audience, starts to cry properly, pushing his fists into his eyes. Mme Dufour pouts more deeply, lines springing up around her mouth, and turns away from him. You don't blame her; he's embarrassing (could you really sell him to the gypsies?) saying over and over, *Maman never said you could borrow the bicycle ...*

You pedal faster. The heat has made you vague on all things apart from the plan. What you'll do if his window is unlocked, and what you'll do if it isn't.

Mme Dufour's is the last house before the road starts downhill, curving away in a white strip into the trees. The wheels kick up dust, and you go over the lip, with a lurching feeling. *I was never like that*, you say to yourself, as Rémy's howls get higher and farther behind, *never like that*, with the wheels clicking, and your hair behind you; your thin cardigan fluttering and not enough to keep you warm, now you're into the tunnel of trees.

It's all right. Mme Dufour will give him something to eat, and he'll go home. It's for the best, because what would you have done with him once you got there, anyway?

This part of the mountain, the road between your village and Compiègne, is haunted. A woman in a blue coat. She'll stop you and ask if you've seen her husband, the Germans had him, he had only just joined the Resistance – then when you say no she'll ask you it over and over, until you run away. Madeleine Terroir's brother saw the woman one night last autumn, and he got so annoyed with her questions he took a swing at her. His fist felt cool as it went through her face.

You glance sideways, in case the woman is there today, running along keeping pace with you, but there's nothing; just the gummy smell of the chestnut leaves, and the flickering glimpses of the pasture, through the trees – yellow – and the high blue of the hills in the distance. Places you'll go, but not yet.

The trees give way on one side of the road to a fence marking the boundary of his property. Trail your toes in the gravel, slow and stop the bike; peer over the handlebars at the front of his house.

It's set back from the road a little way, and at first it looks like the other houses further up, in the village proper: single storey, stone base, shingle roof, green shutters. It's the garden that's different. (People in the village say, *of course, his garden*, waving their hands as if it's too delicious to talk about, and there's a nudging of ribs, too, as if actually the garden isn't delicious after all. You haven't understood yet the significance of a man who gardens.) The grass in front of the house is fussily trimmed; there are pots of geraniums in wooden tubs, twin miniature conifers ringed with pebble-circles and a bird-table, which is deserted.

His car, still gone. Good. You saw him drive away, earlier: both hands gripping the wheel, sliding past your house. You'd turned away, helping your mother with the laundry, in case your plan was written all over your face.

Unlatch the gate and lug the bicycle through into the front garden; and so far, all of this is all right, because you could be just coming to pay a visit, or bring him a message or a neighbourly gift. And it still feels almost fine to lower the bicycle in the shadow of the fence, where it isn't visible from the road, and to walk up the path as if you're going to knock on the door.

Instead, you step over the grass towards the front windows; reach over the pretty window boxes and tug the corner of one shutter. It opens outwards. And then you reach in – picturing what it must look like from the inside, your hand, white and small, extending into the dark room – and feel empty, warm, hovering space. The window is open on the inside – left like that, to air the room while he's out.

You snatch your hand back. Trembling with relief that nobody on the inside reached out and took it.

You clamber up on to the sill and pull your leg over, straddling it awkwardly, and land on the boards inside, in a delicate arabesque. Then go still.

Shapes in the room come clear: a form in a chair in the corner could be a person asleep; it isn't, it's just a cushion.

The room looks different to home; here, it is neat. Sunlight speckles the bare pine floor. The stove is smart black, logs piled to one side. There is a little side table, a perfect circle of polished wood. And in the corner of the room are shelves, and on the shelves a set of books, bound in real brown leather. Somewhere, in another room, a clock's softly ticking the minutes away.

You'll inspect each room in turn, like a policeman would. Press on floorboards, knock on walls for hidden compartments. Starting with the room you're in: picking up the books from the shelves, shaking and fluttering the pages one by one, in case anything falls out. Lifting through the log pile, lifting them one by one, getting sawdust all over your hands; picking up the portrait photograph on the mantelpiece and checking behind the image in case anything has been slipped down the back. Tapping on the bricks; on the stovepipe. It echoes; from outside there's the startled clap of birds' wings, ascending from the roof.

At the back of the house is a kitchen. A window looks over the back garden, letting in bright light; a dark wood table and bench occupies most of the free space. It is already set for one person's dinner: spoon and soup-bowl, plate and knife.

You pick up the shining cutlery and turn it over and over. There is a drowsy smell: turning, you see a vase on the sideboard, full of cut flowers.

You pass through the house, as light as a ghost, brushing your fingers along the waxen surfaces of his furniture, opening the larder to study the neatly turned cans of powdered milk, inspecting a soap by the hip bath in case there's a key in it.

In his bedroom, you lift the crocheted coverlet to look under the bed, and find only a line of shoes; waxed nutty-brown, the laces trailing. Pick up a photograph from the windowsill; it looks like M. Arnaud, but younger. For a moment you think this could be it; but then you see he's wearing a white shirt, not any kind of uniform, and he isn't carrying a weapon. And he's alone. It's just him, standing there, in a field, his back to a tree; squinting uncertainly into the camera, one hand up to his forehead. Whoever is taking the photo is someone he likes, from the smile on his face. Their long shadow stretches out across the grass towards M. Arnaud.

Another photograph: this time the hair is starting to recede from his forehead. He has that thin, long-jawed look, but the same smile. This time, he has his arm looped around the shoulders of another man. They are in a cornfield, the stalks thigh high and pale gold. The face of this man is turned in three-quarter profile towards M. Arnaud, slightly blurred, but you think he looks like a dog with his tongue hanging out for more.

You almost think it can't be M. Arnaud; that wide, open grin, because how can a man like him look so free? Madeleine Terroir whispered it to you, behind cupped hands, earlier this summer: *that's where his money comes from*; he was a *collabo*, he was in the Militia, he took away the Resistants and shot them, and when the fighting stopped, he wasn't rounded up with the others. He got away and hid. And that's why he's moved here, because it's up in the mountains and far away. But somebody knew somebody who knew somebody he knew. And so now we all know, too. That's why the grocer won't serve him. That's why the butcher doesn't deliver his meat.

When you repeated it to your mother, she smacked your hand and said *we don't spread gossip*, which was how you knew it was true.

Into his bedroom again. Sun, slatted by the shutters, falls on the coverlet. You sit on the edge of the bed to test its weight; make the springs bounce.

There are people who can divine water with a stick. But perhaps your gift isn't for finding water; perhaps if you listen, the house will give up its secrets.

The roof shingles creak. The wind makes the shutters rattle. The birds, outside, hurrying around the table; the flutter of letters that you pulled from his desk drawers, held down by a paperweight, trying to escape.

Nothing sings out to you from the darkness.

The disappointment you feel is unreasonable. You alone have come to find him out; just you, not Madeleine Terroir, not her brother, not the butcher, with his foul-smelling hands and sweaty bald head. You alone have been brave.

Then there is another sound: a humming, becoming the crackle of wheels on gravel. The woman in the blue coat brushes swiftly past the window – her pointing fingers: *you're next*. And you think you already know, in these elastic few seconds, what will happen; can already see the sweat stains under the arms of his shirt, the glint of his spectacles, how his combed-over hair lifts in the breeze as he stands looking at you. So then, all there is to do is move along towards the point where that happens; which you do by running to the back door, and out into the garden, discarding the possibility of escape into the woods (what about the bicycle?), and round the side of the house, to wait by the corner, looking out at him walking up the garden path.

There's a point where the you who you are most of the time would lie; would step out from the angle of the wall and say something like *You weren't in so I left the jam round the back, Maman sends her compliments*, and then run to the bicycle and away before he could get inside to the back door and see that the jam was made up. Lying has always come naturally to you and it is a shock to find yourself out of smooth words.

Here he is now, almost at the front door, the jingle of keys, a parcel of meat staining blood through the waxy paper, held in his other hand. The key pointing at the lock, like a sixth finger.

Bright sunlight, dappling the garden; birds scatter upwards from the bird table as you move your hand, just flicker the fingers accidentally, a tic; but they have gone up and now he can tell you're here.

A lock of his hair lifts; light on spectacles; you step out so he can see you.

Oh, he says, and he puts one hand up to his chest, flattening the palm, as though he's got a cough. *Oh.*

Then he says: *It's Juliette, isn't it? From the village?*

Speaking your name might give him power, so you just nod.

He shifts his weight on to his other hip. *Everything all right?*

You nod. He is staring, and the way he is looking at you seems kind, but you don't like how it feels. You want to say *don't you know it's rude to gawp?*

He says: *Your mother all right?*

You nod again. Your hands clutching each other at the level of your waist.

Well, he says. Pushes his flyaway hair out of his face.

You are disgusted – he is unseemly. You can see a lot of different hims, fleeting one after the other across his face. He could be seven, now, Rémy's age, that time you took him fishing, smiling widely at you in complicit delight; then there's doubt at the corners of his mouth, and he could be your mother, rolling out dough too hard, staring at the tabletop; and now he's someone you don't know, a much older person, a watchful person, who peers at other people from behind half-closed shutters. Now his face has dragged down even further, and he is someone older still, whom you've never met; and also someone you do know, again. Rémy, after the fish escaped his net, flipping silver into the rush of water. Looking up at you. Bewilderment, sadness.

You back away from him at first, palms up to fend him off if he comes; but he doesn't, he just stands there, the material under his armpits a different colour, looking at you as if you, too, are an entirely new person.

Halfway down the path, you turn to run, your feet scuffing little granite pebbles on to the lawn at either side.

Up comes the bicycle, fitting into your hands; you slip on to the saddle. *He is behind you!* He isn't behind you, he is still standing by the house, watching. The bicycle wobbles, threatens to fall. You hurt yourself manoeuvring it through the open gate, the frame bashes into your private parts and your thighs, the pedals scrape the insides of your ankles. By some miracle, he isn't coming. You think that you will vomit when you get a safe way away. Then there's speed underneath you and your shaking legs are going for all they're worth.

In the field outside your house, you fling the bicycle down and yourself next to it, smearing your dress all over the grass and reeds, sure it'll stain. And when your mother asks you later why you've ruined it, how she'll get the stains out, why you're in such a temper tonight, will you tell her? *Never*, say the rattling seed heads by your ear. You can never tell.

Madeleine Terroir comes to your house after school one day, just at the edge of the autumn; brown chestnut leaves crackling under her feet, and the chimney has just begun to whistle its winter song. Your mother has started cookery classes in Compiègne; she goes there every Thursday evening and comes back smiling, vague, to kiss Rémy's hair: *my boy's getting big.* There have been no reports of the woman in the blue coat for some time.

Madeleine Terroir stands on one foot on the doorstep, then the other, her face lit up, and says: *M. Arnaud's leaving, my brother saw him packing his car this morning, the agent says a new family's moving in next week.*

You look at each other. Your faces are saying something different, but she doesn't realise that for a few seconds. *My mother says she doesn't see your mother much any more*, she says, defiant, once she understands you won't invite her in.

When Madeleine Terroir is gone you go back and sit at the table and try not to look out of the window. You focus your attention on your books. The schoolwork, not that you find it difficult, has increased this year.

In a few minutes his car slides up the hill, going slowly because it's completely loaded with furniture and crates. There's a trailer rattling behind it, with plants in pots packed carefully in, blankets between them, to stop them getting broken. The bird table is tied to the roof with red twine.

You leap to your feet and pull the curtains across, tight shut so not an ounce of the view can get in. But this is new, too: things don't stay outside your mind just because you can't see them, in the way they used to. As the car passes the house he may or may not turn his head to look at you; his face may or may not be a pale blur; may or may not be any number of things.

Valedictorian Speech: Moments of Magic

ALYSSA HOLLINGSWORTH

First, I want to thank my family, and particularly my parents, for enthusiastically supporting my work through many horrifying drafts. Thank you to all the tutors and staff on the MA Writing for Young People—it was a joy to work with you, especially Lucy Christopher with her sparkly stickers.

I thought about taking advantage of my American-ness and simply reciting a few country songs, with no one the wiser. Because 'I'm proud to be an American, where at least I know I'm free'. But since I am a collector of stories, I decided instead to share one with you.

Recently, a fellow student and I were at Iford Gardens. We'd climbed out on a boulder to the centre of the Japanese pond. Soon we realized literally hundreds of newts covered the pool's floor.

A little boy ran up and stared into the water. Then he whispered to his sister, 'Look! It's a kingdom of water lizards!'

I turned to my friend Annie and said, 'This is why I write for young people.'

During my year of study, the Writing for Young People course gave me many moments of magic like this one. I'm sure all of us have similar memories, across our studies—where the world went sharp and lovely, and we knew we'd chosen right.

Sometimes it got hard to see, when we had to get out of bed at 5 am to write before our jobs, or arrived at Corsham with something to turn in having had only two hours of sleep. But I have stored up these glimpses of joy to remind myself that all the work—and it is a *lot* of work—is worth it.

As co-editor for the Writing for Young People anthology, since the course's end I've watched my classmates fly on to the next stages of their writing careers. Some have signed with agents. Some have publishers knocking on their doors.

All of us, regardless of subject, regardless of degree, are standing on a threshold. We have accomplished great things, and now we begin to see what the real world holds.

Like the children and young people my course mates write for, it is in our nature as artists to create kingdoms out of lizards, and to uncover the enchanted in the ordinary. Study, jobs and bills can conspire against us to turn the magic mundane again.

But remember the times that illuminated you. The time we heard the bells of Venice singing to each other. Or the time when we rode three-metre waves in search of the whales. Or the time when we walked through fairy woods and dipped our hands in fresh red earth.

Hold tight to your wonder, labour hard and always be a joy to work with.

from *Esc&Ctrl*

At exactly 6 pm I return to the underpass. There is a shadow of a man stand-ing beneath the archway. He is wearing a long black woollen coat and a grey trilby.

He is standing at a right-angle to me, and his facial aspect is strikingly perpendicular. He has birdlike features, and small, round spectacles perch on the end of his nose. He is holding a canvas case in his left hand and a fold-ed-up tripod in the other. He looks like a Russian spy.

The case looks about the correct size to hold a laptop computer. I walk over to him. I say, 'I think you're waiting for me.'

The man turns round. 'I presume Davison sent you?'

'Davison?' The word is like a razorblade in my mouth and I don't know why.

'Yes,' the man says.

I say, 'I'm here to collect a laptop and some software.'

The man holds the canvas case aloft and nods at it proudly, as if he's showing me the head of a beast he has recently decapitated. 'You're Vincent Ballone, I presume?'

'Yes.'

He places the canvas bag and the tripod on the floor. 'I must say,' the man announces, 'that I am most impressed by your punctuality. It must be six o'clock, on the dot.' He pulls back his coat sleeve and frowns at his watch. 'Would you look at that,' he says. 'Damn thing has stopped.'

'Mine too,' I say.

The man smiles a wry smile. 'Well, look on the bright side. Still tells the correct time twice a day, doesn't it?'

I try to smile back but I think it looks more like a grimace. 'Would you mind telling me how you and this "Davison" know each other?' I ask.

'We don't,' the man replies, still looking at his watch.

'What?'

He looks up. 'I don't know him and he doesn't know me.'

'I thought you were friends?'

'No, no. We've never met. We speak online.'

I nod towards the canvas bag and the tripod. 'And you just agreed to meet a stranger with all of this expensive equipment?'

'Not exactly.'

'What, then?'

The man pushes his spectacles further up his nose. 'If you must know,' he says, 'he paid me.'

'Paid you?'

'Yes. Handsomely.'

'How much?'

The man coughs. 'I'm afraid I'm not at liberty to say.'

'Was it more than a thousand dollars?' I ask.

He removes his spectacles and breathes on them. He takes a handkerchief from his pocket and uses it to wipe the lenses in a circular motion. 'Yes,' he says. 'It was considerably more than a thousand dollars.'

'Was it more than ten thousand dollars?'

'No.'

'How did he pay you?'

'Bank transfer. He sent the money online.'

'Did he say why he was paying you so much?'

'Mr Ballone,' the man says. 'I'm not sure how much you know about my work in the science of lie detection. But allow me to divulge one piece of information: I risk losing my job over this meeting. The laptop computer and the software I am availing you of are the property of the university. I have no idea what you hope to gain from using this equipment and, to be frank, I would rather it be kept that way. Had Mr Davison not offered me such an agreeable sum then I'm afraid I would have had to decline his request. You can keep the computer and the disc. As far as my colleagues in the department are concerned, some miscreant has broken into the laboratory and stolen a laptop whose CD drive happens to contain a prototype of the most up-to-date version of our software. For that reason, my association with you, and with Mr Davison, ends here.'

He picks up the laptop case and tripod and hands them to me.

'I'm not technologically minded,' I say. 'How am I supposed to use this thing?'

'You're going to have to figure that out by yourself,' he says. 'The camera is inside the front pocket. Good day.'

'What if I can't get it to work?' I ask.

'Good day, Mr Ballone,' the man says, firmly.

I expect him to walk away but he doesn't. He just stands there, looking at me. I think he's waiting for me to leave. I think it's a power thing. He wants me to back down first.

I shoulder the bag and begin the walk back to the Explorer.

I sit in the hotel room, making notes. I'm trying to come up with a list of questions to answer when I take the lie detector test. I'm writing the list of questions on some of the blank sheets of paper I found in the envelope.

The questions must have answers which are statements of truth or falsity as opposed to opinions. Coming up with these sorts of questions is more difficult than it first appears, since it is necessary to anticipate what the answer might be and to then construct a question around it. I realise that life would be much easier if all conversations were structured in this way – if the answer came before the question to which it corresponds. At this point, the phone rings.

'Did you collect the laptop?' he says.

'Listen to me,' I say. 'Is your name Davison?'

'You can call me whatever you like.'

(Where the hell have I heard that name before?)

The realisation hits me with such force that I feel as though I am falling, falling through layers and layers of reality with nothing to break my fall until.

Until.

'You've got it, haven't you?' he asks. 'You know who you are.'

I drop the phone on the bed. I can hear the voice repeating my name, over and over, louder and louder, asking whether I'm still there. There is a word in my head and the word is 'obloquy'. I imagine a clock ticking and I remember the computer in the Belleclaire Hotel with the timer ticking down to cut-off point and I think that the computer is me.

Time is running out. I have to take the test. I shoulder the laptop bag and find the tripod. I hesitate at the door and grab the red telephone. Seconds later I'm outside the elevator, repeatedly and impatiently banging my fist on the buttons. It's broken down. I hurtle along the corridor, burst through double doors and descend the stairs; two, three, four at a time. Fifteen blocks to Perry Street. I run the whole way. My path takes me across Manhattan, from East Side to West, diagonally downwards, an arrow piercing the city's heart.

Beginnings: A Tribute to Les Arnold

Les Arnold was the prime mover of the MA in Creative Writing at the college that would become Bath Spa University. He was a poet, whose poems were as alive as the man himself. 'Running' shows Les as I knew him; an athletic, dynamic man, who was always on the move:

> My heart crows along this morning
> road. Running zippy zappy through
> the day, blue-frost, ice-sun, hearing
> only thud of distant blood, my body
> felt from a great height.
>
> I merge with the road's indirection.
> I can't die. I can only go on like
> this, amplifying the world's pulse
> under a clear sky, drawing after me
> the trees, the early flowers, sleight
> of fox & deer in celebratory
> silent marathon.

I had joined the college to teach English Literature and Creative Writing in 1988, and initially I lodged with Les and his wife Sandra at Leigh House Farm, on the Cotswold ridge above Bradford on Avon. Les was Head of English and Creative Writing at the college. He was also a smallholder; he and Sandra kept sheep on about eight acres of grassland. One of his publications was *The Golden Fleece: A Celebration in Text and Photographs of Cotswold Sheep & Shepherds*,[1] drawing upon H. J. Massingham's *Shepherd's Country*,[2] but informed by personal experience. He included his poem 'The Brassrubbing'[3] in this book:

> The Unknown Sheepman at Northleach
> and his Unknown Wife have been sleeping in
> the same stone bed for more than 400
> years Both are fully clothed He is always
> the perfect gentleman Sheep explain
> his success His unknown wife
> lies perfectly still with hands crossed
> in prayer But he cannot touch her
> Lord I have covered her body with paper
> rubbing until nipples again shine through
> in the exhausted cold at Northleach
> we go about our business Whilst the
> sheepman dreams of the brass he has made
> and the fleecing that remains to be done

As a poet and a teacher, Les owed a lot to his roots in the country. After his death, a student said: 'He was close to nature, he inspired us.' Les was indeed an inspiring teacher. When I first saw him with a class, I knew at once he was the finest teacher I had ever met. He was vital, dynamic – a colleague with whom he had worked at a Canadian university described him accurately as a 'dervish of energy' – and natural, friendly, approachable. As Colin Edwards once remarked to me, teaching with Les was fun. Les was a great encourager. He liked to speak of himself as an enabler, and he helped students to discover in themselves creative abilities they didn't know they had. This was at undergraduate level, in courses that prepared the ground for the MA, which from the beginning was marked by Les's ideals

Tragically, weeks into the MA, early in November 1992, after a short illness, Les died. We lost a dear friend and, also, a man who was due to play a major part in teaching the course he had initiated. For me, that semester was a grievous time. My mother died in October, weeks before Les, and my eldest brother at the beginning of December. As director of the course, I had, as far as possible, to set aside personal feelings and attend to the work in hand. That I was able to do so owed a lot to the support of colleagues and the enthusiasm of the first cohort of students. Fortunately, we were able to get invaluable part-time help from writers living in the area, initially Lindsay Clarke and Rosie Jackson, who joined us as tutors. What helped me too was the knowledge that we were working in Les's spirit.

The MA in Creative Writing at Bath Spa University has gone on to establish itself as one of the best in the country. Les Arnold will be a memory to only a few associated with the course now, and it is important for the history of the course that his part in making it possible should be recognised. In responding to a request to write something about the course, therefore, I deem it vital to remember its founder, who did not live to enjoy its success.

Les and I were of a generation; we had similar ideals, though in some respects we were very different as people. We had both written theses on the early poetry of W. H. Auden. We had been influenced by the Beat culture of the 1960s. Les had written his doctoral thesis on William Carlos Williams, the poet he loved best, and we admired the poetics and spirit of Black Mountain College. We shared a passion for nature and rural life. Les was originally from Blackpool, but his heart was in the Cotswolds. We talked about one day collaborating on a sequence of poems, with his ground being Cotswold limestone, and mine the chalk of my native south. After his death, we (family and colleagues) planted a wood in his memory on the land at Leigh House Farm. The small trees included oak and whitebeam and hollies; alders and aspens; and other varieties. 'Hopeful young trees,' Richard Kerridge said. This plantation is now a flourishing wood that bears Les's name. In the years after his death I wrote the poems in *Arnolds Wood*[4], feeling it to be a kind of conversation with Les.

Les spoke with characteristic modesty about his own poetry, and told funny stories about its fate: publishers who undertook to publish it suddenly went bankrupt, or their premises burnt down. This was all part of the history of experimental modernist verse, for Les was a modernist, and a poet too good to be fashionable. I remember his delight when he told me Rupert Loydell was going to publish his book, which Les called *Joy Riding*[5]. But when the box with the first copies arrived, I was the one who opened it. He read to us in college from 'Shaker City', the title sequence of what would be his second posthumous collection. Introducing him on that occasion, I praised him by joking about how hard he was to praise – open and playful as he was, he was shy of acknowledging any of his own achievements, and given to doubting them.

On 17 March 1993, on what would have been Les's 50th birthday, we held a celebration of Les through his writings at Newton Park. The Tippett Centre was crowded for the event. Les's wife, Sandra, and their daughter, Megan, were present, together with many of Les's students and former students and colleagues. Colin and a group of students gave readings from *Joy Riding*, and Richard, with two students on the MA in Creative Writing, read from *Shaker City*[6]. Laughter broke the tension as we reminisced about Les. At the time, I wrote: 'there was a quality of concentration in the room that I have never seen before; on people's faces, in their stillness, in their quickness to respond. What Les meant to us all could be felt; his spirit breathed in his words and the words spoken about him.'

On a cold day of spring rain in 1993, I sat at Les's desk at Leigh House Farm and looked through his papers for unpublished poems and stories and scripts that would make a posthumous collection. These subsequently appeared, together with poems and prose tributes from students and colleagues, in *Uncollected Writing and Tributes Written for Les Arnold*[7]. On that cold day, alone in his study, in the house where I had enjoyed so much good talk and laughter, the world inside and outside the window seemed desolate indeed, and the rain fell on the vegetation outside and against the window with a frisson of chilly green. Spring rain brings back that day, and in recent years it led me to write another poem for Les.

Green rain
Remembering Les Arnold

1

Once you told me
you didn't trust a slow driver.

You were fast –
            driving, writing, teaching
with energy, awakening
in others their creative life,
and quick to leave us.

One day the man
most alive, the next
            gone.

2

I sat over your papers
on a cold, wet morning
in April,
            rain on the window
reflected leafing trees –

this flesh of the world!

I sat at your desk
with your words for company:

            work-in-progress:

quick notations,
poems half-finished,
a story for children
about a red bus.

Looking up, I expected
to see you dashing past.

But of course there was no one.
Only rain drops
            in green light, moving
slowly down the window pane.

How Les would fume when we drove in to college together and were held up by a traffic jam at the misnamed Rush Hill! I remember his brother telling me that when Les played hockey, he frightened his own team as much as the opposition by the way he charged about the field. He was an active, restless, quick-witted man and he had to get things done. The MA in Creative Writing at Bath Spa University was primarily his doing, the work, initially, of his energy and his commitment, and his belief in encouraging others to realize their creative potential. It is right that I should end this tribute with his words from 'Shaker City', a celebration of the dynamic people of whom he said: 'It is in the coherence of their lives that the Shakers serve as images of wholeness.'

Shaker City [8]

They're coming down to paint the town

white. The sisters are wearing shovel bonnets &
white dresses and the brothers are wearing homespun
suits of penitent black and great beards and they're

shooting up the main drag in horse-buggies and sending
the grey dust along Bloor pluming upwards until all the
chromed burger-bars are ghostly this unlit evening

and their brown and black cobs are stamping through
streets where we're all on the point of surrender
with nothing to light our way and our neon signs

flagging in an air where whips and whoops! are the only
signs of a life we never knew until too late. Now in
sunset storm outside our dustsheeted best parlour damp

Brothers and Sisters ride the sidewalks breaking shop-
front windows with their singing.

[1] *The Golden Fleece: A Celebration in Text and Photographs of Cotswold Sheep & Shepherds.*

[2] H. J. Massingham, *Shepherd's Country: A Record of the Crafts and People of the Hills*, (London, 1938).

[3] Author, *The Golden Fleece.*

[4] Jeremy Hooker, *Arnolds Wood*, (Birmingham, 2005).

[5] Les Arnold, *Joy Riding: New and Selected Poems*, (Devon, 1993).

[6] Les Arnold, *Shaker City*, (Devon, 1998).

[7] *Uncollected Writing and Tributes Written for Les Arnold*, (Bath, 1995).

[8] Arnold, *Shaker City.*

The Accidental Novelist

CLAIRE KENDAL

If I hadn't worked at Bath Spa, it probably wouldn't have happened. So many novelists tell stories about how they knew pretty much from the day they were born that they would be writers. I didn't.

I never considered writing novels. For as long as I can remember, my biggest obsession was reading them. The only way I could imagine being paid for that was to become an academic. So I did a PhD in English Literature, then applied for jobs.

Bath Spa was very different, back then. Even the name wasn't the same. The English department was run by Les Arnold, who had presided over my job interview and was beginning to introduce Creative Writing into the department's offerings. Les was a poet and an academic. Meeting him, I saw for the first time that you could be both of those things. There would be countless others to reinforce this principle.

When I started work a few months later, the department was in shock and grief over Les's sudden death. Jeremy Hooker stepped in to run the MA in Creative Writing, wanting to ensure that Les's creative vision would not be lost. I was struck by the idea that everyone around me had been given a legacy, and taken on a trust.

It soon emerged that the arrangements for teaching a group of MA students had somehow fallen through. With seeming casualness, Jeremy asked if I would take the class. He'd stopped me as I passed by his open office door, making me wonder if anyone would do. But he peered at me and stroked his beard in that thoughtful and wise way of his, so perhaps it had always been part of his plan. I said yes. I was excited, but also nervous that the students would feel cheated – I didn't even know what a writing workshop was.

It is likely that the students taught me more than I taught them. One of my first lessons was that you can learn a lot from other people's writing mistakes. Somehow, you are more open to seeing what is wrong with somebody else's opening chapter than your own. You aren't invested. Your critical faculties engage in a different way, and much less personally.

It quickly became clear that I wasn't just teaching a how-to course in Creative Writing – I was taking it.

I began to realise that the techniques I'd been honing as a literary critic were relevant. It struck me, too, that the kind of nitty gritty work I was doing with these novels-in-progress was as fascinating as anything I had done with the literary works of the canonical greats. I was inside the writing, somehow, instead of out.

But these early recognitions didn't prevent some awful pitfalls. My stomach was always in knots when I was teaching. Who was I to run a workshop? I had never written anything creative, let alone published it. I feared I wouldn't know what to say about the students' work. I scribbled pages of notes that I never looked at, just in case I ran out of thoughts.

The wonderful – and scary – thing about a writing workshop is that all of your interventions in the work are on show. It's a kind of public operation you can't rehearse for, but I wrongly used to believe I had to be the best person in the room at. All you can do, really, is read as deeply and thoughtfully as possible. Perhaps that is the best thing any writer can hope for. But I was still full of questions about how to do it.

Managing the group dynamics was delicate, and involved so many paradoxes. I could see how sensitive they were to any hint that tutors might admire some work more than others. How could I be diplomatic about weaker pieces, yet make the points that would help the students to improve them? How was I to maintain credibility if I failed to address problems?

One of my worst mistakes was to feel like I had to plunge in and be first to identify all of the flaws in any submission. Then, with what must have been embarrassing crudeness, I would find something nice to say. Writing this now, it seems obvious that I was doing these things back to front.

A crucial technique, and learned only by getting it wrong so many times, is to trust the students to make the key points. They nearly always do. They hear the difficult things better from one another than the teacher. There are always refinements that the tutor can offer at the right moment. When you relax and share the responsibility with the whole workshop, this happens naturally.

I watched Richard Francis run one of his prose fiction workshops. So this is how it is done, I thought. Richard was so at ease, but so acute. He would effortlessly stage-manage feedback, with each student having their say in turn, but magically ensuring it never felt forced. He would come in at just the right time, with the exact and absolutely needed thing the student needed to hear to make their work better. The students loved him so much they tried to outdo one another by making him cakes. Richard joked that his class had become a bake off, and his clothes would no longer fit.

Somehow, barely conscious of it, I began my first novel. It was like breathing. Not deliberate. Not an effort. Almost inexplicably, the novel was there. It was as if I had caught something from the people around me. Looking back, I am certain that this happened because of the inspirational feel of the department, a kind of force field. The novel was awful. It is now in a deep, dark drawer, where it will stay locked away forever. But the pleasure of writing it stayed with me.

I taught more and more Creative Writing classes, and realised that at some point I had begun to feel at ease in them, even purposeful and competent. It is thrilling to work with brilliant students, and see some of them achieve publication.

Along the way, I managed to write a book of literary criticism and a fair number of scholarly articles. I was proud of these pieces, and my love for the subject matter was intense. But writing novels was different. I had to tear myself away from them, rather than force myself to work on them in the way I did with traditional academic research.

One failed novel turned into two.

Then something happened. I doubt anybody will remember this small moment, but it has stayed with me. We were at Kingcombe, where we used to take the MA in Creative Writing students for an intensive residential weekend. This one was rare, and rather special, because Steve May was there too, and he didn't usually come to them. Somebody thought it would be a good idea if the staff sat at a table in front of the students and performed a writing workshop. Steve chaired it. Richard Kerridge was at the table. Tessa Hadley, too. Probably Colin Edwards as well. Maybe Philip Gross. Perhaps others, but those are the people I seem to remember.

We workshopped one of Steve's poems, and an extract of Tess's prose. The members of staff were supposed to take turns saying constructive things about each piece, just like in a real writing workshop. It all felt exciting, at least to me, and I remember feeling proud that I was part of it. At the end of the workshop, Steve asked Tess whose comment had been the most useful to her. She said mine. I glowed. For me to tell this little story is a kind of bragging, and I hope you will forgive me for it. But that moment meant a lot to me. And it illustrates the power of even a small number of positive words from someone we admire.

That moment made me think, *I really can do this. I'm learning how writing works, and how to make it better, at quite a high level.* The extraordinary benefit from such an activity is that if you can look sharply at other people's novels, and practise doing this for many years, it becomes a skill you can turn on your own.

Two failed novels turned into three.

I had my yearly 'Staff Development and Review' meeting with Steve. I expected him to be horrified by my inability to stop wasting my time with novels. I feared he would tell me to devote myself to academic research and say I wasn't qualified to supervise Creative Writing PhDs any more.

'I'm not a novelist,' I said. 'I haven't published any fiction.'

'But you are a novelist,' Steve said, 'if you write novels.'

It made a huge difference to have someone I respected tell me that what I was doing was legitimate. Until then, writing novels felt illicit – certainly not part of my job description. Steve even said that he admired me for my drive to continue, to do the thing because I loved it, despite the lack of any external validation for it. He knew it was hard. That he could think these things about me was a revelation. Although I still didn't feel that I could publicly call myself a novelist, Steve gave me permission to think of myself as one. And from then on, I did. At least secretly.

I wrote novel number four. There was a meeting in the English Department, something I was compelled to go to even though there wasn't a single item on the agenda that had anything to do with me. I was cross that they'd dragged me in on a rare non-teaching day that I could have used to write. I piled books all around me so nobody would see what I was doing. I sneakily edited my novel, and was rehearsing defiant speeches in case I got caught. There was no longer anything unconscious about the process. I knew what I was doing and had the dark circles under my eyes to prove it.

I told Gerard Woodward I had written another novel. 'How exciting,' he said, 'I'd love to read it.' I was startled, and touched, that Gerard would volunteer his time like that. But one of the other things about Creative Writing at Bath Spa is how generous our writers are to one another. Gerard's encouragement was a huge boost.

Fittingly, the news came while I was at Bath Spa. The Barn at Corsham Court was filled with academic staff. We were on some kind of training day. I looked at my phone during the coffee break. A literary agent's name was in my inbox. His response had come so unexpectedly soon it took me a few seconds to process what it was. I had to read his letter over and over before I could believe it. There had been too many rejections to count, usually coming after I had waited many months, so I hadn't properly imagined getting anything else. But the agent liked my novel. He wanted to meet me. I floated through the rest of the training event.

Sometimes I think Bath Spa is like a Tardis. It may seem small compared to some universities, but it expands magically, to fit what its staff and students can offer, and makes a place for them, changing as they change. I have had two different careers at Bath Spa, and the university has embraced that. The first career was in the English Department, and that will always be part of my identity – I wouldn't write if I hadn't read. The second career is as a novelist and teacher of Creative Writing, working with doctoral students and doing a job I love in a place that helped to make me into the writer I didn't know I wanted to be.

What Workshops Do (Ideally)

RICHARD KERRIDGE

Sometimes I think about designing a 'context' module on the topic of
sentences. We would spend the term asking what makes a sentence beautiful. Students would analyse the sentence styles of writers, including some
famous for long sentences and some for terseness. They would pastiche these
different sentence styles, and experiment with mixing them up. We would see
how changes of length and rhythm produce changes of mood. A short sentence snaps into action after a long and contemplative one. Long sentences
surge, falter, regroup and become decisive. We would look at structures and
rhythms, at simple and complex sentences, at the placing of the main verb,
and whether no-verb sentences, the ones Stephen King calls 'frags', are ever
a good idea. How can sentences be metrical, like lines of poetry? Does that
intensify the drama? If we compose sentences with that in mind, do they
become too artificial?

I imagine us relishing the ironies of Anglo-Indian sentences in Rushdie,
and the precision with which Sarah Waters pastiches 1940s sentence structures. Students would write their own sentences with much more attention
to style, and with awareness of a greater range of possibilities. We could, in
fact, make this a Learning Outcome: 'By the end of the module, you will be
able to demonstrate a subtle and wide-ranging awareness of the qualities
and techniques that produce eloquence and dramatic intensity in single

sentences and sentence combinations, in your own writing and in selected examples from other writers.'

Perhaps we will introduce this module one day, but I began to see reasons for wariness. Would it slow writers down too much, making them hesitate over each sentence for too long? Would their styles become too self-conscious and artificial? What I wanted was for students to think about these basic units of writing: what beautiful and challenging things they can be in themselves, as well as in their contribution to larger textual effects. I *wanted* student writers to pause over each one. But as I sketched the plan, mission creep started. Thoughts about sentences led on to sentence combinations, paragraphs, dialogue. I saw that every question about whether a sentence was good had to be context specific. Does it work in the right way for *this* part of *this* book?

That is what the workshops do, and why the workshop is the heart of the MA. They mediate between the general principle and the needs of the particular manuscript. What follows here is an account of how workshops work when they go well; an account prompted by my hopes and hesitations over this imagined context module.

In a workshop, the agenda is set by the manuscripts students are writing, rather than by topics and set texts. Every two weeks or so, each person sends a piece out: usually a few pages of prose or a single poem. In the class, one by one, the others say what they think are the main strengths and weaknesses, giving reasons, which are then debated. The tutor may then expand on a question and suggest further reading; in practice there is likely to be considerable overlap between the series of topics the workshop produces and the curriculum the tutor would have designed for a skills module for novelists or poets.

The difference is that in the workshop each topic remains attached to the one piece of writing. If the discussion moves into general principles, it will soon return to the question of what is best for this book, at this point. As the term continues, the students will get to know each other's books-in-progress, and understand more deeply the implication of each decision. One of the dangers in Creative Writing classes generally is that principles, such as 'show, don't tell' will become items of dogma, applied without question. This is less likely in a good workshop, because the question will be, is it right *here*?

Recently I have heard the term 'information dumping' rather a lot, perhaps because of the popularity of historical and futuristic novels. In these genres there is a special need for the provision of background facts, since the rules of the world are unknown to the readers. How is that information to be provided without the energy of the story disappearing under prolonged explanations? What is the right mixture? There is no general answer. The judgment depends on the quality of tone and pace in the whole narrative. Another necessary but potentially dogmatic term is 'over-written'. Elaborate sentences with lots of adjectives are out of fashion, but done precisely, in the right context, they can delight readers with intelligent observation.

The strength of the workshop is that general propositions and particular passages of writing are continually tested against each other. Each student gives a reaction to the piece of writing, offering a judgment. Some of these reactions will be disconcerting to the writer of the piece, who has to think carefully about what is said, and decide, in all rigour, whether any of the advice should be followed. Is it compatible, finally, with the writer's instinct for the book they want to write? The most important word here is 'finally'. To make that decision conscientiously, and to inhabit it and see it as one's own, is to take creative responsibility for one's writing. That should be one of our Learning Outcomes too.

Books come from inside their writers, and also from outside – from things that the writers have observed, researched, imitated, internalised. Sometimes it is a moving experience for writers to recognise, suddenly, that in their own work they are echoing sentences, or cadences, that have stayed with them from books read in childhood. Among the things observed and imitated are the conventions of genre, which shape the personal material the author pours in. The relationship is much more complicated than this quick way of putting it suggests. Inside and outside can seldom be cleanly distinguished, and we cannot disentangle them back to a time when they were separate. Nevertheless, the distinction between them is worth making, because it helps us see another kind of mediation that the workshop provides.

By 'personal material', I mean more than the writer's advance vision of the completed book. I mean also the personal concerns that will go into the book, even if they are not obviously connected to the plot and the genre – sub-texts from the desires and fears of the author's life. Sometimes there will be recurrent motifs that represent these concerns symbolically or metaphorically. An author's interest in the ocean might do that, or in clothes, paintings, birds, the sky, children, streets and buildings. These things can become sets of poetic images in the background of a story.

From the earliest stages of writing, these hidden subject matters come into contact with the shaping models provided by genre, plot structure and narrative viewpoint, or for poets stanzaic and metrical form. These models too can work their way deeply into a writer's instinct, but I put them in this second, more purely external order of influences because teachers, editors, publishers and the literary community in general hold them out for examination and imitation. They are topics on the curriculum. A literary criticism module may teach them systematically, using a range of literary examples and dipping into theory and philosophy for critical questions. But the workshop does something different. It makes explicit the encounter between these models and each writer's more personal material, honouring both, and helping the writer bring that material for the first time into public view.

The Woman Among the Nerudas

TIM LIARDET

I hunger for your sleek laugh
— Neruda

All the Nerudas muster, as if from nowhere,
like a flash-flood of doubles. There is not one of them
who feels he does not own that lugubrious smile.
Each draws around him like an overcoat the air
of *I am the Neruda.* Some great men, for security,
hire twenty men who look exactly like themselves.
Bonaparte's asylum-garden was crowded out
with loonies in bicorns and tails. A similar purpose
infuses the Nerudas: they blend and are safe.
This cloud of lookalikes seems to make it clear
that your uncommon, very un-Chilean voice
and umbrella which is firewalled and not grey
down with the grey umbrella of caps might be
the perfect Neruda, among the Nerudas, disguise.

Extract from a Radio Play

Dean Jim Blunt is interviewed for the vacant Vice Chancellor role at Hayborough University by Dame Sheila Gore-Butt, chair of governors.

RADIO   And today, after a flexible but robust selection process, led by headhunter agency Vulture and Crowe, interviews for the post of Vice Chancellor are taking place at this very moment.

UNIVERSITY BOARD ROOM

SHEILA   So, Jim, why this job, and why now?

JIM   That's a very good question.

SHEILA   And that's a very poor answer.

JIM   I haven't finished yet ...

SHEILA   It's what low-grade politicians say when they're stuck.

JIM   I'm not stuck.

SHEILA   You're floundering like a flounder.

JIM   What was the question?

SHEILA   That's worse, that's footballers.

JIM   (*Clears throat haughtily*) There comes a time in any distin-
          guished career where one longs, indeed aches, for the chance to
          give something back.

SHEILA   Did you take something, then?

JIM   Take what?

SHEILA   Any spoons, paper clips, copier fluid, that kind of thing?

JIM   I've taken nothing from my time at Hayborough but immense
          personal satisfaction in a job well done.

SHEILA   But why this job?

JIM   I just told you.

SHEILA   But if you wanted to give something back you could have
          applied to be a cleaner or a gardener.

JIM   What? And waste the benefits of my immense talents and
          experience?

SHEILA   But why this job?

JIM   You keep asking the same question.

SHEILA   And I will until you answer it.

JIM   Very well, Dame Sheila. Why this job? Isn't it obvious?

SHEILA	Not to me.
JIM	For goodness sake, because it's highly paid with plenty of scope for embezzlement.
SHEILA	And why now?
JIM	Because you've just advertised it, there wouldn't be much point in applying if there wasn't a vacancy, would there, you stupid woman?
SHEILA	But why now in your career trajectory?
JIM	My career has been marooned on a plateau for some years, and this is a last desperate attempt to better myself and augment my pension.
SHEILA	And what would you say your vision is for Hayborough University?
JIM	Well, as I see it, higher education should be about excellence. If it's not excellent, we ought to shut it down.
SHEILA	So we ought to close the university?
JIM	Not entirely, no. But we should concentrate our resources on those areas that have the chance to make a world impact.
SHEILA	This would sound like a policy of contraction?
JIM	And why not, what's so wonderful about expansion? Is bigger necessarily better? If that was the case, wouldn't everyone want to be grossly obese like you? Is a huge pile of shit more desirable than a single gleaming well-cut gem? Is a broken-down bus superior to a Porsche Tapiro, to which incidentally I will certainly treat myself were you so misguided as to give me this job.

SHEILA   And modernisation? What's your stance on education in the digital future?

JIM   If you ask me, madam, the so called digital revolution is nothing but an aberration, a momentary blip in the wide scroll of history. My vision is, that in ten years time, once all the digital nonsense has run its course, and all the money and information in the world is lost due to a gigantic explosion of sunspot activity, then we will revert to the tried and tested methods of paper, or stone tablets, or even shards of broken pots.

SHEILA   And do you have any questions for us?

Postcards From Paris

BRITTANY McCOMAS

'I will never be a hundred per cent again.' That's all I kept thinking. Sitting in my parent's house. Filled with grief. When I was a child, my parents had a figurine music box that played Francis Lai's infamous *Love Story*. Maybe it was there that my love of another world was born. I used to think the man and woman in the music box were my mother and father. My father had this love about him that was so romantic. He was everything I ever dreamed of and so much more. For a woman, the first man she meets will always be the first love of her life. For me, that was my Daddy.

Life can be an emotional roller coaster – especially for a writer. There are moments you want to throw in the towel. Moments of complete exhaustion, both physical and emotional. You think of the people who got you to where you are, and often ask God for help in moments of despair. Because you think 'I will never be 100 per cent again' when personal tragedy rocks your world. I'm not sure why, but in the worst moment of my life the words from writer Mimi Thebo popped into my mind. 'Not if, when you make it as a writer.'

We were on our way home from the anthology launch of the 2009 Bath Spa University Alumni Anthologies and I was the editor for the scriptwriting anthology *Blood, Sweat and Structure*. The launch was a lovely affair at Foyles Bookshop in London, where every editor was thanked in a very grand speech – except me. Even in that moment, I knew I had a hard road ahead of me if I was going to be a scriptwriter. On the bus ride home I was chatting away to some tutors and said, 'If I ever make it as a writer', and Mimi Thebo immediately interrupted me with 'Not if, when ... '

You're never quite prepared for the roller coaster ride that makes you think you are going to die. You are never prepared to drop your life when your writing is about to take off, hop a red-eye flight home from London, and watch the first man you ever loved die. The odd thing for someone in the middle of a massive amount of grief is to have it all together, and I had it all together. In my family, I took after my grandfather. Emotional, I was often referred to as having a flair for drama. I loved telling stories and creating worlds of magic, and I cry – a lot. The grieving me was the exact opposite. She was stone cold, organized, and didn't shed a dang tear.

My best friend Brandy came to me, 'You're scaring me.' 'Why?' I asked very calm, cool, and collected. 'Because you have it together way too well for this.' She knew grief was going to hit me and when it did – it would be cruel, and scary, and bloody awful. I got an email that a short film I wrote, *Dr. Sugarloaf*, produced with Pinewood Studios in London, was to world premiere at THE Cannes Film Festival. In that moment my grief was instantaneously tucked away, and I booked a flight to Cannes.

When I got to Cannes, my friend Laura was waiting on me. Laura is an amazing woman who works in film and had become so very special to me over the years. In a strange world full of red carpets and celebrities, it was so nice to see a friendly face. She could light up a room with hers, and I knew in that moment that Cannes was going to be amazing.

Cannes was exhausting. You are constantly selling yourself as a writer. You get up, you have breakfast meetings. You watch films that are emotionally draining and lovely. You walk a lot. You are pushed around by paparazzi. You do it with a smile on your face, in the most perfect pose. You attend party after party. You drink a little and keep your composure. You might not eat all day. You go to bed at 4 a.m. You get up at 8 a.m., and you do it all over again.

A few days into the festival, I had been invited to a vodka mixer with my Finnish friends. I went to a meeting, and decided afterwards to just let loose for the evening. The mixer was on a rooftop terrace full of sun and fierce industry professionals. Laura introduced me to some amazing people, including a producer from Paris. The light in my world instantly got a little brighter the moment he smiled.

Everyone was having such a lovely time – what with endless vodka, white wine, and the most tantalizing hors d'oeuvres I have ever seen. The producer and I couldn't quit talking. Even Laura noticed the strange connection between us. As the sun began to set, I took my sunglasses off. 'Wow,' he said. 'What?' 'Why you hide your eyes?' 'The sun was bright.' 'Your eyes are brighter.' In that moment I fell head over heels for this beautiful man from Paris. 'No really, Brittany. Your eyes, your smile. You are beautiful. Keep your glasses off.'

So, I did what every girl would do in this situation. After Cannes I followed him to Paris. I was in a very weird place in my life, hiding from grief. Cocktails and conversations about religion, with a beautiful man in a speakeasy in Paris, just seemed more fitting than falling in love under the bright lights of that intoxicating city. What I didn't know, I was falling in love under the bright lights of that intoxicating city. One eve, I was afraid in my grief that I was going to do something really stupid with this beautiful man so I told him I should go home. He walked me to a taxi. He twirled me around like Fred Astaire would Cyd Charisse and he kissed me. He looked me deep in the eyes and said, 'You need to find your smile, the beauty in the world.'

I jumped a flight to Pisa the very next day to do just that. Italy was my second home. After spending time there writing a beautiful film, *American Fango*, with a lovely and insanely talented Italian director Gabriele Altobelli. I knew I could find solace there. Pisa would be the city where I found my feet again. There I met the most amazing German woman who was going through the same thing. She had lost her father as well, and would become my rock. The person I could share my fears, hopes and dreams with – in just knowing one another for three days Marleen and I would be comrades in life, love, and all things travel. We both shared a beautiful lust for life.

A week later, I was on a bus from Pisa to Viareggio where I was going to spend the day by the Italian seaside. I decided after having a film world premiere at The 69th Cannes Film Festival that I couldn't go home from France and face what was there for me. An empty house with my heartbroken Mum and the rest of my family – always talking about my Dad. I didn't want to forget him, but I didn't want to deal with what happened that last day in the hospital. But, it crept in when I least expected it and big, fat tears just rolled down my face on this Italian bus filled with strangers.

Missing this man in Paris something fierce, I thought about what he said to me. Something in my world changed in that brief moment. A little African girl began to play 'peekaboo' with me. She had the brightest smile ever. It was magical. My tears became tears of joy, because this little girl – all she could do was smile. Which in turn made me 'find' my smile, and I took my sunglasses off.

I cried every day in Italy. Every. Damn. Day. I found my grief and started to deal with it. I still came home to America bitter, jaded, and full of booze. I would pretend I was fine when I really hated everything. I quit writing. I quit going to church. I started drinking more. I didn't sleep at home, because it reminded me of my Dad. I didn't want to be around anyone in my family. I was ruining my life. Failing at my job. I was missing deadlines and just forgetting to turn things in.

In the middle of all this self-loathing and grief, that I tried to hide from everyone around me, things just kept getting more dark. I quit talking to my best friend on the regular. That was the moment I knew I was lost, and I wasn't sure how to get the hell out of the black hole that was this grief. I was doing everything my father taught me not to do. In a moment of profound darkness I messaged the beautiful Parisian man, 'I miss you. Everything has been horrible for me lately. I miss Europe. I try so hard to stay positive.'

A few days later I got a postcard from Paris. No return address. Just a stamp of priority from France. This postcard wasn't your typical postcard. This was a handmade card. On the front, *Giraffes by the Evening Light* ...

On the back, a simple note reminding me of who I was, who I was meant to be, and just how amazing I am. No, I'm not going to tell you what it actually said – because it was the single most sweet sentence anyone has ever said to me – and I treasure it that much.

I didn't know it then, in Cannes, but this man would become my soulmate. My shining light. The one who could unknowingly pull me out of the darkness. From the moment I read that letter, I decided that grief did not own me. My smile did. My tenacity to be one helluva scriptwriter. My love for comedy and all things hilarious. My wit, my charm, my drive, my awesome – all things I got from my Daddy and unknowingly let go of the moment he let go of my hand. All it took to get them back was a postcard from Paris. A note from a beautiful man that I met, one gorgeous day, under the sunlight of Cannes. Where I had followed my dream to be a writer.

Since then my feature film, *American Fango*, has rocked the film festival circuit and become a multiple award winning film. Every month I get a postcard from the beautiful Parisian man reminding me of who I am, something to encourage me to keep going. I have written him a hundred letters, and never sent them. Because no one seems perfect enough for what I want to say. Funny, even writers struggle with words.

Recently, I went with *American Fango* to the North Hollywood Cinefest. We sat on edge at the awards ceremony having been nominated for Best Picture. When you hear the words 'Best Picture' followed by the title of your film – you realize you only live once. You only get once chance to '*carpe diem*'. So many people walk through life with a '*c'est la vie*' attitude. That is not who I am.

When I attended Bath Spa University I longed to break barriers, show that I wasn't just your typical scriptwriter, and above everything show that scriptwriting is just as intellectually stimulating and academic as all other forms of writing. I didn't see it then, but tutors there saw that I was a bright, young writer on her way to something. The person who graduated from Bath Spa University is still that bright, young writer on her way to something big.

As a person in grief, I needed to figure out who that woman was – everything had changed me. My time of grief and success, on my way to one amazing writing career, both needed to be embraced. When I broke down in Italy, the only person who could save me was 'me' and my faith in God. I simply prayed for forgiveness, light, and hope. Because when you are on your way to greatness, nothing can stop the path you are on. Your destiny is set, and you have to trust in the bad, the good, and the ugly moments.

As I unpacked from my award winning film festival tour in LA and New York, I found a vest top I bought in Sicily. Bright, like a light, it reads, '*Lu vie faite de petits bonheurs.*' Which means, 'Life is full of little pleasures'. In the process of finding the magic of being a writer, the fantastical world I once lived in full of wild adventures, I always had him with me. My father. Big, fat tears burst from my eyes and I cried into that shirt. Only to realize every single thing I worked for at Bath Spa University had come to light.

The tutors who pushed me so hard: Jonathan Neal, Doug Chamberlin, Hattie Naylor, Steve May, Chris Jury, and especially Robin Mukherjee. Those beautiful moments I spent with poet and friend Carrie Etter, hashing out what I should do with my writing and where to look for work, over posh dinners and beautiful conversation in Bath. The eternal words from Mimi Thebo that I will always hold dear. Thank you. All of you. For believing in this writer.

In that moment of emotional release, crying into a shirt, I remembered Paris. Where I found my feet through the beautiful words of a very extraordinary man. Probably the only man who came close to reminding me of the love of my father … it is a beautiful thing when you finally realize there is only one person in the world that you can love as much as you love yourself. I jumped up from my bedroom floor, grabbed a piece of paper and a pen. Then simply jot down three words, 'I love you'. I stood, staring at those three little, magical words the beautiful Parisian man had taught me. Wondering if I would ever have the courage to mail them on a postcard to Paris.

from *Being Kennedy*

SUSAN McMILLAN

Kenny Wilmot, an attention seeking Australian teenager, is avoiding the problems of real life by broadcasting a bizarre fictional one on the internet. Kenny has no friends and receives little attention from his self-obsessed mother. He's clever, rich, bored, and, since the death of his father, has retreated into his own virtual world using webcams, mobile phones and YouTube to obsessively film and broadcast his life. But, in his virtual world, Kenny is not himself – he is a teenage girl called Kennedy. *Being Kennedy* is a rites of passage black comedy about a troubled teen who discovers that, when real life goes wrong, you can't just log off. This is an extract from the full screenplay:

INT. DINING ROOM, WILMOT HOUSE – EVENING

At the dinner table are Kenny's mum Val and her five guests: BERNARD (fifties – a developer); DR EVANS (forties – a mild mannered psychotherapist); MRS EVANS (forties – a walking ad for Botox); the GLAM NEIGHBOUR (thirties) and RANKIN (fifties – a Northern Territory cattle station owner). They are Sydney nouveau riche: squeaky clean, ostentatious, and a little rough around the edges.

There is a spare chair – Kenny hasn't arrived yet. The chat is easy, relaxed, until

Kenny walks in, dressed normally, but wearing full makeup. He's playing with his smartphone as he slumps down at the table. Everyone stares. Kenny looks up from his phone briefly, stares back blankly, accustomed to this awkward response from his mother's friends.

KENNY

What?

Val stares at Kenny maliciously, then turns a pathetic face to the men.

Dr Evans takes Val's hand, smiles sympathetically.

DR EVANS

Hard bringing a boy up ...

VAL

... On my own.

Val stares flirtingly at Dr Evans, she needs – no, wants – the attention.

Kenny stares at his mother for a moment. Wrong attention, wrong person.

KENNY

And your point is?

He ignores the continued stares and begins filming people's feet under the table.

CUT TO:

INT. UNDER TABLE, SMARTPHONE POV – EVENING (continuous)

Val's expensive mules play footsie with Dr Evans.

Rankin tries to reach her other foot but fails.

As each person speaks – the feet react. A pair of Italian leather slip-ons, tap nervously.

BERNARD OS

It's not normal.

A pair of red kickers rise and fall thoughtfully, from heel to toe, heel to toe ...

DR EVANS OS

He's obsessive.

BERNARD OS

He needs to get out more.

The expensive mule is slipped off and a stockinged foot (Val's stockinged foot) is placed on Dr Evans's inner thigh.

DR EVANS OS
(*loving it*)

He's egotistical.

The kickers rise and fall in time with the massaging stockinged foot.

A hand reaches down and scratches a purple painted toenail.

NEIGHBOUR OS

He needs a girlfriend.

And Val's stockinged foot finally reaches Dr Evans groin ...

RESUME: INT. ABOVE THE TABLE – EVENING

Kenny looks up. He can't quite believe the contrast between the grown-up calm above the table and the foot orgy below. The foot orgy in which his mother is an active participant with someone else's husband.

NEIGHBOUR
(*to Kenny*)

You OK, love?

The table all turn to stare at Kenny again.

DR EVANS

He's probably gay.

RANKIN

Fuckin' A.

Bernard and Rankin stare at Kenny uneasily.

Dr Evans closes his eyes in private rapture.

Everyone stares at Kenny. Their expressions are variations on a theme: what a screw-up this boy is. Kenny stares. They stare.

Silence.

Then Kenny smiles sweetly at Dr Evans's wife.

KENNY

You on Facebook?

MRS EVANS

Yes, why?

Kenny smiles, looks down and sends her what he has just been filming. Mrs Evans's iPhone beeps. Beat between them all then.

EXT: WILMOT HOUSE – NIGHT, A FEW MINUTES LATER

The guests are leaving. A tense atmosphere. Mrs Evans sweeps past.

VAL

I'm so sorry.

Everyone is po-faced except the Glam Neighbour, who howls with laughter. A glance between Dr Evans and Val. She mouths ...

VAL

Sorry.

INT. WEBCAM POV, WILMOT HOUSE, BEDROOM – NIGHT

Kennedy talks to the webcam in her bedroom. Smiles sweetly.

> **KENNEDY**
> I'm not.

INT. CONSULTING ROOM – DAY

Kenny sits in a comfy chair, looking pleased with himself. He is filming Dr Evans, the psychotherapist, with his smartphone.

Dr Evans takes the smartphone from him, puts it on the table.

> **DR EVANS**
> *(eventually)*
> So apart from making your little films, Kenneth,
> do you have any plans for life?

> **KENNY**
> No.

> **DR EVANS**
> But, the more you publish yourself online the
> lonelier you seem to be.

Kenny shrugs.

> **DR EVANS**
> Didn't you have a happy childhood Kenneth?

Silence.

> **DR EVANS**
> You liked your expensive school?

> **KENNY**
> Sometimes.

INSERT

EXT. SCHOOL GROUNDS, YOUTUBE FILM – DAY

A calm, perfect school. Squeaky clean, privileged and academic and, well...

Kenny hides behind a bush wearing a safety helmet and some goggles. He holds a detonator. He watches almost wistfully as ...

The sports hall BLOWS UP.

RESUME: INT. CONSULTING ROOM – DAY

> DR EVANS
> Do you do it to get attention?

Kenny doesn't answer.

> DR EVANS
> From your mother ...?

Kenny doesn't answer.

> DR EVANS
> She's a very attentive woman. A real woman.
> A woman.

Kenny still doesn't answer.

> DR EVANS
> Is it about your mother, Kenny?

INT. WILMOT HOUSE, UPSTAIRS LANDING – NIGHT

Val is ready for a bath after dinner.

She walks towards the bathroom but stops halfway when she sees that wires lead across the landing to the bathroom.

She knocks on the door.

> VAL
>
> Kenneth?

She sees a webcam is clipped on to a picture rail. Not good.

Troubled, she pushes at the door. It opens.

INT. BATHROOM – NIGHT

Val enters.

She sees a camera on the shower rail. She sees a camera on the toilet. She sees a camera on the vanity cupboard. Not good.

She PULLS back the shower curtain.

> VAL
>
> Haven't you done enough damage this evening,
> Kenneth?

She turns and runs out.

WEBCAM POV:

Kenny is in the shower. He is dressed in an expensive bikini. His legs are covered in shaving cream. He's holding a razor.

Kenny listens to his mum running down the landing crying.

> VAL OS
>
> My Dior bikini!

Kenny turns to the web camera on the shower rail and smiles.

INT. CONSULTING ROOM – DAY

> DR EVANS
>
> Are you angry with her Kenny?

Kenny ignores him.

> DR EVANS
>
> Are you angry with me? Your mother and I are
> very close.

Kenny snorts.

Kenny notices the nameplate on Dr Evans's desk. It says:
DOCTOR EDWARD EVANS: PSYCHOTHERAPIST. Kenny studies it.

> DR EVANS
>
> Obsessive use of technology stops you
> experiencing the real world.

Kenny experiments with shutting his left eye. He holds his hand in front of his right
eye, blocks out the word 'therapist' leaving just 'psycho'. Kenny smiles to himself.

> DR EVANS
>
> What about your relationship with your mother,
> Kenny. Would you class that as real?

Kenny tries his hand over his other eye. He sees – The. Rapist. Psycho. This amazes
and amuses him.

> DR EVANS
> (eventually, impatient)
> Kenny! I am trying to help.

> KENNY
>
> But are you helping?

Dr Evans pulls his chair forward, invading Kenny's personal space. He lowers his voice.

                    DR EVANS
            Does dressing up turn you on?

                      KENNY
                  (sarcastically)
            Hell, yes. You?

                    DR EVANS
            This is not about me, Kenny.

                      KENNY
            Says PSYCHO THE RAPIST.

Dr Evans pulls back. Puts a little space between them.

                    DR EVANS
            Well, perhaps we could think about finding another
            way to express yourself creatively?

*Kenny glowers at him, then calmly gets up and goes to the door. It is locked electroni-
cally. The unlock button is on Dr Evans's desk. He is all too aware of his control over
the situation. His hand hovers.*

                    DR EVANS
            That would be a start, wouldn't it?

*Dr Evans hand hovers over the unlock button. Click. Kenny exits. The door clunks
shut after him.*

                    DR EVANS
            Have a nice day, Kenny.

INT. WEBCAM POV, WILMOT HOUSE, BEDROOM – DAY

Kennedy talks to the webcam and paints a picture in her bedroom. It's a self-portrait.

                     KENNEDY
            Kennedy loves art. Kennedy's a mucho creative

creature. Kennedy apparently needs to express herself. I love trying to capture the 'essence' of people. What I think they really are. And you know, the wonderful thing about the web is that … *(leans towards to the webcam, whispers)* your greatest work can be seen by the whole world!

INT. WILMOT'S HOUSE, KITCHEN – MORNING

Val and Dr Evans stand accusingly in front of Kenny.

Kenny's laptop is on the worktop.

> VAL
>
> It took seven workmen to clean it off … and it's caused a lot of embarrassment to Dr Evans. *(beat)* And to me. *(beat)* How does that make you feel Kenneth?

> KENNY
>
> Dunno really.

> DR EVANS
>
> Do you have a penis fixation, Kenneth?

> KENNY
>
> Dunno really.

> VAL
>
> Did you think that no one would see it?

> KENNY
>
> Only if they Googled it.

Val and Dr Evans stare, horrified, at Kenny's laptop on which Google Earth is displayed. The image zooms in on a property with a flat roof: Dr Evans's house in the leafy Sydney 'burbs'.

On the roof is a huge graffiti penis.

                              VAL
          It's certainly large.

                            KENNY
                          (proudly)
          Took twenty-five cans of spray paint.

from *Two Dead, One Missing*

PAUL MEYER

CHAPTER ONE

When she found the handgun, Katie Maitland was thinking about teeth. The gun was just sitting there, on top of a white plastic bag, in the garbage can behind her family's house on Messenger Street. How it had ended up in the Maitlands' garbage can was anyone's guess. But there it was. She stared at it for a minute, and then she put down the other garbage bag – the one that she'd carried from the house – and tried to decide what she was going to do next.

Katie's mom and dad had introduced the family to a new schedule over the weekend, and this was the first day it had taken effect. On Tuesday mornings before getting ready for school, Katie would empty the trash and on Thursdays her brother Anthony would do the same. Today was her day to take out the garbage and Anthony's day to clear the breakfast dishes. This is why she had been thinking about teeth: she'd eaten a bowl of Kellogg's Frosted Flakes at breakfast, and one errant flake had become lodged in a molar at the back of her mouth. After bringing the bag of trash to the garbage cans, Katie was meant to go back inside, take a shower and get ready for school.

The handgun was black and heavy. She lifted it out of the garbage can by its rubbery handles, and then placed it ever-so-carefully on the cover for the water meter – as one might place a letter on a scrabble board or an unhatched egg back in its nest. The handgun, she noticed, had a dab of barbecue sauce on one side of it. The barbecue sauce had come from dinner two nights before, when Katie and her friends had a pool party to celebrate Katie's fifteenth birthday and her parents barbecued chicken. When Katie placed the handgun on the cover for the water meter she found that she had some red sticky substance on her fingers which, she thought at first, could have been blood but then she realized. The sauce clung to the left side of the gun, along the part that goes back and forth when it fires. She could smell the barbecue sauce and studied it on the tips of her fingers. It reminded her of her birthday, which had been mostly enjoyable but then later, when a couple of boys showed up, some of the girls became different and one of them had reminded her that she was an average student and probably wouldn't get into the University of Wisconsin, in Madison, where many of the girls talked about going after high school. She didn't understand why her friends, her actual friends, singled her out for abuse, when she was actually quite nice to them and invited them to her parties and gave them presents on their birthdays even though she was not always invited to their parties. When she looked at herself in the mirror, she saw a serious girl with pursed lips who – she decided – looked as if she were listening to something, a sound or a voice perhaps, in the distance: she was attentive, but not quite understanding what she heard.

Why didn't Katie march right back into the house and tell her parents about the handgun? She wasn't sure. It just felt to her as if she had found something valuable, and she wasn't quite ready to share this valuable object with the rest of the world yet. Instead she decided to hide the gun. Improvising, she tried to cover the handgun with weeds she pulled from big clumps growing close to the fence, but then she concluded that any gust of wind would blow the weeds away and any person walking past it would see the gun. She lifted the heavy handgun again, and with her fingernails she picked off the blades of grass which had stuck to the barbecue sauce. There were some bricks stacked haphazardly near the back gate, also with weeds growing between them, and after a moment Katie decided to hide the pistol under some of the bricks. What on earth was she doing, hiding a handgun in a pile of bricks? Just moments before, she had been a relatively normal young lady, and now here she was concealing a handgun. It gave her a sudden thrill to think she was doing something so illegal, just like the people on television.

She thought about the handgun when she was in the shower, and then again when she was getting dressed for school. It came to mind a few times when Anthony's friend, Don Weist, gave Anthony and Katie a ride to school, and then when she was in her morning classes. By lunchtime, she had forgotten about the thing and sat with her friend Mary Black, chatting about school and boys and their upcoming softball game against the Chetek-Weyerhauser Bulldogs, who had come in first place the previous season and against whom their team – Rice Lake – had very little chance of winning.

In fifth hour, Katie sat with a group of girls who weren't her friends but they were the only girls in class and it was either that or sit apart from them, with the boys, and this would cause even more trouble for Katie so she sat with the girls she didn't like very much. These were the same girls who'd said the mean things to her at her birthday party – her own birthday party at her own house, if that gives you some idea about these girls.

One of them in particular liked to pick on Katie: Rachel DeFrancesco, a tiny girl with skinny arms and straight brown hair and long white socks – you'd consider her inoffensive, to look at her – a nerd, but she controlled most of the other tenth-grade girls in the school with her will and her wit, and she loved nothing more than to pick on Katie Maitland in fifth hour – Science.

'I don't even think they're going to take you to the softball game on Saturday,' Rachel said to Katie while the two of them were working on an experiment together, burning a green wire with a torch and noting its effects. 'This is such an important game; I think the coach is only going to bring the best players. Besides, you should probably stay home and study anyway. There's no sense playing softball if you're only getting Bs and Cs in your classes. You're better off doing your homework so you can go to Madison after you graduate with the rest of us.'

Katie hadn't thought much about the handgun after lunch, but she thought of it now. What would it be like to hide the handgun in her backpack, bring it to school, to point the handgun at Rachel and whap: pull the trigger? Would she aim it at Rachel's face, or her chest, or just an arm or leg perhaps? It would be Katie's choice, Katie would be in charge of the situation, not Rachel. Afterwards, Katie would run out of the classroom and down the hallway, and at some point someone – a football player, perhaps, or one of the teachers, would tackle her and wrestle the handgun away from her. And then she would go to prison.

CHAPTER TWO

Dallis Flowers chose to drive his car down the narrow alleyway instead of walking because he figured driving would make him seem less like a thief – less like someone casing the neighbourhood for a later break-in, and more like a citizen completing a task, a chore. His white 1997 Toyota Camry, too, had been selected to draw minimum attention to itself. Dallis paid eleven hundred dollars for it at a used car lot in La Crosse to ensure he had Wisconsin plates and would fit right in. Just some kind of dipshit from Wisconsin in a 1997 Camry: invisible. That is exactly what he wanted.

Dallis stopped at the set of green garbage cans behind 215 Messenger Street, as he had been instructed to do, left the engine running, and then opened one of the garbage can lids. Nothing. He opened a second, and then the third and final garbage can lid, and still didn't find the Beretta he'd been promised. Nervously, because he wanted to get out of there as quickly as possible, he pulled out the white garbage bags and eventually he found the money – two rolls of hundred dollar bills totalling five thousand dollars – but no Beretta. He put the rolled-up cash in the pocket of his Levi's and then decided to tear into the garbage bags, hoping that the person who'd left the Beretta actually had actually hidden it inside one of the bags and not on top of it.

Dallis had a folding Buck Bantam in a black canvas sheath on his belt. He unsnapped it and pulled it open, revealing its matt-finish drop-point blade, and it felt good using it to slash open the garbage bags. A nice weight and balance. You couldn't even hear it slashing through the plastic bags. That's how sharp it was. He didn't use this knife as much as he should have, in his opinion. Chicken bones, oatmeal, packaging for a new digital camera, empty cans of chopped tomatoes, beans, Campbell's Cream of Mushroom Soup, paper towels that looked like they had been used to mop up a massive vegetable oil spill. Potato chip bags. An empty box that once contained Oreo Snack Pack Classics. But no Berretta. Unused celery stalks, a bag of salad leaves which had gone bad, a can of tuna, some cat food. But no Beretta. He found a paper towel that didn't have too much oil on it, and wiped his blade clean. Surveying the results of his handiwork, Dallis kicked some of the garbage around with his boots, just to make sure he hadn't missed anything. Eventually he climbed back into the Toyota and left the mess behind.

No one saw him come. No one saw him go.

He drove south-east about a hundred miles to a town called Marathon City, and there he bought a cell phone and a pay-as-you-go SIM card at a Walgreens, and called The Lorax from the parking lot of a frozen custard stand called Kurt and Jo's Eats and Treats. Dallis actually liked sitting in his Camry – it was roomy and welcoming and offered big windows to look around at the customers walking in and out of the frozen custard stand. His father back in California had a similar car, last time Dallis had visited him around 2003, 2004, before Dallis had fallen off the radar and gone to work for a fellow named Mike Granger who lived in Yankee Blade, Nevada, up on the north side of the Humboldt National Forest, known affectionately by those close to him as The Lorax.

Dallis missed his dad – his mother had killed herself and his sister along with another family in a car accident more than twenty years before, when she'd had too much to drink at lunch with her friends at a restaurant called the Branding Iron and hit another car head-on bringing Dallis' sister home from school in Fresno, where they lived at the time. His dad still lived near there, in Merced, about thirty miles north of Fresno on Highway 99. For most of his adult life, Dallis's father had been a fence builder but he also was a certified welder and made dozens of horse trailers for wealthy people up and down the central valley. Dallis could easily call to mind an image of his father's hands and fingers – stained with oil and criss-crossed by dozens of tiny scars from years working in the shop and on the farms where he'd helped the owners string their properties with barbed wire for a hundred dollars here, a hundred dollars there.

These memories crossed his mind as he waited for The Lorax to answer his phone. Eventually someone said hello at the other end – a woman, who sounded vaguely Latin American or European. Finally, The Lorax came on: 'Dallis,' he said. 'Dallis Alice. What's up?'

'Well, the money was there, in the garbage can, like you said, but no pistola.'

'No pistola?'

'I dug through all the bags. My hands smell like shit.'

'You always smell like shit.'

A fat man and his family came out of the frozen custard stand. The fat man was digging at his teeth with a wooden toothpick, and he let his wife open the door to their Oldsmobile for him. It took him a long time for the fat man to seat himself in the car, and by the time he had, the rest of his family was already buckled up and ready to go.

'We need that pistola, my friend. That is an important piece of the puzzle. You have to go back and find it.'

'I told you, I looked for it.'

'Well, you need to look again,' The Lorax said, with an air of finality. Dallis hated the fact that he was almost fifty years old and still had to follow basic instructions like this. By this age, he would have liked to achieve a certain station in life – the manager of an auto repair shop, for instance, or the boss of a construction crew. He was pretty sure that the future held no such promise for him, though, and he would spend the remainder of his life taking orders from people like The Lorax.

'You get the fucking gun, and take it down to Chicago, and do what we talked about. And then you leave it there, out in the open, for people to find it. This is important: it cannot be any old Berretta but that exact one. I don't know why, but that is the instruction I have been given and that is what we – meaning you – need to do.'

The fat man and his family were driving away when another one of their children – also fat – ran out of the restaurant and chased down the car just as it was pulling out of the parking lot.

Halfway between Marathon City and Rice Lake, Dallis pulled off to the side of the road and placed his new cell phone under the front tire of the Camry, and then he got back into the driver's seat and drove over the phone. There was a satisfying crack as the plastic case shattered under the weight of the car. He took some of the pieces with him and left some of the pieces there by the roadside. In a town called Boyd, he traded in the Camry for a rusted-out Oldsmobile Cutlass Supreme, also from the mid-nineties, with an automatic transmission and a crappy V6. Then he drove back to Rice Lake to find the gun.

Stuffed:
The Curious Case of the Hastings Rarities

STEPHEN MOSS

AUTHOR'S NOTE *this is the first draft of a book examining one of the most unusual cases of fraud ever exposed. The narrative approach deliberately blends techniques from fiction and non-fiction.*

PROLOGUE: JULY 1911

The door opened, allowing a narrow shaft of summer sunshine to penetrate the shop's murky interior, and momentarily illuminating the millions of dust particles that swarmed in the air like angry gnats. The customer paused for a moment before entering, to remove his top hat, before entering the Aladdin's cave within.

As his sunstruck eyes became accustomed to the gloom, so dark shapes – indistinct at first, like half-forgotten dreams – began to metamorphose into birds. Birds of every shape and size: eagles and egrets, sandpipers and shearwaters, buzzards and buntings, rollers and redstarts, and many, many more. Birds in flight, birds perched, birds hovering ready for the kill, birds cowering in terror in the claws of a predator. Birds, birds and even more birds. For a brief second or two, he felt quite faint; though whether this was because of the oppressive summer heat, the smell of formaldehyde, or simply a delicious anticipation of what he might find here, he wasn't altogether sure.

The visitor's name was Sir Vauncey Harpur Crewe, 10th Baronet, one-time High Sheriff of Derbyshire, and a genuine British eccentric. He lived in Calke Abbey, a vast, shambling stately home from whose grounds he banned all forms of transport: not just the new-fangled motor car, but even the humble bicycle. Over the years he had gained a reputation for being generous and caring towards his many employees and tenant farmers, while simultaneously displaying a haughty aloofness – some might say a wilful disregard – towards members of his own family. He communicated with his children via letters delivered by a footman, and when one of his daughters displeased her father by not only getting married, but also having the temerity to smoke a cigarette in the best drawing room, he banished her from the family home forever.

Amongst Harpur Crewe's many idiosyncrasies, quirks and foibles, one obsession reigned supreme. He had spent his whole life building up one of the largest private collections of natural objects in the world: cabinet after cabinet containing drawer after drawer of butterflies, moths and birds' eggs. Mostly these were for his eyes only, but occasionally a privileged visitor – invariably another collector like himself – would gain access to the inner sanctum to marvel at these precious treasures.

Of all the many thousands of objects he amassed during his long lifetime, just one category was on public display: his prized collection of rare birds. Shot, stuffed and mounted, they gazed down at visitors from every shelf, table and available surface in every one of Calke Abbey's many rooms. Hence today's visit by train to the south coast, more than two hundred miles from his Derbyshire home, to 15, Silchester Road, St. Leonards-on-Sea, Sussex.

As the sound of the shop's bell began to die away, a rather shabbily dressed man appeared from the back of the premises, and greeted his customer with a practised deference. His name was George Bristow, and he was a taxidermist.

A short, stout man in his late forties, bespectacled and with greying hair swept back from his forehead, Bristow had succeeded his father as proprietor of the family business many years earlier. By this time – the long, hot summer of 1911 – he was firmly established as one of the finest procurers of rare birds not just in Sussex, but also throughout the whole of England. This was why Harpur Crewe had made the tedious and uncomfortable rail journey from Derbyshire to meet him.

Letters had already been exchanged between the two men, so Bristow knew what his visitor had come to see. Walking slowly across to a cabinet, he pulled open a drawer. Gingerly he lifted out the corpses of two birds, both about the size of a song thrush, but with the plump body and long legs that marked them out as waders.

Carrying them across, he laid them down side by side on the counter.

'Caspian plovers', he announced in his soft Sussex burr. 'A pair – male and female. Shot at Brenzett, down by Lydd. First I've ever had.'

Harpur Crewe remained silent and, he hoped, inexpressive. But his heart was beating beneath his moleskin waistcoat as never before, and he longed to reach out and touch their soft and silky plumage. He knew just how rare these birds were – only the second to be found in Britain, after a pair obtained at Great Yarmouth in May 1890. But did Bristow know this?

'Very fine specimens, as well,' continued the taxidermist. 'Hardly damaged by the shot – not so's you'd see, anyhow. Look at this chap – that orange patch on his breast, the white above and below. Really lovely.'

'How much do you want for them?' Harpur Crewe enquired, trying, without success, to keep the excitement out of his voice.

'Well ...' replied Bristow, pensively. 'You're looking at a very nice pair there, sir, of really scarce birds ... In fact if I'm not mistaken there's only been one other pair of these Caspian plovers ever seen in England, shot in Norfolk during the old queen's time, back in '90 or '91, if my memory serves me right ...'

Harpur Crewe knew the game was up. Bristow was far too canny, and had delivered far too many rare birds into the hands of wealthy collectors, to have the wool pulled over his eyes.

'I'll give you five guineas for them', he pronounced, with a confidence he did not feel.

A pause. 'They're worth ten.'

Another, even longer pause, and Bristow spoke again. 'That Mr Nicoll, he's already been in to take a look ...'

The mention of a rival collector's name had an immediate – and desired – effect.

'Seven.'

'Eight, sir, and I'll throw in the case for free.'

A pause so long Harpur Crewe wondered if both he and Bristow had lost the power of speech. But he was well and truly beaten.

'Eight guineas it is.'

Hands were shaken, the money was counted out and, his business concluded, Sir Vauncey Harpur Crewe emerged back into the dazzling sunlight, to begin the long and wearying journey back home.

A week later, one of Bristow's young assistants arrived at the abbey's grandiose entrance. He was delivering, as agreed, a glass case containing the two Caspian plovers, united in death as in life. Minutes later, after some hasty wiping to remove the dust and grime accumulated on the long trip from Sussex, they took pride of place in Harpur Crewe's ever-expanding and remarkable collection of stuffed specimens.

Some 13 years later, on 13 December 1924, Sir Vauncey Harpur Crewe died, aged 78. His only son Richard had predeceased him three years before, as had his brother Hugo, and under the rules of the time his daughters were ineligible to succeed to the baronetcy. So this ancient honour, which had been granted to Harpur Crewe's ancestor Henry Harpur by Queen Elizabeth I, died with him.

The estate itself did stay in the family, passing down through the eldest daughter and eventually reaching his grandson Charles. But the efforts of keeping up such a vast and rambling property took their toll, and when Charles died in 1981 it had to be sold to pay punitive death duties. Four years later, it was bought by the National Trust, in whose hands it remains today.

As for those thousands of cases of stuffed birds, they might have simply become an historical curiosity, were it not for one significant and rather curious fact. For, like so many of Harpur Crewe's prized specimens, the pair of Caspian plovers he had so eagerly bought from Bristow – for a sum equivalent to almost £1000 today – were not quite what they seemed.

Their identity was not in dispute; it was their provenance that was doubtful. For they had not arrived on our shores under their own steam, lost waifs gone astray on their migratory journey, as Bristow had claimed. Not only had they never seen the delights of Brenzett, they had never been within a thousand miles of Britain – at least not while they were still alive.

Those long-forgotten Caspian plovers, now lying moth-eaten and faded somewhere in the attics of Calke Abbey, tell a fascinating story: an ornithological whodunit that takes us from a sleepy English seaside town to the banks of the Suez Canal. It is a tale of greed and one-upmanship, barefaced deception and the betrayal of friends, underhand practices, sharp dealings and fraud.

So how had they ended up in George Bristow's shop, in a back street of this shabby seaside resort, where Sir Vauncey Harpur Crewe had been persuaded to part with his eight guineas? To unravel this mystery, we must delve deeper into this murky affair – one that rivals even the celebrated 'Piltdown Man' scandal as one of the greatest frauds of all time – the curious case of the Hastings Rarities.

Kenwood House (Autumn)

ROBIN MUKHERJEE

It isn't quite winter, with its sapless stumps hunched in sterile hedgerows. But close.

We meet on the heath. She springs up to me; her boots sound like paper, ruffling the unread pages of a weeping tree, kicking through the leaves of a cliché.

Daddy, she says. Her breath is damp against me. We hug and hold. You're looking great, she says. And then, shall we?

Rembrandt, hot soup? Or the other way round?

Hot soup, Rembrandt. I say. I think I need bracing. For him.

He's a cuddly, old man, she says. Like you. And she takes my hand, pulls me forward. I know where the path turns, and turns again, I know its trees. And I have seen them in every season.

I love autumn, she says. Love it.

But I see only the downward spiral of Persephone, and the rape of her mind, which turns formidable, unforgiving. She will slip you up and break your wrists, and gently peel the skin back from your lips in the frigid fury of a kiss.

Can I dunk? Of course you can. She plunges her roll. But I cannot taste the food any more. Even her smile. I cannot taste it. How's your mother? I think to ask, but don't. She takes her scarf off, drapes it behind her. It'll fall,

I think to say, but don't. I want to tell you about Tom, she says. Tell me about Tom. She'll go back to him later. Into his heat. For now, it's soup with the old man, an autumn Rembrandt. Nobody loves you forever, I want to say but don't. Nobody can.

We nod to the woman, pass the Gainsborough. You have this moment and the next, and the next. She stops. And then it's winter.

Well, look at me, says the old Dutch master. You think I'm old. And he laughs.

from *Queen Bea*

JO NADIN

www.blogster.com/TheBellJar
Sunday June 1st
High school high

Welcome to a new term, Bellies. Or should I say, good fucking luck. Because high school is everything you've read about, everything you've seen on screen in the sticky seats of cinema back rows and your so-called best friend's bedroom. And then some.

It is *Mean Girls* and *Heathers* and *Easy A*. It is *The Breakfast Club*. It is *Sixteen Candles*. It is the special edition, twentieth anniversary John Hughes box set.

It is Lord of the fucking Flies.

Forget primary. Primary is nothing. It is a game of kick-can in the park compared to high school; its pigtail-pulling and name-calling rounds of 'you're gay', 'no, you're gay' just line-writing practise for bigger and badder things.

No, high school is where it really starts. A battlefield in ballet flats; an Edith Wharton world in which conspicuousness passes for distinction, and the wrong shoes can buy you a ticket to seven years of, at best, obscurity, and, at worst, daily humiliation. A decision as seemingly simple as where you sit in the refectory can dictate your social ranking for your entire scholastic life.

Sure, your stock might rise with a new haircut or if you suck Dexter Wilton's dick behind the bike sheds. But, believe me, you are the sum of your dumbest utterings, your skankiest outfits, and your least flattering profile pictures. And hey, The Bell Jar will publish them all. Because truth is everything.

Right?

----

43 comments
Click to add a comment

Who am I? by Boeatrice Gillespie
A Level Philosophy and Ethics (S. Harris)

If a tree falls in a forest and there is no one to see it or hear it, does it still make a sound?

Does it even exist?

Do I?

Not according to the men and women in white coats. Undoubtedly my body is here, and my brain. And somehow together they create and collect and contain enough information to generate a girl that my parents cruelly christened Beatrice. But endless experiments have failed to distinguish the self separately from the body; they have failed to find a tangible, actual, assessable entity. Neuroscience, trailing for years in the wake of philosophy, has finally caught up with Buddha in that respect.

So, what am I, then?

I am a clever conceit, they think. A trick of the ego to convince my poor, pathetic human head and heart that I matter. And so they conspire, working together to recognise faces, keep hold of memories, make plans.

But it's all an illusion, a sleight of hand.

If you took me apart you'd find nothing there. There is no pearl of Bea-ness buried within me, hidden in some crevice or sacred cave. There is no eternal soul. There is nothing but muscle and blood and bundles of nerves. Seven stone eleven of flesh, stretched to a nice national average of one metre sixty-three, draped in a kilt and blazer and accessorised with a freakishly low hairline, a birthmark on my right ankle shaped like a heart, and an ability to recite entire episodes of *Gilmore Girls* at will.

So, I am nothing special. In fact, I am not at all.

There is no me.

I do not exist.

I am nobody.

But if you'd asked around, you'd have known that anyway.

Mary Palmer: A Short Poetic Life

ANTHONY NANSON

Mary Taylor, as she was then known, went to Iona in the summer of 1993. She was thirty-six. It was a pivotal time in her life. She was halfway through the brand new MA in Creative Writing at Bath Spa University College, through whose stringent discipline she was refining her craft as a poet; and she was grappling with difficulties in her personal and spiritual life, and especially the emotional legacy of nine years as a hospital dietitian. The outcome of her time on Iona was the sequence of poems that became *Iona*, the first draft of which she wrote as her MA creative project under the tutelage of Philip Gross. The poems can't easily be read as a memoir of her pilgrimage to Iona, for they are framed in a fictional narrative. What Mary actually experienced there, in solitude, she kept to herself. That holy island, that 'thin place', as Mary calls it in 'Pasture of the Geese', seems like a mythic space of uncertainty within the story of her life. My sense is that on that tiny island, for a brief interval of time, everything that was most important to her came together: a truly nourishing form of spirituality, a delight in nature's beauty and a soul-healing creativity.

Though Mary had always enjoyed drawing and painting, she discovered poetry fairly late, while working as a dietitian. Her training in nutrition and dietetics simply had not prepared her emotionally for the harrowing experience of what she witnessed in hospital. 'It was the start of a search for meaning, an awakening and a loss of innocence.'[1] Poetry, she discovered, was a way of connecting with and expressing feelings that might otherwise be suppressed. She subsequently wrote a number of poems based on her hospital experiences, some of which she published in a leaflet called 'Hospital Heaven' (2002). She became engaged with the concept of 'writing therapy', and in presentations and letters shared her ideas about the utility of this practice to the healthcare professions.

Mary's completion of the MA in Creative Writing meant a lot to her: not only the sense of accomplishment, especially in completing Iona, but also the validation as a writer. Remember that back in the early 1990s, before the explosion of Creative Writing programmes in British universities, there were few opportunities for advanced study in this subject. Mary now embraced with great commitment the identity of being a poet and devoted herself in every way she could to the bardic triple path of writing, performing and teaching.

This artistic commitment became one with her faith commitment as a Christian. She was introduced by the Revd Richard Russell to the 'Reformational worldview', originating in the Netherlands, which breaks down the dualism between spiritual and physical to seek a redemptive transformation of the whole of life, including body, work and art. Mary was one of the many artistic, young Christians attracted to St Matthew's Church, Bath, where Richard was putting theory into practice to build a dynamic creative community and transform the church building into an arts venue. In 1995 she published a set of poems, celebrating this project of transformation, as a leaflet called 'Take 2'. She began to meet with fellow poet Rachel Laurence to critique each other's work. They set up a 'Writers Support Group' at St Matthew's, offered creative workshops more widely and contributed poetry to church worship. Mary ran the poetry and writing strand of the Cross Rhythms festival at Launceston and performed poems at Greenbelt.

In the late 1990s the St Matthew's community began to fragment. One of its offspring was 'Sanctuary', a monthly meeting for Celtic-style worship, which Mary attended and for which she wrote devotional poems in the style of the traditional Gaelic prayers of Carmina Gadelica.[2] These were another fruit of her exploration of Celtic spirituality on Iona; a number of them have been included in devotional anthologies produced by Wild Goose, the publishing arm of the Iona Community, and in Coracle, its magazine.[3]

Soon after finishing the MA, Mary was getting work published in many other anthologies and magazines, including ones as prestigious as Acumen and Tears in the Fence.[4] Her big ambition, though, was to publish Iona. She continued to revise its constituent poems, as she did all her work, and assiduously approached potential publishers. Some key figures in poetry publishing praised the quality of *Iona*, but always in the end the story was they couldn't publish it because so little poetry sells these days that they'd probably lose money.

Meanwhile, Mary was not only writing, but also performing. On the Bath and Bristol poetry circuit she met Rose Flint. They clicked at once. With a third poet, Rachael Clyne, they put together a performance of readings from women poets for International Women's Day; and then, as 'Erato', performed in diverse venues over a period of five years, gradually augmenting their shows with music, costume and props. They were united by a feminist impulse, conceived both spiritually and internationally; Mary was always drawn to the plight of people, women especially, in poorer countries. The Celtic dimension of her faith – the spirit of Iona, sacred to pagans as well as Christians – allowed her a sympathetic connection with Rose's Goddess-centred spirituality.

Mary gained immensely in confidence, in her sense of being, through performing her poems. The 'no reading' rule at Bath Storytelling Circle, which she often attended, spurred her to commit her poems to memory; in doing so, she was able to inhabit them more deeply and to perform them with power, nuance and a sensual physical presence. Philip Gross, who remembers her shyness during the MA, was struck at a performance years later by the sight of her on stage, 'visibly glowing in the light of the audience's attention'. Mary always had in her bag whatever poem she was currently memorising; motorists halted at traffic lights on the Wellsway were sometimes startled by her reciting aloud as she hiked the interminable distance between the city centre and the little flat she rented in Odd Down.

For her subsistence she worked for several years at Bath's Waterstones, where she was active in helping to put on events and encouraged colleagues to perform poems for National Poetry Day and the like. The shop at that time served as a transit camp for graduates of the MA in Creative Writing; so in 1998 Mary and her colleague and fellow MA graduate Adam Death started a writers group, which initially met in the shop but soon moved to Hannah Bagnell's flat, where it got misnamed 'Apartment 4'. The group had a preponderance of prose writers, who often troubled Mary's aesthetic of concision and spareness with their extravagant use of adjectives. When Apartment 4 came to an end in 2002, she immediately started yet another group, the 'Poetry Salon', dedicated to poetry, which initially met in her own flat. Later she joined the 'Natural Words' writing group, which had originated from a course at the Envolve Environmental Consultancy and now met at the house of Judith Young; she continued to attend its meetings, when she could, right into her final illness.

Participation in this succession of groups was an essential part of Mary's life, for the camaraderie they provided – everyone remembers Mary's laughter – as well as the opportunity for incisive criticism, which she was able to both give and receive. It's a mark of her dedication to her art that often she would bring multiple versions of the same poem, differing radically in approach, and invite listeners to critically compare them. She was still inviting criticism in this way when friends came to visit during the last few weeks of her life.

Her capacity to encourage others in their creativity had greatest scope in teaching. In 2002, realising that her low-paid bookselling job had become a dead end, she took steps to kick-start her career in a new direction. She put herself through an A level in English and a PGCE and then took on a smorgasbord of teaching jobs, for Bath City College, the Open University, the University of Bath, plus workshops at, for example, Bristol Poetry Festival, Bath Literature Festival, St Gregory's Catholic College – and Black Swan Arts Gallery, Frome, where she exercised her interest in making connections between writing and visual art. In her final years, she also taught English as a foreign language at Languages United.

Mary Palmer – the maiden name she'd returned to – was much loved by her students. So many of them turned out to support the launch of *Iona*, alongside two other Awen titles, at Mr B's Emporium of Reading Delights, that people were literally spilling out of the shop into the street. It was a special day for Mary, 9 April 2008, to see her book finally in print after fifteen years of revision and hammering on publishers' doors. She was in her glory, shimmering with energy, reciting poems with her characteristic strength and conviction. During the ensuing year, she performed an *Iona* set in diverse venues, using simple items of costume to distinguish Aelia and Mordec from 'the poet'. The power of these performances was superior to anything she'd done before.[5]

Though inspired by the austere landscape and spirituality of the Celtic north, Mary was also drawn to the sensuality of tropical Africa, which seems in some way to have symbolised the other pole of her being – rather as Aelia and Mordec represent two poles in *Iona* – though her engagement was also a heartfelt response to African people's history of suffering. Right in the middle of *Iona* stands the poem 'Black Madonna', about an African image of the Virgin Mary. In 2002 Mary went to Africa for the first time, to Kenya and Tanzania. The following year she went back, at her own expense, to teach English for eight weeks in Pangani on the coast of Tanzania. This experience, limited in space and time, like her visit to Iona, had a similarly momentous impact. The poems it inspired reveal a widening of emotional range, a kaleidoscopic world of places and people and an extension of form to include longer, more narrative poems; she also wrote some creative prose. She assembled some of the poems, with photographs, to make an exhibit called 'Teaching English' for an exhibition in the Grant Bradley Gallery, Bristol, marking the two-hundredth anniversary, in 2007, of the abolition of the slave trade, and began to put out feelers for the publication of an Africa sequence comparable in scale to *Iona*.

Sometime after her return from Tanzania she had to have a melanoma removed from her foot. The skin had got sunburnt there. Unfortunately, it seems, the surgery was too late. Tumours cropped up elsewhere. They were dealt with each time, but early in 2009 the cancer came back in more aggressive form. It seems a dreadful irony that the time in Africa, so nourishing to Mary in so many ways, should also – so she believed – have led to her demise. In an unpublished prose piece, 'Mashaka', she wrote of bathing in the Indian Ocean: 'Fall, seduced by Africa, and roll in the waves, letting them swallow me, reword me and speak me out changed … I finally swim out, and then back along the path of the sun and wonder if this is what dying is like, dissolving into water and life.'

In March 2009 Mary performed some *Iona* poems in Waterstones, Bath, in support of another Awen book launch. It was the most powerful performance I ever saw her do. In her introduction she spoke with unusual boldness about her faith. I sensed that something had changed, and she told me afterwards that there was bad news from the doctors and she had come to accept the possibility it might be God's will she should not be physically healed.

The cancer advanced with startling speed. Sometimes unable to sleep because of the pain, and promised publication of her 'selected poems' by Awen, she worked night and day to sort out and revise the best of her oeuvre. She also wrote new poems. For Mary was now in the storm's eye of the greatest challenge and mystery of faith: she knew she'd done nothing to deserve such suffering, she believed in a loving God, and yet she suffered. 'It really does help,' she said of her faith in the teeth of this illness, yet she spoke also of a relentlessly intensifying 'battle'. Not a battle to fight her illness, for the cancer was overwhelming her body, but one to sustain a positive state of mind in spite of everything. When I visited her at Dorothy House Hospice, the spring light shining through her window, she spoke with searing authority: 'Only love matters. If someone offends you, forgive. Just forgive! Don't hang on to it and let it twist you up inside.' Her 'Last Poems' give expression to this struggle; they were sparked by her wish to communicate these final hard-won insights to members of the last church she belonged to, Bath City Church, who had been so supportive during her years of illness.

Mary died on 9 June 2009, a week before her fifty-second birthday. Four days earlier she'd handed over the body of poems from which Jay Ramsay made the selection that became *Tidal Shift*. The book was published three months later. The day after the launch in Waterstones, Kevan Manwaring and I travelled north to Iona. In our bags were copies of the book for the Iona Community Shop, which already stocked *Iona*. We gave a presentation, attended mainly by Americans staying at the Abbey, and read poems from *Tidal Shift*, including 'Black Madonna', reprinted from *Iona*. Reading *Iona* while I was on the island, I discovered how intricately it mediates the island's topography. I had to ask for help to locate 'St Michael's Chapel', hidden behind the Abbey. In the sunlight streaming through a window was the beautifully sculpted ebony head of a young African woman. In this spot, I knew, Mary had sat to contemplate this sculpture and germinate her poem: 'candles gutter / and your skin gleams / as if stained by tears'.

'Mary distilled so much of herself into her poetry,' says Rose Flint. Poetry made her feel alive, facilitated an experience of intimacy, mattered all the more to her because her options in life were so limited by lack of money, by being single and then by illness. Though you'd never know it from her ability to look on the bright side, Mary was never free from worry about the material necessities of life. In 'The Way', Mary writes, 'following the Way / can damage your health / and hasten death'.[6] The 'Way' is the way of Christian faith and at the same time of poetic integrity. It is radically defiant of contemporary materialism. In an essay titled 'Write to Heal', she says, 'Poets who model Jesus are needed to counter the perverse and pseudo poetry of pop, slogans and jingles that brainwash us all. Their poetry should be good news to the poor, point another way to those captive to the idol of economic progress.'

The evening when Mary handed over her poems, she asked Jay and me to take a look in Dorothy House's chapel: an elegant octagonal structure, three adjacent sides of which are giant windows upon a panorama of Wiltshire countryside. She impressed upon us how this embodied her vision of a harmony of the human, the spiritual and nature. That night Jay told me that he believed Mary to be 'a major Christian poet'. The poems she left behind are the generous legacy of her commitment to poetry and to faith. A considerable body of her writing remains uncollected or unpublished. I hope that in time it will be and that, though she's no longer with us, she will get the recognition her work deserves. Her epiphany on Iona speaks to all of us in our brief lives on earth: 'Here, in this thin place / I choose to dream.'

This afterword draws on not only my own memories and Mary's papers but also the memories and insights of a number of people who knew Mary. Many thanks therefore to: Hannah Bagnell, Verona Bass, Nikki Bennett, Rose Flint, Adele Gardner, Philip Gross, Liz Hendries, Jeremy Hooker, Rachel Laurence, Liz Newman, Ita O'Donnell, Ione Parkin and Richard Selby.

1   Mary Palmer, *Tidal Shift: Selected Poems*, (Bath, 2009), 169.

2   Alexander Carmichael, ed., *Carmina Gadelica: Hymns and Incantations from the Gaelic*, (Edinburgh, 1992).

3   For example, in: *A Book of Blessings*, Ruth Burgess, ed., (Glasgow, 2001); *Barefeet & Buttercups*, Ruth Burgess, ed., (Glasgow, 2008); *Acorns and Archangels*, Ruth Burgess, ed., (Glasgow, 2009).

4   A provisional list of Mary's publications can be found at awenpublications.co.uk/mary-palmer. The publisher welcomes details of further publications not yet listed.

5   A video clip can be viewed at www.youtube.com/watch?v=y4jsYJNVTkk

6   Palmer, *Tidal Shift*, 156.

A Novel in 25 Words

In the Spring of 2017, Bath Spa University and its PR agency, Speed Communications, hosted a competition to find the best novel containing just twenty-five words. We received more than a thousand submissions from across the world, and in July the judges – Jonathan Dent, Beatrice Hitchman and Philip Hensher – met at our campus in Corsham Court to select the winners.

WINNER
FYI by Kelly Anne Doran

Obviously I'm not judging Carl; I just think it would've been nice to know about the whole pineapple situation before I moved in with him.

FINALIST
Early Learning by Clare Gallagher

With boys she hit harder. Hit at the child he once was. Thirty years' 'exemplary classroom practice'. The soft palm of so many small hands.

FINALIST
Rise of the Shy Horticulturalist by Michael Hunt

Veni, vedi, Aesculus hippocastanum: I came, I saw, I conkered. Caesar of playgrounds, bullied no more, commander of string, nut and a smattering of Latin.

from *Peg and Art*

The lake was as still as a bucket of water, heat shimmying off the dusty road that ran along beside the beach. Art trotted behind Peg; why was she always so much faster than him? He'd catch up one day. They'd finished their chores early and quickly and not very well, and had made their escape before their mother had a chance to inspect their work, before the day grew too hot to move.

They were going to find the jungle. They'd been hearing about it all spring, as the numbers of men coming to town to look for work grew. Sometimes it felt like the grown-ups talked about nothing else; there were town meetings that his mother attended and articles in the newspaper that his father read aloud: 'Local "Jungle" Creates Problems'. Art and Peg knew where it was, at least they thought they knew where it was. Rumour had it placed on the west side of the lake, then the east, then way up the railway line toward Midway.

The town ended quickly. Art followed Peg along the railway line, jumping over the rails, avoiding the freshly-creosote-soaked ties. Art wanted to remain on the tracks as they cut up through the hillside – he liked walking along the tracks, knowing they led to his father.

'But that's the wrong direction,' Peg said, and Art knew she was right. Peg was usually right. She was one whole year older than him, and one whole year smarter as well. Art chided himself, he should be doing this with Archie.

Archie was his best pal, with his wild, curly red hair that he claimed had never been touched by brush or comb, and his layers and layers and layers upon layers of freckles covering every inch of his skinny body. Archie would be hopping mad when he heard that Art found the jungle without him. But Art reckoned he was better off going with Peg. It might be more fun going on the hunt for the jungle with Archie, but the truth was that if you wanted to get something done you were better off doing it with Peg. It was annoying, but Peg was unaccountably brave. And when he was with her, Art was brave too.

They'd walked through what remained of the cluster of old railway workers' cottages which were really no more than glorified lean-tos as far as Art could see; he found it difficult to believe his parents had ever lived in one, but they had. The house they lived in now – the house his dad had built – was a palace in comparison.

Art was looking forward to the day he'd be old enough to go to work with his father. His dad left home on Monday morning and returned on Friday afternoon most weeks, layered with coal dust and sweat. He worked up and down the Kettle Valley Railway line, wherever the bridge and tunnel crew was needed. He'd promised Art that when he was ten – his mum said twelve, but his dad had said ten, and that's what Art was sticking with – he could spend his summers working with the railway crew. He'd learn to drive the handcar; he'd be able to pump the handcar up the line faster than anybody, he was sure. But he wouldn't be ten for ages.

The spring had been hotter and drier than normal and the cherry harvest was underway already. This year the farm workers were camping out among the trees, due to the scale of pilfering that was going on. 'They've got guns,' Peg had warned him as they set out that morning.

'Guns?' Art replied.

'Rifles. Shotguns.' She gave her head a little shake, which Art knew meant she wasn't entirely confident about her story but she didn't want Art to ask questions. 'We need to be careful not to startle them. We might get shot.' But there was little chance of that happening; Art had his father's canvas-covered canteen slung around his neck, two tin mugs dangling off that, and they made a racket with every step he took. 'That'll scare away the snakes,' Peg had said by way of convincing him that he was the one who ought to carry it. She was full of information about the rattlesnakes that had been spotted in the hills above the lake; of the farmhand she heard about who had stepped backwards unaware, flushing the snake out of its lair. 'He got bit,' Peg said. 'He died.'

Sometimes at night when Art was lying in bed he'd hear the wind move through the trees at the end of their street, rattling the branches with a hiss, as though an enormous serpent was making its way through the town. He'd never believed the stories about the monster that lived in the dark depths of the lake, but the stories of the rattlers, well, he knew for a fact that they were true. He'd seen enough snakeskins; in fact, most of his friends had snakeskins that they displayed like trophies, keeping them folded up in their fathers' hankies in their back pockets until the skins crumpled and fell apart. Last summer Archie found a snakeskin that was more than five feet long. He spent several days showing it off as though it was evidence of his own bravery. It turned out to belong to a rattlesnake that was living in the crawlspace under his house; their dog Jolly got bit one day. Archie's dad, Mr Pemberton, killed the snake and then the dog with a shovel while Archie screamed the house down and the whole street came out to see what was happening. As the kids from the town paraded through Archie's backyard to inspect the carnage, Mr Pemberton lectured that it was a freak occurrence, that rattlers were shy and normally stayed well away from town, well away from people, only striking out when cornered, and even then if you stood still, the snake would calm down and slither away. The little dog hadn't had this information. Art rehearsed it in his head now.

He was afraid of rattlesnakes, but as the possibility that they might actually find it came closer, Art realised with a shudder that the idea of the jungle was even more frightening. Just the word on its own. Jungle.

It was some kind of hobo camp. That was all Art knew. There was a big one down in Vancouver, Art's mother read about it in the newspaper. And now their town had one of its own. The grown-ups didn't like it; it worried them. But Art couldn't wait to see it.

They were in one of Templeton's orchards now, on the access road that led across the back of the bench. Peg was up ahead, moving through the stony orchard like a goat, jumping over the irrigation flumes and furrows, compact and sure-footed. Finding the jungle had been his idea, but she'd latched on to it as though he was some kind of genius, and they'd made it their project. Art had heard his father say to Mr Pemberton that there were so many homeless men walking back and forth across the province, they had to stop somewhere, and why not here, where it was warm and the trees were dense with fruit instead of pinecones and needles like most places this side of the Rockies. Jumping on trains without a ticket, knocking on doors looking for food and work as well as taking over any building they could get into – like the railway roundhouse – the hobos set up these camps, these so-called 'jungles'.

According to Mr Pemberton it was a like an almost-town on the outskirts of their real town. Art had no idea what they'd do if they actually found it; he hoped at the very least it would make a good story to tell his friends, one to rival Archie Pemberton's rattlesnake.

The trees around Art were heavy with fruit, the ground so parched it was as though the peaches had sucked up all the available water and were storing it inside their flesh which, Art thought, was pretty much true. Most years by mid-August the whole town would be drenched in sweetness as the smell of fruit ripening on the trees drifted down from the orchards and out from the kitchens of countless houses where the annual canning spree took place. Canning was one of the only times his father helped out in the kitchen; all that boiling water and steam was familiar territory for him, he said, like running a locomotive. This year it had already been so warm for so long that the early peaches were nearly ready, would be ready in a couple of weeks, and now that Art was in the orchard, the smell of the fruit was slowing him down, making his legs heavy, making him feel like he was moving through syrup.

Art loved peaches. Fresh, canned, in pies, in puddings, in jam. Of all the fruit in the Okanagan – cherries, apricots, apples, plums – he loved peaches best. Yellow peaches, with a red blush, eaten on the grass near the water while wearing a bathing suit so that you could run into the lake afterwards when you were covered with juice, run away from the ants and the wasps, washing yourself down. There was even a town called Peachland along the lake; Art thought he might like to live there one day. Peg always insisted on peeling the skin off hers, she had this idea that if you ate the skin you might choke to death on it; she claimed she'd heard about a girl in Vernon who had died that way. Art was too impatient for that. He longed to put aside his worries about snakes, to forget about this quest to find the jungle, to pick a peach from a tree and sit down right here and eat it, then run all the way back down the hill, over the railway tracks and into the lake. The workers usually picked the fruit before they were ripe so it was easier to pack and ship them, but the fruit in this orchard hadn't been harvested yet, and these peaches looked perfect. He stopped to take a drink of water from his dad's flask, not bothering to use the tin mug, Peg wouldn't see. He felt a bit swoony.

He took another swig. Someone was watching him, he felt it. He turned quickly, the tin mugs clanking. At the end of the long row of trees was a man, standing there, in plain sight, holding something – a gun, Art thought, or maybe it was a stick. Art couldn't tell if the man was a farmworker or a hobo – they dressed the same, more or less, sweaty and dirty. In fact, they often were the same, at least according to Art's dad, the hope of seasonal work in the orchards was why so many men had come to the Okanagan this year. The man was watching Art. Art stared at the man. He wasn't sure what to do. He could tell the man knew he had been about to steal a peach.

Then he heard Peg calling in the distance. 'Hurry up Art! Come on!'

He took off, running.

When he caught up with her, she had a peach in one hand. She held it up and he could see she'd peeled away a patch of skin and taken a bite. 'Not ripe,' she said, and she put on an extravagant pout. 'Very sad.' She handed the peach to Art and he hauled back and chucked it as hard as he could in the direction of the lake. Peg whispered, 'Splash.'

They were out above the orchards now. Trees were sparse and the sun beat down on their bare heads. They'd passed the graveyard a while back, lower down the slope. He was relieved that Peg hadn't noticed; she claimed to love the graveyard and was forever trying to convince Art it was a place they should sneak out of the house at night to visit. As if that was a good idea. 'It's hot,' Art complained, looking at the lake below.

'It's hot because it's semi-arid,' Peg announced.

'Do you remember everything those teachers tell you?'

'Yes.'

'Semi-arid.'

'It's like a desert, but not quite.'

Art scoffed. 'Semi-my-derriere,' he replied.

Peg laughed, liked he knew she would.

The going was tough. They were on a footpath that cut along the side of the hill, but the ground was uneven, the dirt crumbly and full of gravel, prone to shifting and slipping away beneath their feet. They were surrounded by blackberry brambles and prickly bushes – everything sharp and spiky and liable to lash and whip. Art had on short trousers and his bare skin was scratched and bleeding. There was a road up above but Peg said she figured you wouldn't be able to see the jungle from the road and, besides, someone from town might see them and ask where they were heading.

'Is this really the right way?' Art asked, though he knew Peg didn't know the answer.

'Who do you think made this footpath? It's not as though anyone else would come up here,' Peg said over her shoulder as she marched ahead.

'Who d'you think made this footpath?' Art whispered to himself in a snidey voice. He'd turn around and go back home if he thought he could escape the teasing that would come later when Peg told everyone he was too afraid to continue. There was no escape.

Up ahead Peg had stopped at the crest of the hill. Art scrambled to catch up with her. She was on the rim of a steep ravine with a dry creek at the bottom. Art looked in the direction of the lake and saw the ravine broadened out into a small, neat field where it met the lake, the green crop luminous against the dry brown earth that surrounded it. On the far side of the ravine, the slope rose from the lake on a series of broad flat benches, just like where they had walked. The ravine was a crack in the earth at their feet, a deep slash into the broad brown hillside.

'Look,' Peg was pointing into the ravine, the opposite direction from where he'd been looking. The valley narrowed and steepened as it tore up through the hill. And there it was. The jungle.

Art couldn't believe he hadn't seen it straightaway. It teemed with men. Even from here Art could see how busy it was – though busy was not the right word. It was a raggedy and decrepit-looking collection of lean-tos and bivouacs, constructed from tin sheeting, canvas tarps, broken apple crates and brushweed. There were several small fires burning, thin smoke-trails moving skyward. Men were sitting around the fires, Art could see they were cooking, and other men were moving around the camp, and as well as that, men were lying flat out on the ground with their hats pulled down over their faces, sleeping in the middle of the day. Sleeping in the middle of the day!

It didn't look anything like how Art had imagined. He knew that it was a hobo camp they were looking for; he knew that just because it was called a 'jungle' it wouldn't actually be a jungle. He knew that Tarzan wouldn't necessarily be living there. But he realised now, looking down at it, that part of him had been hoping there'd be ropes to swing from, and green pools of water to jump into, and maybe, just maybe, a monkey to play with. He didn't think it was unreasonable to imagine that a hobo might be accompanied by a monkey. He kicked the dirt with embarrassment. At least he hadn't told anybody about that. He hadn't told Peg about the monkeys.

'There's a lot of them,' she said, and her voice sounded small. 'Daddy said there was a lot of men living rough out here.'

'Yes,' said Art. 'Maybe we won't go down there after all.'

Peg took Art's hand. He didn't mind.

They heard a sound behind them on the footpath, and they both whirled round. The man Art had seen in the orchard was standing right there, less than three feet away, close enough to reach out and grab them. He was tall and thin with hollowed-out cheeks and a scraggly beard; his brow jutted out, casting his eyes into shade. He kept flexing his hands into fists and his extra-long fingers made Art think of the white spiders he'd once seen coming out of a drain. He smelled bad and he looked hungry.

'What are you kids up to?' he asked.

Art waited for Peg to reply. She didn't. 'We're playing,' Art said.

'You're not playing. You're spying.'

'No, we –'

'Someone from town sent you.'

'Nobody sent us,' Art said. 'Nobody knows we're here.' As soon as he said it, he knew he shouldn't have.

'You shouldn't be out here. It's dangerous. You should go home.'

That woke up Peg; she didn't like to be told what to do. 'We can go where we like.' It didn't take much to make Peg indignant. 'You can't tell us what to do.' Art had never heard Peg speak to a grown-up in that way. He wanted to tell her to be polite.

The man laughed, but not in a nice way. 'Have you got anything to eat?' he asked.

Peg put her hand on the satchel she was carrying. 'No,' she lied.

Peg stared at the man. The man stared at Peg. Art looked from one to the other. Then, in one swift unexpected move, the man picked up Art and slung him over his shoulder and took off, running down the hill toward the jungle.

Afloat with the Baul Emperor

JOE ROBERTS

We were staying at Shantiniketan in the winter of 2005. Jayabrato told me about an interesting temple no more than an hour's drive away: Kankalitala, beside the Kopai river, in the Birbhum district of West Bengal. Kankalitala is a Shakti-Pitha, a shrine where a part of Kali's body fell to earth when the Goddess was chopped to bits by Vishnu's bladed discus. There are lots of these shrines and I have visited a few of them. I was keen to visit another and so was Miles, three at the time, and up for adventure. The temple at Kankalitala is built where a bone from the Goddess fell – what bone I wanted to know; the one at Kalighat has a toe. Just a piece, apparently, from the spine. He said it was a small temple, deep in a wood and the murthi, instead of an idol, was an oil painting.

Off we set in the Maruti, the three of us and Jayabrato's driver Sukumar. A short journey through red dust, laterite dunes and saal woods. We passed thatched villages, each screened by a fringe of trees. The temple was far from the road, down rutted tracks, its approach heralded by flags through the sparse woods; and then we were walking towards it among crowd of villagers on a late Sunday afternoon. There was one inquisitive man who spoke persistently in English to us. There were plenty of sadhus. The bonfire smell of wild ganja filled the air. The path to the shrine was lined with stalls selling sweets for prasad, and garlands, malas of red hibiscus. The temple itself looked a bit like a shelter in a Victorian park. Inside the garbagriha, the sanctuary, the painting was festooned with so many garlands of hibiscus it looked like a strange contemporary installation. The image itself was 19th century in the manner of Ravi Varma, Indian Pre-Raphaelite. We approached the priest to make puja. Jayabrato gave some rupees, I copied him, and the priest spent a long time blessing Miles, shuffling backwards and forwards with lamps, sweets, nectar, holy water. We left the temple (passing, I remember, a contortionist-sadhu who had folded himself up, as if packed into an invisible box) and wandered through the trees for a while.

I saw a tall man, twenty yards away, setting up camp for the evening. We could tell from his outfit that he was a Baul, one of the musical gypsies of Bengal, a troubadour. We were hoping he would perform. The Baul wore a patchwork shawl of orange, pink and red over a loose crimson robe and orange pyjamas; the bright colours singing out from the green shade. He untied his loose orange pugree and combed his long hair. He had no beard, just a few long catfish whiskers about his lower lip. Around his ankles he wore strings of bells in the shape of rosebuds. His instruments were beside him: the single-stringed gopiyantra, the small hand drum. He allowed me to photograph him, but politely declined to perform. As we walked away, the English-speaking man said that the Baul had been performing all day; now he was resting.

I was impressed that he hadn't leapt up for the money; perhaps he had made enough already. I had seen Bauls before. Their songs can be very beautiful. The music sounds a bit like Flamenco at times (both, like gypsy music, use the Phrygian scale). There had even been a Baul aboard the Bolpur Express train from Kolkata we came up on. He came singing along the aisle preceded by some small children dressed as blue gods, bahurupis – they just happened to be busking the same carriage but it lent the performance *A Midsummer Night's Dream*-quality and, perhaps because of this, his song had sounded like a madrigal. The English-speaker said that when this Baul danced and stamped his feet, the ground shook. When he sang, his voice was as loud as a trumpet; pots sometimes cracked. When he danced, he spun like a dervish. They didn't know his name, nor his caste; he could even be a Muslim. I looked back at the Baul, who was sitting now against a tree. His eyes blazed red. Smoke flared from his nostrils.

Exactly three years later, the first week of 2008, and I am in Kolkata for four days, with Emma and the three boys. We have just been in Bangladesh. The newspaper said Kolkata was having a cold snap, the temperature dipping to nine degrees, but it is much warmer than that – at least fifteen. No matter, the people are wrapped in shawls and mufflers, especially first thing in the morning. At this time of the year, the people of Kolkata tend to sleep longer; apart from newspaper stalls, street barbers and chai stalls, no business really gets going until nine, even ten – New Market opens at ten – so the streets are exceptionally quiet when we drive from AJC Bose Road to Dhakuria. We had been invited to a picnic by the great singer, Purna Das Baul.

Rabindranath Tagore had written and spoken about the Bauls; among those the great writer befriended was Nabani Das, Purna Das's father. Tagore, who composed both the Indian and the Bangladeshi national anthems, is said to have taken the melody for the latter, Amar Shonar Bangla, from a Nabani sang.

We arrive at Purna Das's house at 6:30 a.m. It's in the Dhakuria area of Kolkata, quiet, middle-class, largely residential. It's not difficult to find; on the wall is written Purna Das Baul Samrat – Purna Das, Emperor of the Bauls – the title is official, it was bestowed in 1967 by the president of India.

The house consists of several apartments leading off a central staircase, the steps covered in shoes. Lots of people are here. Some children, among them two of Purna Das's grandsons, come pouring down from the kitchen.

A grandson called Mishook wears a Batman body warmer. He has a friend with him, aged he tells us, 'Seven – whereas I am seven plus.' He has a dog called Peggy that looks like a little fox; she is thirteen years old and still performs tricks. When Mishook shouts 'Boxer', Peggy jumps and twists in the air. My youngest son Barty is greatly impressed.

We are led into a sitting room. There we meet Chotton, whose real name is Dibyendu Das Baul, one of Purna Das's sons, in his early forties I'd guess. Chotton (it means 'little one', he's the youngest brother) speaks English with an American lilt – he spends part of each year in San Diego. He's charismatic, with long hair and a round-eyed face like a clown or a Chinese mask. He's in Western (as in cowboy) clothes, a fringed buckskin jacket like General Custer's. Chotton is an innovative musician himself, performing and broadening the Baul repertoire – besides the traditional instruments, Chotton plays a steel-string banjo.

He introduces us to the family members and friends, there are lots – and the other Bauls, who are wearing full regalia: rudraksha beads, malas, even Mardi Gras beads, orange robes, patchwork cloaks. One, Haradhan, wears a tall peaked turban like an Ottoman pasha. Madan, whom I later discover is from a Muslim family, has a full prophetic beard and gold earrings. They all look glamorous, hippy-chic; the bright fabrics vivid against the dark walls.

Chotton shows me photographs on a laptop, of his father with various American musicians: Dylan, of course, Mahalia Jackson, Garth Hudson, Levon Helm, Robbie Robertson, Joan Baez. We're all given tea, while Peggy the Fox leaps from one child to another.

Women come in, wrapped in winter shawls. Chotton's mother, the folk singer Manju Das, is recovering from an illness in hospital, so cannot join the picnic. Everybody wishes her well.

The walls are decorated with posters from Purna Das's performances across the world – there are lots from America and some European ones, including the Albert Hall. There are posters too of his various sons' performances. Purna Das represents the eighth generation of Bauls in his family – his sons are the ninth and their children (there are several about) will be the tenth.

There is a large poster of Nabani Das Baul, the father of Purna Das; it is one of the most well-known images of a Baul.

A graphic based on this picture is on the cover of a very rare album, *The Bengali Bauls at the Big Pink*, produced by Garth Hudson and exactly contemporary with Bob Dylan's *Basement Tapes*. There is another, more easily available recording from that time, *The Bauls of Bengal*. Chotton says that album was so popular in the West – first on vinyl, then cassette, now on compact disc – that anybody with any interest at all in Indian culture owned a copy. I wondered if the Bengali words were a problem for Western audiences and Chotton says that, with a minimal explanation, most people can understand the message of Baul songs. At American concerts in the 1960s, sheets were distributed of the lyrics translated by the rock writer Al Aronowitz. I remark that the visit must have been one of the earliest tastes of Indian culture the baby boom generation experienced. Purna Das smiles and Chotton says that there were three of these spiritual ambassadors to the West: Swami Prabhupada (the Hare Krishna founder), Ravi Shankar and Purna Das Baul.

What is striking, listening to *The Bauls of Bengal* forty years on, is how accessible the music is – as folk music, it is much 'easier' than the Hindustani classical music of Ravi Shankar whose album *Sound of the Sitar* was more or less contemporary in its appearance in the West. I can remember seeing *The Bauls of Bengal* in record shops well into the late 1970s.

Most people will have seen Purna Das, and his brother Luxman Das, on the cover of Dylan's *John Wesley Harding* album. They're the two men most people take for anonymous Mexican hippies; the other man in the photo is a gardener called Charlie Joy. The picture was one of a series of Polaroids taken by John Berg in Woodstock, New York. I notice that there are other photos from that series reproduced around the room. The Das brothers wear cowboy hats that they bought at a roadside souvenir stall. Dylan, at 26, looks like a gunslinger.

Purna Das comes into the room. We make the namaskar gesture and I introduce my wife and my sons. He is in his seventies now, so that the John Wesley Harding picture looks more like Chotton than it does of him. Purna Das has a face that reminds me of an Elizabethan courtier – fine features and liquid eyes – as if he should be wearing a ruff. He still wears his hair long, though now it's more flinty than black. He is dressed in long orange robes; with countless necklaces, some of rudraksha beans, others of coloured stones, metal and plastic beads; and his fingers on both hands are covered in rings, moonstones and other stones. Bauls often wear patchwork clothes, the idea being that their garments are stitched from the cast-off clothes of both Hindus and Muslims. I have seen footage of Purna Das on stage wearing a patchwork gown.

Today he is dressed informally, yet there is something regal, even imperial, in his demeanour. He's quite softly spoken and has become forgetful of his English so that Chotton often finishes his sentences.

Purna Das is still performing. Over the winter, he has been part of a tour organised by the great Carnatic violinist, Dr L. S. Subramaniam. The tour is called *Visions of India* and showcases a range of India's most venerated musicians from the folk and classical fields. Presently he will be performing in Chennai.

Purna Das was the first Baul to perform to the wider world. Now there are Bauls to be found in America and Europe and there are even non-Bengalis becoming Bauls – Kazumi Maki Baul, for instance, is a Japanese woman who can be seen on YouTube.

We have our own car for the day, with a driver called Gobin, so we offer to take some of the party with us. All the children, ours included, and most of the other adults get into a large white tour bus. Purna Das and Haradhan come with us.

Purna sits in the front with Gobin. He unfolds a Bengali newspaper. I sit between Haradhan and Emma. Haradhan takes his turban off because it skims the ceiling of the car. Long black hair, so glossy it must be oiled.

We follow the white bus, driven by Chotton, the children waving at us. Purna waves back, the beloved patriarch.

We drive through the southern stretches of Kolkata and Purna remarks how the city is doubling in size, pointing out the numerous building sites where men work like ants building high-rise condominiums for the new middle classes. We progress slowly past cement trucks and trucks laden with workmen. Sometimes, among all the booming development, I see little patches of agriculture.

Purna skims his paper and tells me about San Diego, its sea air and moderate climate. Haradhan says that he loves Switzerland. Haradhan is not related to Purna but he tells me their families come from the same village. He says Purna Das Baul is his guru. 'I am Baba's student.' He calls his guru Baba, which means 'father'. Haradhan speaks English falteringly and slowly. I wish I could speak Bengali.

There have been Bauls in Bengal for at least 500 years. Traditionally they are wandering mendicants who live by performing songs accompanied by music and dance steps, that propound their syncretistic philosophy. Mixing elements of Bhakti, Sufism and Tantra; Bauls believe that God can only be found within oneself, in the Maner Manush – the Man of the Heart. Their goal is to live in the here and now – to be Sahaja, filled with spontaneous natural joy of a divine nature. Sahaja (almost impossible to translate) can also mean 'natural and unaffected'. In America in the 1960s the word was sometimes translated as 'soulful' and certainly Purna Das's singing is as soulful as the great gospel singers – he sang a duet onstage with Mahalia Jackson, after all.

In 1962 Allen Ginsberg went to India for 15 months. He travelled with his boyfriend Peter Orlovsky and, for some of the time, fellow poets Gary Snyder and Joanne Kyger. The book that resulted from this trip, *Indian Journals*, appeared in 1970. I read it first in 1990. I had just read *The Scent of India* by Pasolini, which had interested me and, looking for something similar, bought the book at Gangaram's in Bangalore. Ginsberg's *Indian Journals* is nothing like *The Scent of India*. it is a muddle of diary entries, first drafts of letters, sketches for poems, remembered dreams and later recollections. Reading it then, I found the book self-indulgent, self-righteous and self-obsessed. Ginsberg came across as absurd, pompous and gushing. Perhaps the worst thing about *Indian Journals* was Ginsberg's bumptious self-belief. At best he came across as silly – the non-Hindu temple visitor, with a tika on his forehead and a mala of marigolds around his neck, indeed we've all been there – but most of the time he wasn't even funny. I remember being irritated by the lack of editing, the misspellings, the bad punctuation. A year or so ago, I read *Indian Journals* again. I was amazed at the difference – not in the book but in myself as a reader; I had found the book formless before, this time I found it propelled along by a nutty energy. Ginsberg had still been alive when I first read the book. I had been to one of his performances in Texas and I hadn't been able to lose the picture I had of a plump elder, rambling away at the harmonium, treated with great respect, but actually rather boring. This time I could see him in 1962 and he was quite a different creature. Now he is far enough in the past to seem interesting again. I still found him foolish, but more of a holy fool than a nincompoop. When I first read it, Ginsberg at the age of 37 sounded middle-aged and phony; reading *Indian Journals* in my own forties, he seemed younger and more sincere. He was certainly crazed, chugging hallucinogens, smoking opium, ganja and once, by accident, datura – but he was the same stoned or straight, a ranting prophetic whirlwind. It's not much of a travel book, though there are dazzling snaps of Calcutta in 1962 – a haunting imagist description of alleys around the old China Town – I can see how open he was to ideas, and how much he absorbed. The book is wild and haphazard because the experience was wild and haphazard. Ginsberg's time in India had taught him to be less cerebral, to focus on the physical rather than the metaphysical dimension of his being: 'A whole series of Indian holy men pointed back to the body – getting in the body rather than getting out of human form.'

Whereas in 1990 Ginsberg had seemed all too predictable, this time he was saying something important and unusual. Remember that in 1962 Westerners of Ginsberg's kind had hardly been seen in India. The Hippy Trail hadn't been established. Ginsberg was right in the vanguard. India as a nation was only 15 years old. When Ginsberg was writing these journals, his statements and declarations were startlingly original. There were plenty of kindred spirits for Ginsberg in India. He was drawn to the outlandish side of temple life, the stoned mystical sadhus and sanyassins – Ginsberg considered himself a mystic, he'd had so many visions and hallucinations. He was invigorated by the chaos, enlightenment banging into him from all sides – innocently he trusted everybody. He was also quite physically tough, for all he put himself through; with Orlovsky's help, he extracted two living worms from a lump in his bottom.

To Ginsberg, Sahaja meant hip or beat, that mixture of weary and beatific – which is what he saw in the Bauls and expressed in his *Indian Journals* – and why in 1966 Albert Grossman, Dylan's manager, on Ginsberg's advice, flew to Kolkata to book Purna and his musicians for an American tour, to perform alongside 'underground' musicians at venues like the Fillmore.

After the tour, the group of Bauls spent several months in Woodstock, New York, staying at Grossman's country house, Bearsville. 'There were no bears,' says Purna, 'but there were deer all around.' And Bob Dylan, convalescing from his motorcycle accident. Dylan spent a good deal of time with the Bengali musicians, discussing Baul philosophy and sometimes jamming – if recordings were ever made of these encounters, they have yet to emerge. Sometimes Dylan arrived on horseback. Purna's wife, Manju Das, cooked Bengali curries for him.

Haradhan tells me that before Purna Das made his journey to the West, Bauls were barely known outside Bengal. They had only performed where Bengali was spoken. Then we are trundling through the outer suburbs in the direction of the 24 Parganas. We pass through small market towns, Rajpur, Kulpi, then off the main road on a detour to visit the Ramakrishna Mission at Nimpith. The countryside of low fields and reed beds, buffalos and attendant egrets. The company of these serene men instills its own Sahaja in me. We arrive ten minutes before the white bus, as Chotton has phoned to say he's taking a different route to Nimpith.

It is funny how things tie together in Bengal; I hadn't associated the Bauls with Ramakrishna at all, but it made sense: they share a syncretist approach – Ramakrishna accepted Jesus and Muhammad as great teachers – the Bauls say all religions are equally true and equally false. There is a Ramakrishna temple at Nimpith, its Hindu imagery mixed with Christian and Muslim symbols. A great welcome is accorded to Purna Das Baul. The leader of the Mission, described to me as the Abbot, comes to greet us; but that all his clothes are sacred-orange, he looks and dresses exactly like a Catholic abbot – a fat jolly monk with a skullcap, as in the 19th-century genre paintings of Eduard von Grützner or those paintings of monks fishing. Everyone touches the Abbot's feet, so Emma and I do the same. The Mission gardens are crowded with beds of chrysanthemums, in every shade, beds of pom-poms. The Abbot holds my hand as he shows us about the chrysanthemum garden. He is very pleased with the gardeners' efforts; every time we meet one, he shouts encouragement.

We go into a kind of dormitory where there are sofas and beds. We all sit down and a servant brings tea on a tray. Another brings boxes of sweets, a local delicacy called Jayanagar Moya – it's a ball of puffed rice and coconut around a liquid centre of date syrup, extremely sweet. I think Bengalis like sweets more than anyone else in India. The others arrive and the cushioned quiet of the Mission garden is broken with the cries of children.

'Come,' says Purna and I follow him to the temple. There are paintings on the wall depicting events in the life of Ramakrishna, a painting of Vivekananda and one of Jesus. On a raised platform, there's a large framed photograph of Ramakrishna. Purna Das prostrates himself before it. I notice how clean the floor is. When we leave, the children are noticably quieter. They are eating Jayanagar Moyas with the Abbot.

Back into the vehicles, and on to the Sunderbans, Chotton snarling to the children: 'Tiger Islands!' The Sunderbans are some 2,500 square miles of intersecting creeks and channels, swamps and jungles from the mouth of the Hugli to the mouth of the Megna; they are to the Bengal Delta what the bayous are to the Mississippi Delta. The Sunderbans spill over the national border, the greater part being in Bangladesh. We had arrived in Bangladesh just after Cyclone Sidr, so we had rearranged our itinerary to avoid the Sunderbans, the worst stricken area. The Indian side had been far less battered by Sidr. The Sunderbans are notorious for their man-eating tigers — the Indian side even more than the Bangladeshi – and whereas many of the islands on the Bangladeshi side are inhabited, most on the Indian side are not, because of the tigers. Fishermen and reed-cutters working there often wear masks on the back of their heads, because tigers attack from behind. Chotton has chartered a boat called Jhorkeli. It is moored at the end of a stepped jetty. The boat is as brightly painted, in contrasting bands of primary colours, as a roundabout at a fair.

The captain and his two crew-members are dressed in turquoise shirts of glittering synthetic material, a 1970s disco uniform. We all help load the boat with boxes of provisions for the picnic. Soon we are all aboard and we set sail. The boat leaves the sluggish inlet, dropping down into the current of a brisker stream where the water loses its coating of slime and spreads out into a lagoon. Here and there islands rise from the water in which the sky is reflected: the islands become green clouds floating through air. The women and the servants take over the galley. Purna Das does a little unsuccessful fishing with a handline. Chotton takes his shirt off and lies along the bowsprit, arms outstretched.

After an hour, we pass some boats moored in a row. Purna looks up from his handline. On the upper deck of one a boatman is asleep, rolled like a cigar in a brown sheet from head to toe. On another, a man twists some yarn into rope. On the lower deck an old bare-chested man stares back at us with an expression of accusation. On land the people amble slowly, as if without purpose. Some sit at the water's edge or rest on their haunches embracing their knees.

The other musicians, Madan Das Baul, in a long bottle-green kurta and strings of beads and Lucky Kantha who does not dress like a Baul at all – he could be an office worker from BBD Bagh – sit athwart the bow-deck, laughing with Chotton; Madan plucks at his instrument all the time. Lucky drums on an empty polystyrene bottle.

Haradhan takes a bath at the stern, hoisting up the water with a bucket on a rope. The younger children run about the cabins and up and down the nursery-coloured steps. Llewi and Miles talk about cricket with the older boys.

It is all very jolly. Soon stainless-steel bowls of cauliflower chaat are being passed up from the galley, and cups of sweet tea. Hard-boiled eggs and boxes of sweets. Later the younger musicians play while Purna Das Baul takes the wheel of the ship. Madan sings one of his guru's most famous songs – the refrain translates: 'I will take you out to sea, but never let go of you ...'

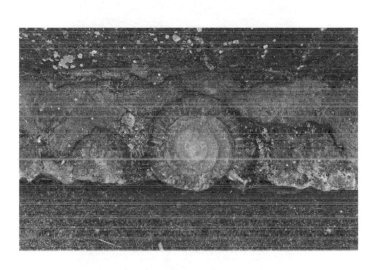

Soham (mantra)

DANNY ROTHSCHILD

I am from the acrylic hands of a painter with long black hair down to her knees, and the arthritic hands of an architect that hold those weak acrylic hands so dear and so close—

I am from the third floor of an apartment building in the African quarters of Rome—from fresh focaccia, ricotta, and pesto for Sunday lunch—I am from the village hidden inside of Rome and I am from the Roman ruins—Caesar's grave and the Colosseum—the Bridge of Angels—I am from the catacombs—I am from bus routes with no timetables—from the walking feet of every local, the tired feet of every tourist—I am from rosemary growing on the balcony, tomatoes we bite into like apples—I am from the park where my brother and I spend hours picking pine nuts to eat on our way home—

I am from my Italian passport and, also, my American accent, my Michigan address—from 4355—the Betsy River, the water flowing into Green Lake—I am from red spots of swimmer's itch from swimming in late July, and pneumonia from swimming in late November—I am from home-cooked meals in the winter—from family dinners and family disasters—I am from mismatched footprints across the frozen lake—from the cracking ice on warmer days—I am from hundreds of daffodils blooming in the spring and—I am from the flight of the mayflies in May—from the summer heat—summer nights—the Cherry Bowl Drive-In and all those cigarettes I never smoked—I am from my bare feet running through the hot sands of the Sleeping Bear Dunes—

I am from sheets of dust rising in the sub-Sahara—from the trade winds, the harmattan—I am from the heat clinging on to the soles of our feet and under the lids of our eyes—I am more and more from Arizona, from the boy I love and the family he is sharing with me—I am from the five-thousand two-hundred and eighty-one miles no longer between us—from golf balls stuck in prickly pears at the base of Daisy Mountain—from the depths of the Grand Canyon and the lack of depth perception—from the way it looks fake like a postcard—I am from the red earth of Sedona and the sunroofs that let it all seep in—

I am from never-ending highways on 6 a.m. drives, from The Great Ocean Road, the 101—I am from the Twelve Apostles eroding two inches each year—from the sharp breaths watching an Uluru sunset, the heavy breaths hiking the Kata Tjuta domes—I am from that special hour when the sky is red and the clouds have bled and then—I am from the crisp clear stars that define the Southern Cross—from a familiar constellation in a foreign land—from the Big Dipper here, and also there—

I am from the source of the Tiber and the mouth of the Blue Nile—the white water of Jinja—I am from a two-day journey across the Mountains of the Moon—I am from nights spent stranded in train stations—sleeping in bus stations, dreaming of jollof rice and rice pilaf—I am from airports too—from Concourse A and Concourse B—from gates 1 to 1,000—from O'Hare, Heathrow, Charles De Gaulle—I am from the window seat of a 747—from the frequent flyer miles that are all too frequent—I am from missing airplanes and missing Jerry, two years gone and still no answers—

I am from lost keys and lost socks—from the things I've forgotten I've lost—I am from the forgotten parts of Tuscany—cinematic drives and switchback turns—from first gear to second and back again—from foggy morning runs up to the monastery—from church bells, St. Francis—from the apple trees and the apples I can't eat because of a chronic illness I would be remiss not to include—I am from stealing pumpkins form our neighbours' garden in the dead of night—from the Milky Way, the night of the shooting stars—from a full-moon Monday—or the dark quiet of a moonless sky—

I am from the bright side of the moon, from the tides, from the mud-slides of Mozambique—I am from torrential downpour interspersed with 90-degree weather—from chasing raindrops on car windows—I am from 200 men shoveling mud out of homes and hospitals and schools—from the sand dunes on Xai Xai beach, long before the mud—from salty cuts trying to break open coconuts with our bare hands—I am from mosquito bites, from sweeter blood—I am from eleven mango trees in our backyard in Bamako—from the fruit bats—and the mangoes, so many mangoes, too many goddamn mangoes rotting on the ground because we can't collect them all—I am from the tires we swung in as children and from tires we'd race down dirt driveways—I am from flashlight tag on Friday nights, capture the flag on Saturdays—I am from the bullets fired off during the Nigerian election—from the man I watched drop dead on Thursday while I was driven to school—

I am from all the things I cannot un-see, from all the things I cannot change—but I am from my dreams to change the world—

I am from dreams of New York and a 16-day road trip that brought me there—and now I am from New York the way everyone is from New York—from the worst in me when riding the L train, the best in me when I see that skyline from a distance, and then—I am from the saddest day in America—I am from western medicine and third-world countries and Africa is a scar on my back—I am from the pain of tattooing the outline, filling in the roots and filling in the branches—I am from the unsteady hands of the painter, who once was from all these things as well—

I am from everything I ever wrote that once was true—the sunflowers wilting on the table across from me—that sunset and the Royal Crescent—wet moons—the rivers and the mountains and the harmattan—the constellations, and everything, almost—I am from tangled roots, tangled branches—I am falling leaves drifting north with the wind.

from *Birdsong*

URSULA RANI SARMA

Birdsong in the darkness. A golden evening light begins to build, the colour and tone of a summer's evening half an hour before sundown. It builds slowly and picks out an open window upstage centre, then spreads to pick up several well-stocked book-shelves complete with volume after volume of expensive looking and aged books. The light spreads further and we see a man sitting at a highly polished rosewood table. This is Fr Christopher Lynch, fifties, he sits with a tea cup in one hand and his head in the other. He exudes fatigue, as if the weight of the world was a heavy cloak on his shoulders and he would like nothing more than to step out from underneath it. He begins to talk with his head down like this but he gradually moves it to face the light as he speaks.

CHRISTOPER: Mya. (*beat*) Miracles and such. Tiny miracles, daily, hour by hour, just enough, just enough to keep you hooked in, tied in, like a drip feed of sorts, like a long chain of ever expanding reasons to believe and not to believe, to stay and not to stay, like a chequered cloth, every second one a different colour, not like the last one but like the one before, not like who you are today but who you were the day before. (*he blinks*) Mya. Soft underfoot, like earth, yes earth, dry and red and soft, like powder between the toes, like a kind of resin as you walked but I have skipped ahead, I must go back. (*beat, deep breath to begin*) To get there you have to take a boat, you have to have

327

a boat take you, some child of a man, tiny brown shoulders hunched over a lunchbox engine. The water is red also, an extension of the approaching earth up ahead. It costs in the region of ten pence to cross the river. There are perhaps, four dozen children waiting on the riverbank, each one with a different western logo emblazoned across their chest, Coca-Cola, adidas, ill-fitting, brightly coloured and ripped shirts. (*beat*) To get there you have to walk through the village which seems to have little design to it, no shape or structure, just these winding lanes with wooden huts that spiral off in every direction and not concentric as you would imagine. The huts themselves seem too small to house the families of five and six that live there, leaning out of doorways preparing food, bathing children out of iron buckets of rust-coloured water, watching and I am thinking of the Ark now for some reason, imagining this place as a giant boat transporting these thousands of people towards something better beyond. (*beat*) But they are not going anywhere. (*beat*) Mya. More children join us as we go until there must be at least a hundred of them now, like a presidential escort, each one more beautiful than the other, some bless themselves when they see me, some do it backwards, some just motion a circle in front of their chests and grin and it is infectious. (*beat*) To get there you have to go to the school, we stand at the window and see the orphans on mats, they are stretched out side to side, like matchsticks. (*beat, he begins to build in pace from here as if anxious to get to his destination*) I was thinking of how tired I felt suddenly, of how long the journey had been, I was thinking these things while we walked that final distance to the house where I would be staying, built from cement unlike the others, with a small wooden cross near the door and a candle burning as I stepped inside. And then, all thoughts are silenced completely. The world became the room and what was in it, which was me, surrounded by a sea of peasant children, a pale wooden table and a chair, a bucket of red water and … you Mya.

(*A young woman's voice interrupts him. We do not see her until indicated.*)

MOLLY: Tired.

(*A tight spotlight picks out the face of Molly Gleeson, late twenties, lying on her back downstage, her face turned towards us. Lights fade down on Christopher until he is invisible.*)

Tired in a way which defies being described in words. Tired in a sense that it brings on a type of nausea, and a dull ache in my bones and a weight in my head like someone or something has crawled inside and placed a brick beneath the plate of my forehead. Tired in a way which makes me think that I have never really known what it meant before, in a way which makes me forget whether I am actually hungry or not, thirsty, angry, in a way which robs me even of my ability to determine what exactly I am ... (*she searches*) feeling? Not feeling? But I have gone too far ahead. To get there I have to drive thirty kilometres through the country before I reach the Burren road. I could go by Ennis but there is something so truly other worldly about this route, something lunar and fantastic that it allows me to believe that I am somewhere else for that forty-minute journey on that winding ribbon road cut from limestone. To get there I have to drive through Kilfenora and Caron, past lonely houses set against sloped grey mountains that look like pale beached whales amongst the greenary, on and on until I climb the hill that brings me down towards Kinvaragh in and on to the Galway road. To get there you have to circle the car park twice to find a space and wrap up against the wind coming in off the sea. Inside there are night staff who are pleasant, some even friendly, they look up from their coffees and smile and they let me pass though they know that visiting time is not for hours yet. To get there I have to walk down a grey corridor and through two dormitory style rooms with countless sedated and sleeping geriatrics. I see these as completely different beings to you, they might as well be from another world altogether, besides the air that you are all breathing, I see you as having nothing in common with them whatsoever. (*beat*) And then there you are, in a corner against the wall, sleeping, peaceful. I pull the plastic red chair closer to the bed and sit for a moment and feel like I should say something over your body as it is stretched out before me but I never know what to say. I feel like I would like to say mass or something, say something epic to verbalise the enormity of what I am feeling, light a candle and bless something, bless the candle, bless you. So I take your hand and rest my head against the bedspread so your fingers are against my cheek, I close my eyes and I let the tired feeling come closer, feel it in the distance, then nearby, descending, like a cloth. (*beat*) This ... is the only place where I find I can sleep, and so I give in ... to the tiredness ...

Giant

C.J. SKUSE

1. JAY

'Freebie please,' Scarlett smiled as the boy behind the snack shack reluctantly slid across the freezer door and pulled out a Feast. He looked over his shoulder to check for his dad, then handed it to her.

'Thank you.' She leant against the counter, licking up her success.

He watched her teeth crack the chocolate. 'I can't believe you did that.'

She shrugged. 'You told me to, Jay.' She said his name slowly. He liked to hear it from her mouth. 'Besides, they could do with skipping a few meals.' They both looked towards the tubby boys telling their parents some girl had buried their chips. 'What's next?'

'All right,' he said, looking round. 'Let's up the ante. There's a woman in the tourist information shed up the hill with an artificial leg. She takes it off every lunchtime for an hour. I dare you to nick it.'

'No way,' Scarlett gasped.

'Knew you'd chicken out,' he smiled, sitting back on his stool and pushing his sweat-flattened hair from his forehead.

'No, I mean I can't believe she has a fake *leg*,' she said. 'I'll nick it, no worries.'

331

A couple came up to the shack in sunglasses and baseball caps. They had a golden retriever puppy on a lead, all jumpy and straining for freedom.

'Sorry,' Jay called out to them. 'No dogs allowed on the beach.' He pointed to the red and white sign nailed to the cliff face, in case they started arguing, but they didn't. They turned and went back up the hill towards town.

Jay turned back to Scarlett. 'Come on, leg time.'

'What, now?' said Scarlett, gesturing with her ice cream. As she did, a milk chocolate trail slid against her collarbone. She didn't wipe it away, just looked at Jay and smiled. Did she expect him to lick it off? Here? In front of everyone? She only had to say and he would. His body ached to be nearer to hers. To move his mouth against hers. His body against hers. Before he could think about it anymore, she plucked a serviette from the dispenser and smoothed the trail away.

'S'gonna cost you,' she said.

'All right, bring the leg back down here to the beach and I'll give you ...' He looked around the shack. 'Flip-flops? Cappuccino? *With* sprinkles?'

'Another ice cream. Strawberry Mivvi.'

'I'm gonna get so done if I give away any more.'

'Now who's a chicken?'

'Okay, okay.'

She finished her Feast, binned the stick and started to climb up the concrete jetty towards the tourism office.

Jay watched her walk away. She had the peachiest arse he'd ever seen, and he had seen every single type of ass on that beach. He thanked God for whatever breeze had blown her into his life; into that dead end soggy tissue of a town he hated so much. He'd have licked ice cream off every section of her if she'd asked him to.

'Five crab sandwiches please ...'

... off her arms, her fingers, her shining calves. Her boobs, oh God her boobs were the best part. Juicy and round and full ...

'I said five crab sandwiches please.'

... just the right size. As if they were made just for him. Lying down next to her, naked, her grasping his buttocks as he ...

'Wakey, wakey.' Jay felt a sharp tap on the back of his hand and instantly snapped out of his daydream. Two dwarves were standing beneath the counter with three even tinier kids.

'God, sorry,' he said, switching into work mode.

'Didn't think you'd be here this year,' said the man, rifling through his wallet.

'Oh, yeah hi,' said Jay, still too distracted to take any interest.

'You were doing your A levels last year, weren't you?' said the man's wife. 'You must be starting university soon.'

'No. I'm not going,' he said.

Jay's dad appeared, moneybelt tinkling. 'No, he failed all his exams. So he'll be shovelling mint choc chip here for the foreseeable.' His scratched his armpit and did the Dad Laugh but to the credit of the dwarf family, none of them laughed along.

Jay left his dad to make the sandwiches and went over to the deckchairs where a new queue had formed, waiting for tickets. His mind was still on Scarlett though. He watched the hill, waiting for her to return and break his suicidal, sweat-soaked monotony once more.

She eventually appeared, strolling back down the hill in her aviator shades, bikini and Nikes, smiling. His heart did a double beat as she made a beeline for him at the deckchairs.

'You haven't,' he scoffed.

'I have,' she said. 'You wait.' She held out her hand. 'Strawberry Mivvi please.'

Jay shook his head. 'Uh, proof? You had to bring it down to the beach.'

He headed back to the shack and she followed, sliding her aviators on to her head. She leant on the counter. It was only as Jay was making two Americanos that there came a commotion from the jetty. They looked across to see the golden retriever puppy from earlier, bounding down the gangplank, lead dragging behind him, plastic leg clamped firmly between his jaws.

Scarlett turned to Jay and smiled her most shit-eating grin, holding out her hand again in expectation.

'I don't believe it,' he laughed, watching the puppy's owners flip-flop along the gangplank after their errant mutt, one-legged Madge shrieking and hopping about like a net-caught seagull behind them.

Jay slid back the freezer door and pulled out a Strawberry Mivvi and banged it on the counter. 'You're gonna get me in trouble!'

'That's the plan.' She pulled off the wrapping.

They both laughed as he watched her lick the frost layer from her ice cream, leaning over the counter towards him.

'I better get back soon,' she said.

He sagged. 'Do you have to? I'm on my break in a minute. We could go up into the town and steal some fudge or knock over a bin or something equally deviant?'

She licked around the top of the ice cream, eyes dazzling. 'Ooh, ruthless! Jeez there really is nothing to do here, is there?'

'Why did you come here then?'

She looked at him. 'Mum and Dad's anniversary. They met down here when they were both on holiday as kids.'

'Can't you have one afternoon without them?'

'No. They want to go to this stupid stately home where I took my first steps. Dad said it's important that we all go together. "As a family."' Scarlett rolled her eyes. 'I couldn't be less in the mood to look at old vases and get lost in some maze.'

'You wanna stay here with me, don't you?' Jay smiled, leaning into her.

'Yeah.' A breeze whipped up, blowing a section of her hair across his face. Strawberries and cream.

She smiled. 'Come on, one more before I go.'

He rolled his T-shirt sleeves into tight knots on his shoulders, looking around the beach until his eyes settled on the shabby teenage boy on the shoreline. 'See him down there?'

Scarlett squinted into the distance, through the clusters of reclining old people and piles of deckchairs towards where Jay was pointing. 'Yeah.'

He folded his arms. 'Go and flash him.'

She didn't even blink, just carried on licking her ice cream. 'Top and bottom?'

He laughed. 'You would too, wouldn't you?'

She nodded. 'Yeah. If you asked me to.'

His hard-on throbbed. 'Top half only. For now.'

She shrugged. 'Okay. I think I deserve a little more than an ice cream though.'

'Crab sandwich?'

She shook her head.

'With chips? For the rest of the week?'

'Nope. And I don't want verruca socks either, before you ask.' She sucked on the stick and dropped it in the trash can beside her on the deck. 'Free boat trip.'

'My dad would tie me to a rock and let the gulls peck out my organs.'

'Ha,' she trilled. 'You're a real pussy when it comes to your dad, aren't you? Come on, live a little.'

'If he finds out I've been taking boats out for free, that's the only life he'll let me have, a little one. Thirty quid a time, mate. Think of something else.'

'You want to see my boobs, I want a boat trip.' She scrunched up her wrapper and reached across the counter to drop it in the bin. Her back shone.

Jay sighed, feeling the ache in his pants again. He leaned in closer to the counter to squash it. 'You realise you're pricing yourself out the market here?'

She laughed. 'Come on, Puss. You in or out?'

'In,' he said. 'All the way in.' He pressed his groin into the counter, suddenly aware how much he was sweating.

She laughed in his face, backing away from the counter and making a bee-line for the shabby boy. Jay watched her approach him. Them talking. Him sitting on his towel, looking up at her. Squinting. Probably thinking the exact same thoughts about her. Without paying any real mind to what he was doing, Jay served three customers. He wasn't even sure he'd given them the right change. He was waiting for the moment to come. To see her breasts. To see what the weird boy did in response.

It didn't happen.

In moments, Scarlett had begun walking back towards him.

'I knew you wouldn't!' he called out. 'What went wrong? Lost your bottle?'

'So, I bottled out, so what? Give me another dare.'

'No.'

'Why not?'

'You're blushing! Do you fancy him?'

'I've seen him before.'

'Seriously?' said Jay.

She wouldn't meet his eyes. 'Yeah. At our hotel. It's just awkward. I feel like he's stalking me.'

'Do you want me to have a word?'

'No. Just leave it.' All the sparkle had gone from her eyes. She leaned on the counter and sagged. 'So, what's my forfeit?'

Jay looked around, pretending to think of an especially heinous punishment. But he'd never wanted to punish anyone less. 'Okay, your forfeit is to meet me here at eight and help me put away the deckchairs. And then come on a boat trip with me.'

Her face lit up again as she leaned across him, removing the lid from the marshmallow kebab jar.

'Uh …' Jay was about to say when she took one out, removed the wrapper and bit two marshmallows from the stick.

'See you tonight then,' she said, wrapping her whole mouth around the two sweets. She plucked the third marshmallow off, shoved it into his open mouth and made her way back up the hill towards the town. He couldn't stop staring.

She only looked back once and it wasn't at him.

2. SCARLETT

She'd have given anything to stay on the beach. Even just sitting on a deck-chair all day, watching the sea and listening to the families squawking and playing Velcro tennis. Even watching Jay sponging seagull crap off the boats was better than being back at their hotel where their suite was cold and the silence was colder.

She thought about the boy on the beach towel all the way back to Palm Court. All the way up the palm-tree-lined driveway and through the marble and dark wood reception and up the winding staircase to their second-floor suite.

Mum was pretending not to touch up her make-up again.

'I'm back.'

'How long do you want to get ready?'

'I'll just get my stuff. Where's Dad?'

'Gone to get the papers, love.'

Nothing different here then. Mum and her acting like they were in a Lenor commercial. Dad gone off to let the dust settle after an argument so loud the chandelier had rattled.

She thought about the boys on the beach all afternoon as she traipsed around Cornell Manor after her parents. The place was old and musty and the day was too hot to enjoy moving about for long; a sweltering, hot, sticky-fore-head, fruit-flies-in-the-mouth kind of day. Their tour guide was a starchy middle-aged woman in tweed called Anne, who did her best to people the house with exciting Tudor and Georgian ancestors who'd gambled away for-tunes and were decapitated for treason, but Scarlett couldn't take any of it in. Not the stories, not the priceless antique tapestries nor the infamous blood spatter on the back staircase where a hidden priest had been murdered dur-ing the dissolution.

Because she knew neither of her parents were taking one word of it in either. They wandered the house like two ghosts past elegant paintings of snooty, old women in lacy gowns and ruddy-cheeked men with dusty faces. Past mounted heads of foxes and stags, eyes screaming in agonized silence. Past cracked ornaments – gold ladies dancing, ivory elephants, a porcelain boy asleep on a little haystack. She saw her mother looking at the ornament and the PLEASE DO NOT HANDLE THE EXHIBITS sign next to it. She thought about posting the ornament into her bag, then thought again. It wouldn't be enough to make her happy. Not when she had the power to give her better.

They broke for lunch. Scarlett found a wobbly, crumb-laden picnic table near the play area as her parents queued for food. She checked her phone – 3:27 pm. Surely they would be going back to the hotel soon so she could go down to the beach again and see Jay? The sooner she was back with him, the sooner she could kiss him. The sooner she could sleep with him.

The sooner she would be pregnant.

The question of where lay heavy on her mind but she was confident this boat trip would take them to the privately-owned cove just along the coast. She'd Google Mapped it. It had caves, hidden from view.

Her mum set out the cutlery. A napkin each. A fork. The cups. The plates. A wasp lingered near the cakes and her dad kept batting it away, only for it to return. By the time everything settled down and the tea had been poured out, tears had come again into her mum's eyes. Scarlett took a large bite out of her Victoria sponge to keep herself from shouting.

For a long time now, she had been in this slowly plummeting lift with the pair of them. And for the last few months at least, it had felt as though they were all dangling on the last wire. Time wasn't healing anything, it was merely a damp plaster that kept sliding off. That's why a new baby seemed the most obvious solution – a new plaster for the gaping wound they all stood around.

'What did you do at the beach today, Scarlett?' asked Dad, stirring his tea.

'Just hung out,' she said.

Dad nodded. Her mum studied the guide map like she was rehearsing lines for a play. Scarlett's eyes went to one then the other then back again. 'I met a boy.'

They weren't even listening.

'I'm going out with him tonight.'

'Will you be back for dinner?' asked Dad, cutting his cake into manageable chunks.

'No. I'll probably spend the night with him.'

If they heard, they didn't say anything. She wasn't even sure she'd said it out loud.

A toddler appeared at the top of the slide, his dad walking alongside him and his mum waiting to catch him at the bottom. On another attempt he got scared at the top and reached out at the steps. 'Daddy, daddy,' the little boy called. The dad swung him round and placed him gently back on the grass. The boy giggled.

Everything else was as it should be. Everything else was sunny and warm. Everyone else was happy. But Scarlett's parents were crying their eyes out. And anger punched a hole right through her.

Scarlett stood up, her mouth still full of cake. 'I'm going into the maze.'

She thought she heard her dad call out but neither of them came after her. Inside the maze it was dead end after dead end of leafy walls and strange families with crying children and over-excited spaniels. She spat out the wodge of cake and an off-lead retriever gobbled it greedily. Everything stank of Christmas trees. It took forever to find the middle and when she eventually did there was no one else there. No reward. No fanfare. She found it by chance – a small, dew-spackled sign that read: CONGRATULATIONS. YOU'VE REACHED THE MIDDLE OF CORNELL MANOR MAZE.

And she was in no hurry to find the way out.

3. REMY

He set up his pitch on the smooth rocks, watching the sun descend as a group of seagulls gathered on the shoreline to peck at leftovers in the fishermen's buckets. He'd have been happy if it had just been him, on holiday, free as a bird. Not hiding like some minnow, waiting for the shark to return.

He saw them before they saw him. That girl and him from the snack shack. Snack Shack Boy was marching over like he meant business.

'What you playing at, mate, eh?' he asked, climbing up on to the rocks in his espadrilles and kicking over his iced bag of fish.

'Hey!' said Remy, righting the bag and placing the fish back inside it.

'Stalking her. I know your game, mate. Fucking weirdo.'

Remy frowned but didn't get to his feet until the girl started clambering up the rocks. 'I'm not stalking her, I'm fishing.'

'Fishing for a shag,' said Snack Shack Boy, pushing him back on to the last rock as the tide lapped against it.

The girl stepped across to them, swinging a carrier bag. He smelled vinegary chips. 'Jay, what are you doing?'

'I'm sorting him out. He knows I'm on to him.'

'He's not stalking me,' she argued.

'You said he was stalking you.'

'I said it *felt* like he was stalking me. He's probably not.'

Jay slumped. 'For fuck's sake.'

'What?'

'I almost decked the guy!'

Remy interrupted. 'If you two are finished, I'm gonna go now.' He slung his bag over his shoulder and picked up his rods with one hand.

'Mate, I'm sorry, all right? I got the wrong end of the stick,' Jay called after him. 'I've got cans. Stay a bit and open one with us, yeah?' The boy turned to see him holding out a can of lager. 'I'm Jay. This is Scarlett.'

'Remy,' the boy replied, putting down his rods and taking the offered can. 'Got anything to eat?'

Scarlett looked into her carrier bag. 'We've brought cod and chips for us.' Jay looked at her. 'You can share if you want?'

They sat down on the rocks and Scarlett doled out the bundles of warm food, handing hers to Remy. He immediately began tucking in.

'So, where you staying?' asked Jay.

'Caravan park, near the Splash 'n' Slide,' said Remy, squeezing out a ketchup sachet on to Scarlett's paper.

'Oh cool, have you been there yet?' asked Jay. 'The Pulsar's wicked. Mind you it's better since the refit. They've got some class rides now.' Jay pointed out the snack kiosk on the beach. 'I run the shack with my dad. We've got free tickets for Splashy if you want some for your family?'

'I'm not there with my family,' the boy replied. He hadn't stopped eating. Scarlett wasn't hungry anyway.

'Who are you with?'

Remy shook his head. 'No one.'

'How come?'

'Ran away from home. Nobody knows I'm here.'

Jay frowned. 'What'd you do, kill someone?'

Remy shrugged, his face a quiet landscape to the marauding giant in his mind.

Scarlett was watching the seagulls pad along the sand. When she looked back at the boys, Remy was staring at her.

'How's your mum?' he asked her.

She nodded 'Fine', but her eyes wouldn't meet his.

'You know her mum?' asked Jay, his mouth full of mashed chips, watching from Scarlett to Remy and back again.

'Yeah.' He motioned towards the looming cliffs behind them. 'I was walking up the hill the other night. Past her hotel ...'

'He saved her life,' Scarlett explained. 'She was drowning in the pool.'

'Seriously?'

'Any normal family would have taken her to hospital. Got help. Then gone home or talked about it at least. Not them. They do these things and then we're just supposed to forget.'

'She fell in?' asked Jay.

Scarlett shook her head. 'No, she walked in. In her dressing gown. There's these decorative rocks around the Jacuzzi. Her pockets were full of them.'

'Jesus Christ,' said Jay quietly, for the first time his mouth empty of chips. 'But she's all right now, yeah?'

'Oh yeah, she's fine. 'Til next month when she'll try something else. I can keep hiding the key to the medicine cabinet and telling her to put her seatbelt on but she's got nothing to live for anymore. So she's just gonna top herself and Dad'll arrange a funeral and we just won't talk about it. Ever.'

'Talk about what?' asked Jay, looking at Remy.

'My brother died. She found him.'

Both boys said nothing. Did nothing. Asked no more questions.

Scarlett looked at them both. 'Don't you want to know how? Cot death. Nobody's fault. Doesn't stop them both from blaming each other though.' The silence between them was sudden and ear-splittingly loud. Scarlett jumped to her feet and unlaced her Nikes. 'I want to go swimming.'

'I've just eaten,' said Jay.

Remy looked at him, then her. 'I will.'

Seeing Remy unlacing his shoes, Jay followed suit, kicking off his espadrilles and unbuttoning his shorts.

The evening sea was just warm enough not to freeze to death and the threesome was soon enveloped within its ripples and waves. Jay wasted no time in showing off for Scarlett, slipping underneath the surface, his legs and feet appearing poker straight above them seconds later.

They stayed in the water until the sky grew darker as the sun dropped further behind Panesea Island. They talked and talked – about *The X Factor*, preferred burger toppings, their star signs, favourite films, milkshakes, dead pets. They played I spy, Bridge Collapse and Cruise, Marry, Shag; and planned what they would do together the next day. They talked about everything but the three giant reasons they were all there; the reasons none of them wanted to go home. Remy wandered through the water, allowing the soles of his feet to explore the pebbles; his hands to grab passing clumps of seaweed and driftwood. He looked up the first time and Jay and Scarlett were splashing each other. He looked up a second time and they were kissing. Mouth to mouth. Tongue lashing against tongue. Hands beneath the water.

Remy didn't know where to look until Scarlett broke free from Jay and turned her head towards him. 'Come here.'

She reached out and pulled him towards her, kissing him too. Mouth to mouth. Tongue lashing against tongue. Hands beneath the water. Then back to Jay. Then Remy. Jay. Remy. Jay. Remy. Eyes closed. Tongue searching for his, whoever he was. Nothing else mattered.

'Let's take the boat over to the cove,' she said, pulling away from them and opening her eyes. They were both staring back at her, expectant. 'We can lie down over there. Together.'

'You want both ...?' asked Remy.

She nodded. 'Yeah.'

'But ...'

'What?' demanded Scarlett. 'Don't you want to?'

Jay nodded eagerly, like he was about to explode, but Remy was unsure. This seemed like more than just a fun hook-up. There was needful desperation in her eyes. He'd seen something similar in her mother's eyes too – the desperation to die.

They made their way back to the boat, Jay and Scarlett all giggly and shivering, practically running while Remy remained sober and thoughtful, his movements slow and uncertain. He shouldn't get close to them. He shouldn't get close to anyone.

As their boat pulled away from the shore, an ambulance meandered up on the cliff road behind them – a large yellow vehicle travelling slowly with flashing lights but no noise. None of them saw the lights. None of them saw it coming.

The Cabildo

ROB MAGNUSON SMITH

I myself have made love to a corpse. It happened during a hurricane in New Orleans, where stories like mine aren't uncommon. That morning my best friend Mike got married—making me, I was certain, no longer his best friend—and I plunged into depths of self-pity. Mike was not only marrying, he was moving to the other side of the country. I took this hurricane as an omen. After the reception, everyone obeyed the warnings to vacate while I roamed the French Quarter, ducking into bars along rain-soaked alleyways and making drunken predictions about the end of the world.

By dawn I landed in Jackson Square facing the Cabildo. I had heard of this building. There, across the trampled grass, the Spanish had built their colonial City Hall. Under its white colonnades and sweeping balustrades, the Louisiana Purchase had been signed. And now, after surviving arson attacks from British spies and serving for decades as a prison for pirates, insurrectionists and murderers, the Cabildo had found genteel retirement as a war museum. At the top of the stone staircase, the lights were on. The double doors stood strangely open. The coming hurricane wasn't supposed to be Katrina-strength, but it still had the potential to be deadly. Standing there drenched in my rented tux, I considered my chances.

I crossed the grass and climbed the steps. Some sort of party was in progress—I could hear people talking and music from the upstairs balcony.

A security guard waved me through. As I stepped out of the wind and rain I noticed a sign for a black-tie gala to pay for the museum's refurbishment.

The Cabildo was humid and smelled of dying flowers. A circular staircase brought me past an enormous diorama depicting the Battle of New Orleans. Under the glass case, miniature soldiers were squaring off in a swamp. British forces numbering over eleven thousand, the placard said, were repulsed by a gaggle of Americans armed with grapeshot. On the wall loomed various oil paintings of Andrew Jackson in profile, his hawk-nose and brushed white hair pointing over the somewhat smaller Napoleon Bonaparte portraits, also in profile, positioned lower down. The next canvas showed the black storm-swept Gulf of Mexico capsizing a fleet of British Royal Navy gunboats. On the decks, hundreds of sailors were captured in their last moments. I looked at one face after another and tried to sober up.

Finally, I reached the top floor, where a string quartet played on a stage. Men in tuxes were smoking cigars in tight clusters. Despite the coming storm couples were dancing—politicians, retired oil executives, war merchants and elderly heiresses with fixed red lips. Only one waiter remained, a dutiful foot soldier in a handlebar moustache and crisp white shirt, carrying plates of canapés. Outside, an open bar stood on the balcony. I had reached the saloon of the *Titanic* in its final hour. I headed for the bar when a voice shouted, 'Don't you *dare* make love to me, honey!'

I turned. A woman of very advanced age stared at me, tugging compulsively at the white lace sleeves of her dress. An apparition would have carried more flesh. She was skeletal, wide-eyed, with sculpted hair the colour of iron. I was immediately attracted to her without knowing why. As the night progressed I *did* know why—it was her smooth acquisitive manner, her apparent seduction of hundreds of men in her lifetime, all more or less duped or willingly vulnerable. I also recognised her. She was the billionaire philanthropist Beverly Stark.

'Lord, save us from this great incursion,' said the man accompanying her. He was much younger, perhaps in his sixties. He wore a white linen suit and chewed a cigar. He regarded my soaking tux with that combination of courtesy and audacity particular to the extremely rich.

'My poor Tommy,' Beverly said, as the two approached. She dipped her outstretched hand toward the balcony and the howling wind. 'Dead and buried seventy-one years. His spirit will be unleashed in this wretched storm ...' She gripped my wrist, leaned in and whispered in my ear: 'I respect my vows when he's likely to be disturbed, honey. He catches us making love, I'll just never forgive myself.'

I tried to find traces of the sun outside. It was too early. It was too late. The whole city, some believed, was populated by ghosts. Even the skeptics kept quiet for fear of repercussions. And maybe Beverly's claim was technically true. Mike's wedding venue had been ringed with yellow crime scene tape. As the couple came out of the church to be showered with confetti, members of staff stood guard beside the more sodden graves. Guests were quietly warned that bodies could start rising.

'He needs a drink,' Beverly's friend said, patting my shoulder. 'What'll you have, son?'

'Martini?'

He made his way to the balcony. Beverly kept her grip on my wrist, and she wouldn't let go for some time. Her hands were strong, and she had white pointy nails. 'Tell me—what are you doing here in the Cabildo, honey?'

'I just wanted to get out of the rain.'

'Of course you did. Were you in a ceremony of some sort? A funeral?'

I told her about Mike. So many years we'd spent, laughing, listening to music, going for drinks. I told her about his wedding and the crime scene tape. As I spoke she moved her eyes over me, top to toe. 'The Cabildo has long been a refuge, honey. This was where the French gave us Louisiana. Where America has always partied and survived. Dick—my sixth husband, there—he hears me fret each hurricane. We never make love when the cemetery floods. Out of respect for Tommy ...' Her fingers tightened around my wrist. 'But when I saw you, I thought, Lord God. What if I want that young thing, there? I've just got to warn him.' She leaned in closer. With her other hand she clutched my chin like an ice cream. 'He died during consummation. Heart attack, right between my legs.'

I laughed—a dry, nervous laugh. Dick returned with my martini. We clinked glasses, and he noticed my living handcuff. He had the guilty smile of a man happy to watch the world end exactly where he stood in life. 'The boy's all wet.'

'A young drowned rat.'

'How old, you figure?'

'Twenty-seven.'

They kept talking about me as if I wasn't there. I tried sipping my drink slowly to pretend I wasn't rattled, but half went down at once. Beverly kept staring. 'Looks like our rat needs something stronger ...'

'That place on Pirate's Alley.'

'That bar that serves absinthe by the bottle. It should be open, wouldn't you think, honey?'

'Yes,' he said, his eyes rolling back to a memory. 'I do indeed.'

'Dick, honey. Do you mind staying on a spell—while this rat and I go and see?'

'I'd rather stay here ...' I stammered, but Beverly waved my words away like a bad odor. She'd paid for the Cabildo's refurbishment, and I was being cleaned out.

The rain blew straight at our faces. The morning was near, the wind strangely warm. Across Jackson Square all the power lines whipped on their poles. Behind us, the Cabildo stood high in the storm.

There were sirens in the distance. A young couple in shorts sloshed over the wet grass and veered into an alley. Debris lay everywhere—abandoned bicycles, heaps of clothes, a hot dog cart on its side with buns spilled on the sidewalk. No pigeons had come to eat, no birds of any kind. The only animals I saw that night were cats, huddled in shop doorways and outside boarded-up bars.

'Not many people left in the quarter,' Beverly said. She had put on a fur coat. She looked like an ancient, poisonous blowfish searching for its last meal. This didn't make me any less attracted—my final dawn had arrived, I had decided, with a cut-throat philanthropist as my companion. While Mike limped along with the evacuees on the highway, I was boldly embracing Thanatos.

'We must find absinthe,' Beverly announced, her heels clicking around a shattered beer bottle. We came down Chartres Street onto Pirate's Alley. It was a little cobblestoned enclave where Faulkner once lived. The houses were shuttered, the suspended flower pots swinging violently. Up on a balcony, a man wobbled impossibly on a ladder, hammering boards. A woman ran by us with her arms full of leather coats.

Beverly held my wrist and walked on. She was aiming for a bar on the corner with its doors open. Inside, a circular velvet sofa stood around a table made of hammered brass. There were cut-glass mirrors, chandeliers clinking in the wind. By the entrance a parakeet swung in a cage with its eyes squeezed shut. The place was empty, but Beverly rang the bell on the bar. I wondered if Tommy's body had surfaced yet. I wondered if he'd had any warning, just before his own end had come.

A woman in thick make-up appeared. 'Closed,' she said. 'Get yourself gone.'

346

Beverly produced a clip of hundreds and fanned them out on the bar. 'Just bring us a bottle of absinthe and a fountain, honey. Then get yourself somewhere safe.'

She pulled me over to the circular sofa. As soon as we sat down, she entwined my legs in hers. The owner hurried over with a glass vessel filled with ice along with a bottle of absinthe and two glasses, arranged on a platter with a bowl of sugar cubes and spoons. The ice fountain had tiny gold taps. She poured out large portions of absinthe into our glasses and balanced the spoons on top. The spoons had holes in the bottom where the sugar cubes dissolved. She put our glasses under the taps and opened the spigots to a trickle. 'Wait 'til it turns green, okay?'

There was a gust of wind outside, and something smashed. The owner closed the doors and bolted the wooden shutters. Back at the bar she emptied the cash register into her purse. 'The hurricane door's out back if you need it ...' She grabbed the parakeet and was gone.

The absinthe in our glasses slowly turned green. I took a sip and my nose caught fire—it was an icy, headily strong drink, bitter as liquid bark. We finished them, poured a second round, added sugar and trickled the taps. Beverly's features softened and her coal-black eyes flashed. 'I remain in love,' she said, 'with a man long gone.'

I thought of Mike on the highway. He was too helpless to be alone. He had moved across a continent to avoid the discomfort of hitting thirty single. I had always taken the other way. By my third absinthe I was thinking of the different ways men die, often in the attempt to preserve their lives, and I noticed that Beverly had taken my trousers down, that her legs had locked me in as she climbed on top. I closed my eyes as the wind shook the doors. One by one, the windows on Pirate's Alley shattered like bells.

'Forgive me, Tommy ...'

Beverly's nails bit into my shoulders. Her lips quivered and she mumbled something I couldn't hear. Later, I would take her back to the Cabildo. The problem was, she'd be dead. But that moment, before she collapsed on my chest with her dress hiked up and her fur coat still on, before I rested her gently back on the sofa, I stared into her open mouth and wondered if she'd found Tommy at last. Then her voice died away and I closed my eyes and prayed for everyone under the coming storm, trying in vain to retreat.

Outdoors

MIMI THEBO

I buckle my helmet on to my head as I walk down the hall. Dog follows, but knows not to step out of the door when I do. He takes a teeth-cleaning chew delicately with his rubbery mouth. 'Take bone to bed,' I say, but he doesn't. He looks at me, and slightly tilts his great golden head. 'Sorry,' I say. 'Jess will come. Jess will come and take you for a walk.' Satisfied, he retreats down the hall and I shut and lock the door.

Sunshine and showers today. Right now, the weather is deciding which to have first.

Council workers park along our road. When I look down, one is smiling at me as she walks past, 'Did you just apologise? To your Labrador?'

I shrug. 'I forgot to tell him about his dog-care arrangements,' I explain. 'He worries.'

Her eyebrows raise and she smiles again, more rigidly. Perhaps she walks a little quicker. I think she's decided I'm not in good mental health.

Seriously? I am cross, slinging my panniers on to the back of the bike. Dog has a vocabulary of around 40 words ... he's about as intelligent as an average two-year-old child. I'm sure the council worker would agree that a two-year-old child is capable of worrying and asking questions about her care. But she thinks that Dog can't – because he's furry, and walks on four legs. Specism has bothered me, my whole life.

It's a relief to begin riding.

My panniers carry a laptop, books, my lunch, bike tools and my hand-bag crammed inside. I do a few swoops and wobbles down my street, just to familiarise myself with how the weight will work today, how I will need to compensate and adjust my steering. Then I pedal hard and swoosh through the little pensioners' bungalows and into traffic. The Chew River is on my right, and, after the roundabout, I pedal over its confluence with the Avon. The big brown result turns left, but I go straight on.

My town was a Roman settlement and later the site of an abbey. I can see Kelston Round Tump, the Roman triangulation point, from my bedroom windows. Here on the bridge, a 13th-century church pokes its tower up above the trees of the park. It hasn't been wild around here for millennia. Everything I see has been moderated by humans.

The water beneath me is carefully managed. All of the trees have been planted. The fish are licenced and stocked. The foxes have learned how to depend upon bin bags. The badgers are dumped on the side of the road after being poisoned or shot by dairy farmers.

Knowing all that doesn't make the birdsong less lovely or the blossom less fragrant.

On the hill, my electric motor kicks in to help. It's as loud as a mosquito in a tent and it doesn't give me superpowers. I'm still gasping by the time I get to the top and I'm still embarrassed. It's been forty-three years since my breathe-way was injured, and yet I'm still self-conscious: about how loud I sound, how unfit I look and often am, about using the electric bike. There's a pub car park at the top of the hill and I wheel on to the pavement there, hop off, and cross at the zebra crossing.

The pavement here is a shared pedestrian and cycle path and a horrible surface for riding. The council has been digging it open for the technologi-cal advances of the last twenty years. Every time, they patch it closed again. There are ripples, ridges, dips and bumps. I know them all now, but they've spilled me off the bike twice. It's slow going, too. I'd make better time on the road and used to ride there. But a forty-three-year-old woman was killed on that roundabout, leaving behind two children under ten. Since I have a teen-aged daughter myself, I stay on the cycle path. My life isn't mine to risk.

The surface of the cycle path jars my teeth together. All the fatty bits of my body wobble and I have to work to keep hold of the handlebar grips. No one is certain where the cycle path begins and even on the marked bits, motorists shout at me to get off the path. On the road, they used to shout at me to use the cycle path. Being a cyclist, like being a mother, means you are always in the wrong.

I taught an MA seminar the day I was taken into hospital to give birth to my daughter. I corrected proof pages during labour. She attended two board meetings before she was six months old and then became a regular at the university nursery. This was all wrong. I was wrong to work away from home. I would have been wrong not to work as well, because I was making the money that kept our family afloat. I was wrong to work, wrong not to work. Wrong to bottle feed, wrong to let her starve. Wrong to teach her baby sign language, wrong not to buy Baby Einstein videos. I wasn't giving her enough opportunities. I was pushing her too hard. It was endless. My legs pump hard, thinking about all this. I pass the roundabout and I'm into the next town.

I've entered a neighbourhood of 1930s detached and semi-detached houses. Even though the A4 traffic has increased to an unforecastable level, these houses have kept their high value. There is a good primary school here. If you want to find good schools in this country … just look for the 1930s housing. This neighbourhood screams 'garden suburb' and I wrestle with envy. I love the clean lines of the deco houses, the perfect proportions, the shutters and the circular drives. I hate that I don't have one of them for myself. I recently heard Baroness Floella Benjamin say contentment is one of our three chief duties and I remember this as I cycle along, feeling my stomach churn with discontent. I think of Dog at the doorway and my little terraced house and I let go of my envy and just enjoy the blossom and startling green leaves from the well tended gardens of the 1930s houses.

The bike path ends, definitely and unmistakably. We suddenly leave the proportions of the 1930s and enter the proportions of the 1600s – the path becomes a narrow ribbon. I use the pelican crossing, nicely marked with a bicycle and cross on to the left-hand side, to re-join the traffic on the road.

Now the Avon comes back from its meanderings and keeps me company. In the winter, it flirts through the trees. In the autumn, it exhales a marker of deep mist. In the early spring, I just know it is there. The hill is steep and I am going faster than the cars and lorries in this 30 mph zone.

There's a speed camera. When they used to flash, it often flashed on my bottom. I ride this hill slightly up on my pedals, crouched over the handlebars, chasing the least wind resistance. Suddenly, you can tell that once I could actually ride a bicycle properly. I love this moment, when I'm the fastest thing on the road. I'm still careful, because one loose stone can send me under the wheels of the vehicle behind me, but I cut a long line down the face of the hill. It feels like flying.

At the bottom is a place named The Shallows. The Avon used to flow across here and would very much like to do so still. Heavy rain will make unplanned tributaries across it, despite great efforts in draining and cambering. It's hard to sell these houses … if the climate goes the way we push it, we won't keep holding the river back. The Shallows will become The Deeps and we will need a bridge or another route from Bristol to Bath.

After The Shallows, the verges of the road become wilder. In late summer, brambles sometimes stretch out under my tyres. Hedges are untidy and self-seeded … baby trees appear in the wrong places. Like the river, the forest tries to come back. It's been held in check for over a thousand years, but it hasn't given up.

On the next road along, there is an Iron Age fort. I climbed it once, tracing the terraces of the ancient fortifications with my feet. It was overgrown and hard walking. In the close undergrowth, my breath wheezed like a train. The hedgerows beneath me were older than my country, nearly as old as Christianity. And still the hornbeams and larches and wee, little oaks pushed at the margins of the fields. The forest is patiently waiting.

After the hill and The Shallows, the traffic picks up speed and I am acutely aware that I am an obstacle. I shift up and let the engine help me again, even though it's flat and I don't really need it.

Lorry drivers are usually solicitous to cyclists. Buses are, in the main, horrible, passing with their noses and then swinging in. But it's not that busy today and I find my mind returning to what I was writing an hour ago, in the shed in my back garden.

My stories start out straightforward, but grow wildly improbable very quickly. My imagination is unruly as the untidy hedges. Why has my character got to be a ballet dancer? Isn't there enough of a narrative with her unknown father, her expulsion from school, her exile with a family she barely knows, her strange friendship with a wild dog? I always hold a bit of anxiety at this point in a manuscript. I push hard on the pedals, consciously draining away adrenaline by pumping my blood around and around through my liver.

When it's time to turn, I am breathing hard and my mouth and throat are dry. I slow, stop, put my left foot on to the pavement, and look behind me.

A large lorry I hadn't even noticed has been waiting to get by. I wave my thanks as he shifts up. There's a whole queue of cars behind him. Their drivers must hate me right now. For a moment, the shame and guilt of being slow, wounded, unfit, hits me again. But, as I wait for them to pass, and my breathing slows down enough to close my mouth and moisten my throat, my mind drifts back to my manuscript … I love the coyote. But seriously, a ballet dancer? Why? I catch my attention wandering and pull it back hard. Concentrate, I tell myself. This turn is dangerous.

At last I'm across and pedalling hard up a little hill on the Corston lane, where the trees make a tunnel. At the top is an old convent, a nursing home now. I never stopped to see my friend Margaret when she was in there ... didn't even know about her funeral when she died. An intense feeling of loss comes over me, for the sisters that made this their home just to see their order die out, for Margaret, for the many things I can no longer do ... I have given almost all my time to my writing and my teaching ... there is little enough left for my family and almost nothing for even my closest friends. But I remember Margaret and I mourn her fierce, bright spirit. I wish I'd said goodbye.

Thinking of Margaret has taken me past the post office and now I start thinking about my students. One has lost her grandmother, one has slipped back into her ME. There are four fugitive boys trying to rejoin the course after losing their way with drink, drugs and, for one, imprisonment. There are administrative tasks due ... some of which I've no doubt forgotten. And what about my SFHEA application?

I find myself on the A39 without knowing how I got there and tell myself, once again, that I must concentrate when riding a bicycle on the road. There's a big queue of cars waiting for the roundabout a quarter mile away. I wait patiently until the road widens and then swing out to the right, zipping down the centre line, until I can turn into the gates of the university.

The cattle guard is tricky. There are two sweet spots that won't damage my wheels or tyres and some mornings I know I won't hit them properly. This is one of those mornings, so I dismount and push the bike across, balancing in dress shoes on the wide bars of the cattle guard.

If Capability Brown had designed the drive with the purpose of making cycling to Newton Park difficult, he couldn't have done a better job. There is a long, slow gradient that looks like nothing, but turns your legs to jelly. And then, just after a disarming little dip down, you face a wall of a hill.

Off to my right, as I shamelessly exploit the electric element of my bicycle, is another Avon tributary ... and sheep. These fields have been farmed for over 900 years. The estate has the remains of a 14th-century castle and an intact Regency manor house. The stable block was standing when Shakespeare was writing. The Dairy is older than Thomas Hardy. Tess D'Ubervilles probably worked in one just like it.

But, panting hard and aching, I finally pull up to an incongruously modern building –panelled with images of nature.

Nature ... we're talking about nature writing today ... is a difficult concept. Today, it's my job to show 200 undergraduates *why* it's so difficult. I'll take some of them outside in an hour. Point to nature, I'll ask them on the carefully created hill. Tell me where it is.

No, not that tree. It was planted and has been meticulously maintained. Not that hill, it was sculpted. Not that field, it's been managed for a millennium. So, where is the nature here, I'll ask. Some bright spark will look up, stick out their tongue to catch the rain.

We'll talk about consumption of nature and specism. I may tell them about the book I'm writing. I may tell them what the council worker said. I may read from one of the four books in my panniers. I may give them a critical insight.

I don't know. I won't know ... until I hear what they're thinking, how they're interacting with the concepts introduced in last week's lecture. I want to see their writing, hear them talk to me. I am ready to challenge and to praise, to help and heal and to gently wound.

I'll make a cup of tea first. I'm looking forward to going into the classroom to talk about nature and writing and how difficult it all is. I wrestle with it all myself, all of the time. It's nice to have some company.

I lock up my bike. And then I look around for one more moment. There's a lovely view here, of a field that I've known used for arable farming, but is now a pasture. I hear a blackbird while I look at the cows and calves ... the calves are putting on weight, grazing now, their hides buttery in a sudden shaft of sunlight.

And then I go inside.

My Brother Saves Things

STEVE VOAKE

My brother saves things
Record players with dusty needles,
old 33s with torn covers
and scratched, shiny vinyl
with names like Captain Beefheart,
Frank Zappa and Pere Ubu while
upstairs there are ticket stubs from concerts
and Spectrum Pursuit Vehicles
and old enamel badges with rusty pins that say
Support the Miners and *Mister Softee* and
Bronze Swimming Award and
I am the Saturday Cat.
My brother saves things

My brother saves things
When the boys trapped a bee inside a coffee jar
I watched, helpless, as they went to fetch
their instruments of torture:
tweezers, scissors, a magnifying glass
'Touch that and you're dead' they told us.
'Don't cry,' he said when they had gone
then he twisted the top off and we watched
the bee fly away into the blue sky.
'Go home now,' he said
and waited patiently on the drive
for the beating he knew was coming
My brother saves things

My brother saves things
Programmes from plays he can't remember
beer mats and bottles and
shirts he no longer wears
old photographs from the 1970s
of people outside their tents in the rain
clutching bottles of scrumpy,
dressed in tank tops and shirts
with collars like the wings of Vulcan bombers
and crushed velvet loons
and Afghans
and unforgiveable hair.
My brother saves things

My brother saves things
Once, long ago,
I came back from the other side of the world
with a battered suitcase and a broken heart
and I pulled the curtains
and lay on my bed in the dark.
'Come on,' he said
'It might be bad. But it's not as bad as all that.'
Then he pulled back the curtains
and opened the door
and pushed me out into the bright street.
My brother saves things

My brother saves things
Beer mats and bottles and
shirts and programmes and
photos of people by their tents in the rain,
record players with dusty needles,
old 33s with worn covers
and scratched, shiny vinyl
with names like Captain Beefheart,
Frank Zappa and Pere Ubu while
Upstairs there are ticket stubs from concerts
and Spectrum Pursuit Vehicles

and old enamel badges with rusty pins that say
Support the Miners and *Mister Softee* and
Bronze Swimming Award and
I am the Saturday Cat.
My brother saves things

My brother saves things

Three Poems

TOM WEIR

Day Trippin'

'I'd ride horses if they'd let me' — Will Oldham

We talked all morning about the horse
that, if we're honest, none of us actually knew existed

but it seemed worth it just to get you into the car,
to stop shouting. We mentioned it so often

you began to repeat it from your child seat
like a mantra, and you'll never know the relief,

having arrived and not been able to see a stable,
having stalled you with an ice cream which you wore

like a glove as it melted over your hand,
of finding the woman who showed us where

the horse rides took place, where you waited
so quietly in line, where I stood and watched

as you approached the man with a five-pound note
scrunched up in your tiny hand. You spent

the rest of the day repeating the words *too little*
like a radio breaking bad news every hour on the hour.

We took you down to the lake and watched
you throw stones at the water, watched clouds fall apart

and mend as rowing boats left the harbour and you
sat still, refusing to join another queue.

Glass

We might as well have all been made of glass
for when the sun broke through the clouds
we wore rainbows round our necks like scarves
and when we held each other our bodies felt hard

and when we shook hands we did so
like our fathers had taught us
and at certain angles there was two of everything
and at certain angles there was nothing at all

and some of us cracked when the temperature dropped
and when some of us passed out we woke
with words fingered on to our foreheads
in dust and some of us were clear and our veins

swirled around our bodies as if we were marbles
and some of us were stained
and some of us were single glazed
and some of us were shipped in from China

and shook on the wind like water
and when it got late some of us carried light
like lanterns in our arms and when
some of us fell over there was no getting up

and when the wind picked up
some of our bodies whined like sirens
and when we drank wine spilled from our lips
like blood and when the cracks began

to appear some of us filled like locks
and when the insects stung none of us
felt a thing and we were all that remained
the following day when the sky fell in.

Monsoon

The lightening, diluted by the orange sheet you hung above the window,
is the same as the lamp's faint glow that twitches with each shock of noise
as each crack of lightning threatens to break the sky.
I don't tell you this isn't normal, that it's never been this bad before;
rain soaking our sheets as it leaks through the ceiling.

I can feel its weight as I make my way across the room where,
above all the noise, I'm not actually sure you ask if everything's okay
or not but I tell you it is anyway. You don't need to know about the women
crying, the men up to their waists in water, the children held high
above their heads like an offering to a god no one believes in.

A Species of its Own

FAY WELDON

I sit in the quiet cafe of Bath Spa's Creative Writing department, drink coffee, and consider the nature of the novelist: a surely species on their own, and unlike any other. The cafe is in the old servants' quarters of Corsham Court as is the department. The Court is a stately home with a major art collection, gardens by Capability Brown, peacocks, ancient yew trees and so forth. It's courting season for the peacocks, and they disturb tutorials with sudden plangent cries. The males parade their full magnificent display – while the dowdy peahens cluster in the shade of the yews and make a point of ignoring them. Or so it seems. But then novelists will find life lessons anywhere. It is what they *do* all day while apparently idling and staring into space. They're famous for it.

A class upstairs ends and the room fills up with aspiring novelists. Post-graduates all, they have joined this course – for better or worse – to polish their craft, and they come in a variety of shapes and sizes, ages and nationalities, mostly female, a few male. They chatter, they laugh – just occasionally someone sobs – but all are instantly companionable. And you can recognise them for what they are – novelists. A separate species.

Non-fiction writers, who are also on the course, seem more serious, more cautious, less relaxed. Why do the fiction writers, whether long-legged beauties or little pebble-spectacled old ladies, speaking in noble tones or the

363

language of the people, reluctantly or fulsomely, already published or novices, have that look only novelists have? It's hard to define. Could that kindly bend of the head, that hint in the eye, suggest some secret, valuable knowledge? Or more likely, whether aspiring to genre writing or great literature, they're all just happy to be living in more worlds than one at the same time and it shows – they're impatient to get back to what's going to happen next in the alternative universe they've chosen to create?

Whatever it is, it's why, when I once recommended a certain student to a selection panel recently, I found myself saying 'At least she *looks* like a novelist' and no one blenched or asked me what I meant.

A gathering of science students I'd suspect to be less gregarious, more judgemental than the writers; of philosophy students to be more remote, perhaps standoffish; of Eng. Lit. students to be more analytical, while misty-eyed. Their queues for coffee and sandwiches would take longer to move forward, decisions as to most pleasing / least calorific being more problematic. Writers are quicker off the mark to make their decisions, not only eager to get back to their inventions, their fantasies, and less selfish, more sensitive to the needs of those behind, better attuned to the zeitgeist. (It's for the same reason that novelists tend to make nervous drivers: too much imagination; too aware of the man with the broken leg lying just over the brow of the hill; the scene when you tell a weeping neighbour you've run over their cat.)

I wonder what the collective noun for a group of novelists could be? A murder of crows, a pride of lions, an ascension of larks – perhaps for writers it's a 'finesse'? All that delicate discrimination between one word and another, that redrafting and redrafting. Or indeed an 'edifice'? All that structuring and bridge-building, the middle strung so and dangerously between the towers of beginning and end?

But I think perhaps an 'empathy' is the best word. Yes, an empathy of novelists. They've spent so much time practising being other people the gift comes easily to then. They know what it's like to be other people. They've had to lose their good opinion of themselves as they walk in the shoes of villains as well as heroes, the thoroughly nasty as well as the nice and all stages in between. They discover their own motivations as they dissect those of their characters. It can be quite a distressing process. No wonder writers get 'blocked'. It's themselves they can't face, not the words on the page.

Well, if the skills that employers most look for when recruiting (as *Forbes* magazine tells us) are the ability to work in a team, make decisions and solve problems; who should be in greater demand than Creative Writing graduates? Those workshop groups have been teams in training; every chapter has needed a hundred creative decisions; every sentence had to solve the problem the previous sentence set up. But it's the empathy that's important. Your CW graduate is not likely to fire off some tactless e-mail which will get everyone (including them) into trouble. They understand the impact of mere words, and the consequences of 'accidents'.

The hubbub decreases, the coffee shop empties, the next class begins – peace descends. A peacock squawks and I jump.

And me? I'm just awed by the courage and stoicism of those who spend years of their life studying a craft without certainty of financial gain or even eventual publication. Dedication indeed.

Spaceman Number One

ANNA WILSON

March 1968

The newspaper lay open on the table, the golden brown of a coffee-cup stain circling the photo, as though marking it out for me. At least I had the luxury, if you could call it that, of reading the news in private.

He's gone. Spaceman Number One. He orbited the Earth. Now he will never walk on it again.

I picked up the paper and stared at the photo. They'd chosen the one of him as a cosmonaut, of course: the picture of his handsome face staring out of the glass front of his helmet. A dead ringer for a film star, were it not for the heavy metal hood encasing him. He was a shinier star than any actor on the silver screen, in any case. In his short life, he had achieved what most men never even dream of.

It was a shame the paper had not printed a different photo, though. One of the real Yuri. The Yuri I'd gone swimming with, chased the girls with, had my first drink with. But that wasn't what people wanted to read about, was it? To the rest of the world, Yuri Gagarin was simply Spaceman Number One. The first man ever to fly out of the Earth's atmosphere into deepest, darkest space. The first man to see the Earth from a spaceship.

367

The day I met Yuri he was sitting on a desk, swinging his legs and telling jokes and stories in front of a small group of my classmates. The new kid on the block. Not that you would have known it from the way the others were listening, eyes fixed on him, mouths slightly open in fascination.

'Think of it – flying as high as a bird!' he was saying. 'We'd soon have the Germans on the run if we could fly away from them!' He held his arms out as if they were wings, and swooped his shoulders down, as though soaring through the air.

The other kids laughed. I didn't want to like this new guy. He was so self-assured, so ... solid. How dare he walk into this place and slot himself in, just like that? It had taken me months to win friends when I'd first arrived.

He looked up and noticed me for the first time, hovering by the door.

'Hallo! What's your name? I'm Yuri – Yuri Gagarin.'

'Ivan,' I said, fighting the urge to smile. I didn't want to yield to this stranger. It should have been me doing the introductions.

But that's the way it was with Yuri. One second was all it took for people to fall for his charms. He had that special something from the very beginning. It's easy to say in hindsight, but I believe I knew from that first meeting that Yuri would turn out to be one of life's stars.

He used to say that he had had a premonition when he first saw me, too.

'You had that look in your eye,' he said once.

'What look?'

'The one you've got now – that determined one. I loved it! That's what made me realise how much I wanted your friendship. You were going to be a tough nut to crack, but I was going to do it,' he said, punching me on the shoulder.

Me, determined? What did that make Yuri? I wondered. He was the one who had come from nothing to take centre stage and receive the world's accolades. He was the country boy with a carpenter for a father who had ended up being the first man in space. Whereas I ... I had been a good boy, studied hard, got my apprenticeship as a metalworker, and stayed in that trade ever since.

Yuri had trained with me after leaving school. There weren't that many opportunities for poor kids from the Moscow suburbs. We weren't exactly encouraged to 'live the dream'. Not like the kids here in the Land of the Free where anything is possible if only you work hard enough.

We worked hard back then in Russia of course, but all we got was enough money to scrape by and the knowledge that the job we were doing day after day was the job we'd do until the day we were too old to be useful any more.

I used to moan to Yuri.

'Don't you ever wish you'd been born in another country – or another time?' I asked him once, as we were slaving away in our freezing workshop.

Yuri laughed. 'No way. I don't wish for things I can't change.'

'So, what *do* you wish for, then?'

Yuri stared straight at me, putting down his tools. 'Look out of the window.'

'What?'

'Look out of the window,' Yuri insisted.

I went over to the grimy panes of glass on the far wall of the workshop. Outside I saw the yard where some of our colleagues were working, the fields and trees beyond. Nothing unusual, in other words. I turned back to Yuri, puzzled.

He was grinning, infuriatingly. 'Look out and *up*,' he insisted.

I did as he said, but all I saw were clouds. It looked as though it would snow again, I thought.

'Don't you ever think about what's up there?' Yuri asked, coming up behind me. He put a hand on my shoulder.

He still talked about flying, just as he had done that first day in the class-room. I tutted and shook my head. 'Don't you ever think about anything else?'

But Yuri looked serious. 'I'm not talking about flying with the birds,' he said, 'I'm talking about what's beyond that – beyond the sky.'

I frowned. 'What do you mean?'

Yuri had dreamy look in his eye. 'Other planets. Outer space.'

'Hey, I knew you were crazy, but you're not telling me you believe in alien life forms—!' I began.

Yuri snapped, 'No.' Then he turned back to work.

'Sorry,' I said, hastening to make amends. I hated to see him upset. Especially with me.

We finished our work in silence that day. But Yuri came back to that conversation many times over the next months. He told me that, as a boy, on the farm where he'd lived, the night sky had always fascinated him.

'I would gaze up into the stars, and pick out the patterns,' he told me. 'Papa taught me how to recognise the different constellations: the Great Bear, Orion's Belt, the Dog Star. But the thing about the night sky is, the more you stare at the stars, the more stars you realise there are. It blew my mind. Still does,' he added.

I knew that wistful look. It was the look Yuri had had on his face when he'd told me he wanted to learn to be a pilot. The other guys at college thought he was out of his mind. 'You, the country bumpkin? A pilot? You don't stand a chance ...' But that merely served to increase his determination. He saved up all the money he made from the casual work he did in the evenings and at weekends, and then enrolled in a local flying school. Typical Yuri: he was a natural.

He took me up with him a couple of times. I have to admit I was scared witless at first.

'I promise you, you won't regret it,' he said, laughing when I told him I'd rather pull my own teeth. His eyes sparkled. 'There's nothing like it, Ivan, being above the clouds, above the towns and villages – above Igor!'

Igor was our boss. And a miserable old so-and-so he was, too. Always grumbling that we didn't work hard enough, well enough, quickly enough. The idea of taking off and flying over his ugly bald head made me chuckle. 'OK, take me up in your plane,' I agreed. 'But only if I can drop rotten eggs on Igor's stinking face.'

I thought I would be sick or panic or scream when the plane took off, but when it came to it I didn't have time. The experience was like nothing I had ever been able to imagine. We rose up into the air so fast, the people and the buildings beneath us shrinking before my eyes as if someone had poured a magic potion on them, or as if I had taken a potion myself and was turning into a giant, sprouting up like a tree, spreading my branches across the world.

Yuri's face shone. 'You get it now, don't you?' he shouted above the noise of the engine.

I nodded, too stunned to answer. Holding my gaze with those intense blue eyes.

So I wasn't surprised when Yuri told me after graduation that he was going to join the Soviet Air Force. I was sad, as I'd privately hoped we would end up working together. The minute he told me, however, I knew it was a case of a dream come true.

'I have to fly,' he said, holding my gaze with that intense gaze. 'You know I do. And this is the only way I'm going to be able to do it. It's not like I'm one of those rich Americans who can have their own jet and zoom around wherever and whenever they feel like it. And look at it this way – I'll be serving our great country, too. Join up with me, Ivan.'

But I couldn't. I was engaged to be married by then. I didn't want to leave my future behind me to roam the skies.

We stayed in touch. Yuri wrote me long letters about his training programme and the other men he made friends with. Very soon the things I'd always known about Yuri became clear to the people he worked for.

5th October, 1955

Dear Ivan,

At last I'm getting the kind of challenges I've craved for so long! No more toeing the line for me; no more run-of-the-mill training and following the same orders as the rest of them. No! I'm being given the chance to test and actually fly new aircraft. Imagine it, Ivan – I'll be flying new planes before anyone else in the world! This is what I joined the Air Force for.

    Your brother-in-arms,

    Yuri

Even this wasn't enough for my determined friend. Yuri was insatiable, it seemed. The Air Force must have been breathless, trying to keep up with his thirst for adventure.

10th April, 1961

My dear Ivan,

This is it – the pinnacle of all I could have hoped and dreamed. I hope you are sitting down while you are reading this, my friend! Are you ready?
    You remember that time I told you to look out of the window of our workshop – when we were still apprentices? Doesn't that seem like a lifetime ago? I told you how I longed to know what was out there, beyond the sky.
    Well, soon I'll be able to tell you. Yes, Ivan ...

I AM GOING INTO SPACE!

This isn't one of my jokes, I promise. Since joining the Force I've heard many whispered stories about secret missions to send a man into space. It seemed too crazy to be true, but somehow I'd always known that we would do it one day. The human race is too valiant, too spirited to stay with its feet on the ground.
    In the end I couldn't stand by, thinking that another man might go soaring into the heavens while I lived my life never knowing what lay out there. So I went to one of my officers and told him I was volunteering to be a cosmonaut.

You would have loved the look on his face! He didn't seem to know whether to laugh out loud or reprimand me for insolence. (Reminded me a bit of that stinker, Igor – remember him?) He certainly was keen to know how I had found out about the space project. But I couldn't have cared what his reaction was, as long as I could convince him to take notice of me. I badgered him, Ivan, like a spoilt child. He gave in to shut me up, I think. (Although the work I'd done for him on the experimental craft I'd been testing cannot have gone completely unnoticed, though I say so myself!)

I wish I could have told you about this before, but it's all been top secret. I've been going through a rigorous testing programme to see if I'm fit enough. The worst of it was when I sat in a human centrifuge … I'd better explain.

Remember you couldn't believe how quickly we took off in that plane back home? Well, you wouldn't believe how much more quickly a fighter jet soars away from the Earth. It's the strangest sensation the first time you experience it, and a lot of men can't handle it – it makes them sick. This is because when you are travelling upwards at a high speed, the force that gravity is exerting on you makes you feel as if you weigh more than usual. We call it 'g-force'. To find out how I would react to a high level of g-force, I had to sit in a machine called a human centrifuge. It's not pleasant. It's designed to test us cosmonauts to see if we can handle the speed at which a rocket needs to be propelled into the sky.

As if that wasn't bad enough, I had to sit in a pitch-black, soundless room for twenty-four hours without a break. Again, not something I would recommend. The whole time I was going through these tests, I kept a picture in my mind of how it would feel to be rocketed into space; to leave the Earth behind and join those constellations my dear Papa showed me.

Very soon, I will know. I am due to carry out my mission on April 12th – in only two days' time! The rest of the world will know about this tomorrow, which is when you will get this letter. I only hope it reaches you before you read about me in the papers. And don't worry – I'll write the moment I return.

Till then, I remain, as always,

Your loving friend,

Yuri

Dear, brave Yuri. He was right: the whole world was watching that day and holding its breath. I prayed for his safe return and couldn't stop from wondering what was going through his mind as he hurtled away from us at what we were told later was 28,260 kilometres per hour.

28,260 kilometres per hour. It doesn't make any kind of sense at all. It is quite unthinkable that a man can travel that fast.

How must he have felt, hurtling out of the Earth's atmosphere in the sputnik, Vostok 1, as they called it? Did the Earth shrink away under his feet in the same way it had in that plane I once sat in? Or was he travelling so fast that he saw nothing at all? I couldn't wait for him to come back and tell me.

We arranged to meet not long after he completed his mission – successfully, of course, as he did everything in his life. He had recently been awarded a medal and the official title Hero of the Soviet Union, and the drinks were on him that day.

'So, come on, Yuri – give me the details!' I urged, leaning over my vodka.

'Haven't you read the papers?' he teased.

I frowned.

'Ivan! I'm only joking. The thing is, however I describe it, I'll never do justice to what I saw up there.' He paused, suddenly serious. 'All I can say is that our planet is extraordinarily beautiful. You wouldn't think it when you look out on to the streets most days and see the dirt and the poverty, the fighting and the sadness. But when you step back as far as I have done, it's a completely different picture. Our planet is a whirlpool of colours – blues, violets and dark, inky, petrol-tinged blacks. And around it all is a pale halo. It's a miracle,' he ended.

I stared at my friend's faraway expression and wondered how he would go about his daily life now that he had met the stars face to face. How could any man live a normal existence after such an experience?

Of course, I had read a full account of the mission and had been horrified to learn that Yuri had not been in control of the spacecraft. If seeing the Earth from space had been miraculous, coming home safely had been more so, it seemed to me. The sputnik had been controlled by computers: Yuri had been given a key in a sealed envelope which he was told he could only use in an emergency if the vessel failed. There was obviously a very real fear that the mission could be a disaster. Yuri had been provided with ten days' worth of food and water in case of rocket failure, but what use would that be when you were cut off from the rest of the world, floating about in the cosmos?

'How did you feel when you had to return to Earth?' I asked him.

Yuri snapped back to the present and looked at me, the twinkle in his eyes returning. 'The parachute fall was interesting,' he said, raising his eyebrows. 'You heard I had to eject at seven thousand kilometres? That's a long way to fall, and there was quite a lot of freefall before that parachute finally decided to open!' He was laughing, but I shuddered as I thought of how I would have felt had I been in Yuri's shoes.

'Guess who the first earthlings were to greet me?' he asked.

'No idea.'

'An old woman, her granddaughter – and a cow!'

Then we both laughed – long and loud.

'To the Hero of the Soviet Union!' I cried, clinking my glass against his. 'Moooo!'

That was the last time I saw Yuri. His picture was all over the place of course, but I never spoke to him face to face again. His life took a different course and it must have become harder and harder to keep in touch with old friends. It's seven years since that day in a small bar in Moscow when he told me how beautiful this planet really is. And now he's left it – for good this time. Not in a spaceship, not even in a plane, though that is how he died. He was flying an MIG-15 as a test pilot, according to the report.

I put the paper down and threw open the doors to the balcony. It was a warm evening – unseasonable for March. I breathed in the city and looked up into the sky. There was Orion's Belt, and the Dog Star.

Ah, Yuri.

I like to think you left this world as you would have wanted. Soaring upwards into the heavens. A star, joining those constellations you loved so much.

Telling Stories Through a Wall, Into the Dark

JACK WOLF

The reality we experience is constructed in the world behind our eyes out of the narratives we like to tell ourselves, and sometimes out of the ones we don't. The fact that, most of the time, we do not know we do this, or that sometimes we would like to pretend we don't, makes no difference. Denial of the neurological and psychological bases of perception is about as useful a technique for understanding and influencing objective reality as refusing to comprehend climate change, or (dis)believing in God; the existential nature of the thing is unaffected by our protests of: 'I only believe what is in front of my eyes', or: 'if it's a raven, it can't be a writing desk'. What we see is what we think we see, and vice versa, because this is how the human brain works, how it has always worked, and how it will continue to work as long as our species perpetuates. It is by understanding this rather inconvenient truth that we may, somewhat paradoxically, begin to prise open Huxley's Doors of Perception – and what we see and what we think we see may at last tentatively begin to approach each other, like two lovers long kept apart at arm's length, Pyramus and Thisbe stuck on either side of the high Wall (which continues to insist it is a Wall, despite all the evidence of our eyes and ears that tells us it's an actor).

According to, among others, the cognitive scientist Donald Hoffman, the real world beyond our senses is essentially a place whose characteristics are best described in terms of number. Human perceptions, like those of every other animal-intelligent being, therefore represent an attempt by the brain to fill in the abstract weirdness of photons landing on the retina or soundwaves in the inner ear with a series of symbolic constructs such as 'big' and 'scary' and 'snake'; with what I will call a Story, of sorts – the unconscious narrative a living being tells itself in order to make sense of the nonsense of the real. Hoffman is far from alone in holding this view of perception, though he is, as far as I know, the only writer so far to state that our perceptions do not represent reality at all. He may be over-egging the pudding, of course – it's quite a stretch from arguing that we must perceive reality via a perceptual interface to arguing that the interface bears no resemblance to that reality. But this doesn't matter to my point; whether the Stories our visual and auditory cortices create are fictions or creative non-fictions, they nonetheless remain Stories. When we see a snake, our brain tells our fast-twitch muscles the old, old Story of the snake: like most primates, (even, in fact, most frogs) we jump out of the way. It doesn't matter to the Story whether the snake we see looks anything like the creature that exists on a molecular, numeric level. It's a symbol, and its symbolic meaning is danger, is death.

This unconscious evolutionary process forms in humankind the ultimate basis for a habit of Storytelling in which our species has become the expert par excellence. Story does not begin and end, for us, in sound and vision. Humans, like all higher animals, have more complex needs than simply to escape a predator, to find food or to identify a potential mate – though all these urges are no less strong, no less vital to us because of that. Our species, perhaps uniquely among animals, possesses the capacity and the will to speak – to develop ways of recording and passing on our experiences, culture, history, genealogy and all the rest so that our perceptions and our thoughts will endure beyond our own lifetimes and become part of our children's. We use our words, and both with them and out of them we create and we construct more, and yet more, Stories.

The Stories we tell ourselves are many and complex, and not always immediately obvious. In this society, that of 21st-century Britain, we tell ourselves the Story of opposition, and the Story of duality; we tell ourselves the Story of gender – that 'male and female, He created them' – and believing this to be so, we perceive in men and women entities whose gendered identity is primary over their humanness. We tell ourselves the Story of hierarchy, and the Story of difference; we tell ourselves the Story of race, and persuade ourselves that this very modern social construction (which was unknown among the Romans) reflects a genuine physical disparity. We tell ourselves the Story of human exceptionalism, and let ourselves assume – like my old philosophical bête noire Descartes – that non-human animals are soulless automata. We tell ourselves the Story of progress. None of these Stories proves to be objectively true, when we call it to mind and thoroughly examine it, and none of them is necessarily good, but they have become psychological and social truths; embedded so deeply into the ways in which we perceive and behave towards each other that they direct how we orient ourselves within the world around us without our even being conscious of knowing them. They allow us to make sense of, and impose sense upon, a social reality that – we fear – could otherwise reveal itself to be nothing but unscripted chaos. But the most important Story we tell ourselves is the Story of the Self – the narrative of continuous identity that we use to make sense of the confusing uncertainty of a lifetime; the Story we impose upon an otherwise random sequence of events that afflict and elevate us from the cradle to the grave. This Story, of course, involves all the other Stories in the unconscious way I have described above: we bring them in – instinctively, interlexically, interconceptually – to give our primary narrative substance and coherence.

Henry David Thoreau, in 1845, went to live at Walden Pond, Massachusetts, in an attempt to redraft his own Story of Self in relation to the natural world around him. He spent two years, two months and two days living a life of deliberate simplicity and self-inflicted hardship in a one room cabin in the woods, of which he writes: 'I went to the woods because I wished to live deliberately, to front only the essential facts of life, and see if I could not learn what it had to teach, and not, when I came to die, discover that I had not lived.' [Thoreau, 'Where I Lived, and What I Lived For' in *Walden*, 1854]. Thoreau was, I think, trying to un-tell himself the Stories within which he had previously subsumed his identity: the Story of Thoreau the Harvard scholar and Concord schoolteacher, Thoreau the Man of Text, in favour of a new narrative: Thoreau the Transcendentalist thinker and insightful Liver of Life, prepared to suck the marrow from its bones and learn whatever lessons wild nature had to teach him. He was deliberately seeking a transformative encounter with the Other during a time and in a culture in which the value of otherness, whether racial or species (not to mention sex!), was denigrated and denied. Escaped Negro slaves were not criminals to Thoreau, and swimming kittens thrown into a river by an Irish cook were not automata: both had subjective lives and a fierce, wholly appropriate desire to hold on to them. The Story he wanted to learn how to tell is, I think, one in which the natural World *speaks*;

a Story within which, if one is brave enough to listen to it, one may hear other Stories by which to measure and comprehend the Self: the Story of God as extant, even self-identical, within all Things; the Story of Land half-wild, circumscribed by logger's path and Indian trail. I could be wrong, of course; but the version of Thoreau which I have made part of the Story of my Self is one of whom these things are true, and so, in a way, whether I am right or wrong is not important; I'm not Thoreau's biographer (and I'm not, of course, Thoreau).

In the steel and glass university building we call Commons, my second-year undergraduates and I study a short section of Thoreau's journal, which he kept religiously – *of course* – between 1837 and the end of his life in 1861. Three entries, three moments of profound insight, three sparkling days out of twenty-six years; republished in Joyce Carol Oates's anthology for writers, *Telling Stories* (1999): not nearly enough to get a clear sense of the overarching narrative of the writer's life, and yet perhaps enough to shine a tiny light on this question to which I think he was seeking an answer.

Why do we keep a journal? I ask my students. Why did Thoreau keep his?

The answers come back, sometimes in a trickle, sometimes (because cliches can hold Stories, too) in a flood: To remind himself of what he was doing that day. To keep a record of his memories. Because the moments he has chosen to record are, somehow, unusually important.

Is he trying to tell himself a Story? I suggest. To tell himself *a Story of himself?*

They're not sure. We're not sure. It's a difficult concept to grasp, when you've not previously encountered it, that the Self in which we live, not just the World which we construct on the page, could be somehow made up of a series of narratives, of characters and metaphors – and though I brush against the notion, I don't take the students anywhere near that far with it. Not today. It would be too large a step, too complex and challenging an idea to get across in an hour-long class on short story construction. But maybe Thoreau could be doing something like it, we conclude. Maybe, maybe, maybe.

Next week, I will show this class the tale of the Watermonster – in a narrative poem by Joy Harjo, the wonderful, contemporary, Mvskoke poet who knows all about Stories, both of the Self and of the World around her. [Harjo, 'The Flood', in *Telling Stories*, 1999] She knows, too, exactly why it *matters* that we should recognise that our perceptions and comprehensions work this way, and why we should embrace this concept of The-World-Being-Understood-by-Story rather than being somehow afraid of it. Because – yes! – we *are* afraid. The notion that we might not see what we think we see, that there might be a Wall who is really an actor who is really a metaphor for something deeper, that we cannot really comprehend the relationship between ourselves and what is real is an intimating one for anyone who has been brought up in the Western educational system. When we are children, we are taught the rational infallibility of oppositional categories: up / down, white / black, alive / dead, human / non-human, male / female, God / nature, fact / Story; and the notion that, in fact, we may be unquestioningly employing these categories and the structure in which they are maintained as foundational myths upon which we build our understanding of who we are and of how the world works is an unsettling one. We like to believe our understanding of reality is rational, not narrative; logical, not mythic. Even worse is the possibility that these myths may be, not only fictions of a sort, but in some cases downright harmful. It is painful to acknowledge that some of our most deeply cherished beliefs are built on deadly quicksand.

Harjo writes that she does not need history books to tell her who she is, or where she came from. She has the earth around her and the sun above her and the Stories she bears (and bares) in her bones and her blood to do that. The Mvskoke nation, it would seem, unlike the British, has not forgotten en masse that Story is where Knowledge is really at. Despite all the odds, Harjo has been able not only to retain, but to return to, that essential truth of storied experience and to honour its creative role within culture. She has held on to her people's Stories (and to those of a fair few others) and has mingled them with her own, so that in her song / narrative / poetry images of video games and aeroplanes appear side by side with those of musk-oxen and spirit-walkers. [Harjo, 'Spirit walking in the Tundra', in *Conflict Resolution for Holy Beings*, 2016] Through the poetry of Harjo and others, the constitutive Story of the Native Peoples of the Americas is being told and retold via language and via Self; old myths reconstructed for the modern age, new Stories written and told afresh to explain via that part of the brain and heart that lies beyond logic, beyond the reach of those who would displace the World and try to beat the Indian out of the child, that the real World is part of the Self, and the Stories of the Self an inherent and vital part of reality. The Sun is our brother. The Gods are real.

The Stories our culture has told itself over the past few hundred years – the Stories of progress, of colonial ambition, of human exceptionalism, to name but three – have not, it seems, been good for us. Yes, there was a time when this did not seem to be so; a time when the victims of the Story – the everywhere Aboriginals, the Africans transported in their tens of thousands from the Ivory Coast, the Jews, the non-human Peoples of supposedly lesser species too numerous to count – could be characterised as its antagonists. Othered by role – and seemingly by nature – their sufferings did not command much sympathy from the supposedly progressive agents of the United States, the British Empire, the oilfield and electricity companies. Progress was considered an unconditional good for the people on the right side of it – and it did not matter to those in power that the people on the other side – the un-humaned, the dispossessed – were suffering because of it. Progress, as a progressive ideal, had not caught up with itself. Perhaps it never will.

Now, of course, the holes in this particular Story are beginning to show through, and we can't ignore them any longer. Climate change, political insanity, over-consumption, pollution and ecological collapse were never supposed to be part of the glorious narrative; we did not write them into it in order to bring about some cruel twist of plot and fate that would knock our species, and many others with it, to its knees, begging for mercy from relentless Nemesis.

As individuals – as a People, as a Species, as a Planet, as a World – we all need new Stories to take us forward into the dark time that is coming. We need new Stories of the Self, and new Stories that reflect the relationship of that new Self to the new World which is, because of our Stories, the way that we have made it. We need Stories that speak of cooperators instead of heroes, listeners instead of leaders. We need Stories that show us women can be strong, and that men can be gentle; and that neither sex exists in opposition to the other, but simply represents a different way of being. We need Stories that explain to us that neither of these categories is necessarily fixed. We need Stories that teach us that the Other – whether because of nation, language, religion, or whatever have you – is both different from us and like us, and that both these circumstances are good. We need Stories that remind us that our species is far from alone in having cognition; that dogs can love, and that the wolves who prowl the darkness were never our enemies, but custodians of the greater ecosystem. We need Stories that warn us, in no uncertain terms, about the dangers of giving in to arrogance. We need new myths to speak to us of how we will win the battle (should it be conceived as a battle? Is 'battle', after all these years of bloody war, a helpful symbol to employ?) against the dying of the light, the meaningless destruction of the natural World within which we exist. Stories that reveal how we can reconnect our fragmented selves with meaning. We need Stories that show us how God – Spirit, Meaning, Life – is not distinct from material reality (which, remember, screams the Wall, we can't really know, either) but an indivisible part of it, and that the vital, transcendental force that so impressed Thoreau and which forms such a potent element of Harjo's World-view is something that should never be denied if we want to retain our humanness.

And it's up to us, as writers, both of fiction and non-fiction and everything in between, to craft these precious Stories. Up to us to take on the awareness of exactly what it is we do when we tell them, and not shirk or shiver from the task. We must tell them by hand and by mouth to those who long and need to hear them, without didacticism, without appeal to spurious logic or rationale. Yes, it's a big responsibility. Yes, a lot to take on board. Too much, probably, some people will say, for a motley gang of random wannabes who just want to tell stories. But as Harjo – and probably Thoreau – would agree, it's always been the Storyteller's inevitable and unenviable job to hold the tribe together, remind the people of who they are, and the Stories that they come from.

We had better get on with it.

Unfair Practice
(scenes from an unwritten campus novel)

GERARD WOODWARD

He was just passing the temple to Aphrodite (it wasn't dedicated to that particular deity but everyone called it that), when a dog appeared from round the corner of the path ahead of him. He recognised the dog immediately, a strange wire haired thing with legs that didn't seem to bend at the joints, so that it ran like a table would run, if it could. The dog was the dog of Professor Jim Stodmarsh, which meant that Professor Stodmarsh himself would shortly round the corner in the wake of his dog. The dog propelled itself towards Arnold, as though an invisible hand were pushing it along. As always, it looked eager and excited, but as soon as it reached Arnold, instead of leaping up and barking or wagging its tail, it just stood there, like a coffee table, puzzled by how it got to be where it was. The dog always seems excited by the idea of human company, but terribly disappointed by the reality.

In the few seconds available to Arnold before Professor Stodmarsh came into view, he made a very poor decision – he went and hid in the temple, concealing himself behind one of the limestone columns. The dog remained standing where it was, regarding Arnold with the faintest trace of puzzlement. Arnold silently urged it away with his hand, before remembering what Dr Tate had said about animals and gestures. You cannot point out something to a dog, it will only be interested in the hand that is pointing. Sure enough, the dog seemed fascinated by Arnold's gesturing hand, and stood there watching it.

Professor Stodmarsh would normally have walked straight past the temple without peering inside it, but not this morning. He did more than just peer inside. To Arnold's horror he entered the structure at the far end, which meant that Arnold had to flatten himself against his column and edge quietly around it, to remain hidden. The absurdity of the situation was painful – he felt like some desperado in a remake of *Zorba the Greek*, avoiding a skirmish in the ruins of the Acropolis. The two professors skirted around each other, the column between them, Arnold inching carefully aside as Professor Stodmarsh approached. A situation of excruciating awkwardness had developed.

'Arnold? Is that you? What on earth are you doing?'

Arnold let out the long breath he'd been holding.

'The same as you, I should think.'

'I'm walking my dog.'

'Yes, well I'm doing the same, minus the dog.'

Stodmarsh laughed. 'Perhaps you should get one, then you would have a valid reason to be hanging around in the temple at this unearthly hour. It's almost as if you're hiding.'

'Perhaps I'm worshipping.'

'Or more likely adding to the anthology of graffitied verses, have you read any of these – they're actually quite witty …'

They both for a moment read some of the scratched poetry, mostly parodies of the romantics dating back to the 1870s. It had become something of a tradition for students of successive generations to add their own versions of the poetry they had to study. There were lines from *The Waste Land* twisted with clumsy mockery; Seamus Heaney was there, author of 'Frigging'. As ever Arnold felt relief that students were even aware of these authors enough to parody them.

'Just because we are neighbours, Professor Proctor, doesn't mean we have to be neighbourly. If you want to borrow my wheelbarrow, I will tell you to go to hell, if you like. And I would expect you to do the same.'

'I don't need a wheelbarrow. If I want someone to clear the leaves off my lawn, all I have to do is log a job.'

'I see you can appreciate the advantages of living on a campus. But let's not keep things hidden that could otherwise be aired, it only leads to ever increasing pressure. I know you will never forgive me for what I said in that article, but as I've tried to say to you before, I may have disliked your poems, but that doesn't make me think any less of you as a person. It may shock you to know that I envy you your creative life, and how it continues to flourish. Little as I may care for the actual output.'

The two men smiled. The dog lifted its leg, then ate a dead mouse.

'Would you care to walk, or are you going to continue hiding?'

Sheepishly Arnold stepped out of the temple after Stodmarsh, and then had the awkward feeling that he was being walked, like the dog.

'Do you know, no one has ever drowned in the lake? Not in one hundred and fifty years. Yet they continue to desecrate the landscape with those ghastly life rings.'

'Perhaps they are the reason no one has drowned?' Arnold ventured.

Stodmarsh didn't reply, knowing that Arnold was being perverse in standing up for the life rings. The lake was nowhere more than three feet deep. And they had had conversations about the health and safety regulations that tended to view the beautiful landscaped grounds of the university as a kind of battlefield. No one had ever been killed by a branch falling off a tree but there were signs all over the campus warning of the danger, as though it was a distinct possibility:

BEWARE OF OLDER TREES LIKELY
TO SHED THEIR BRANCHES

Arnold had taken the trouble to look up the statistics, and discovered that each year, around three people are killed in the UK by falling trees in public places. That amounted to a risk factor of about one in twenty million. And in most cases, deaths by tree occurred during high winds or severe storms. Arnold had thought about mocking up his own notice to go alongside the official ones:

PLEASE DON'T WORRY ABOUT THE TREES. YOU HAVE FAR
MORE CHANCE OF BEING MURDERED BY A HUMAN. AND THAT'S
NOT VERY LIKELY EITHER.

By now Stodmarsh had moved on to discussing unfair practice ('The title of your next campus novel, I shouldn't wonder,' he quipped), and cosmology.

'Surely, if there are an infinite number of universes, it is inevitable that, in one of those universes (and why not this one?), all students will, by chance, write exactly the same essay, word for word.'

'In the world of contemporary poetry, that seems already to have happened,' said Arnold, wistfully.

Can We Talk About Monkeys?

AN INTERVIEW WITH EVIE WYLD

EDITOR'S NOTE *the following discussion took place on 20 April 2017, at Review Bookshop in Peckham.*

INTERVIEWER
What did you want to do when you were a child?

EVIE WYLD
I wanted to be David Attenborough, then I wanted to be a painter. I had this idea of being a painter as most people probably have as a writer that money appears and you just sit in your studio pondering, but the reality of course is that money doesn't appear that much and it's quite a lot of hard work which I find to be really a good thing. Why should you, just because you're doing the thing you want to do, get a bucketload of money for it? It's an incredibly selfish profession. If you get loads of money out of it, that's great. But, at the end of the day, I'm not writing the books for other people. I don't write for a readership. I write for myself and the fact that there appears to be some value in that is lovely but it is a selfish thing I'm producing. I'm just navel-gazing for three or four years at a time.

Are there any skills you've taken from painting and drawing and applied to writing?

Well, I write in a very visual way. I often write from photographs and actually one of the modules I took at Bath Spa – I think it was Creative Arts, which was lovely – the instructor just said at the start, come back at the end and show us what you've done. I spent most of my time in the darkroom of a photography studio for that. It felt really incredible and felt like storytelling, seeing the images appear and seeing how you could make a photograph you'd taken of your nineteen-year-old boyfriend look like something from the 1950s. There was something about photography that was really like storytelling. Also I got that kind of hit of being on my own in the dark which was always really good. Even now if I get stuck on a thread, I do a little collage like a toddler! In my first book, I did a collage of Billy Graham, the evangelist preacher, and the collage is a useless thing, but the act of sitting down and meditating with those images that seemed to unlock something for me.

Can I ask about childhood and your thoughts on the artist's connection to childhood? This seems to come up a lot, and the collage technique reminds me of my own youth. Even as a teenager I found it incredibly helpful to make those things.

Yeah, it's like collecting stuff. When you tear a page out of a magazine, you don't really know what you're going to do with it, you never look at it again really. I keep a lot of notebooks, that I never open again, but somehow by giving them the space and the kind of importance that you've kept them, they go in part of your brain and come out three years later as something else. When I have opened a notebook to see what I was going on about, it's nonsense like a vivid description of a prawn or something. Not much point to it, but it is squirrelled away in your brain somewhere if you write it down or stick it to something and you realise it is an important object, phrase or moment.

People who make creative work ... do they retain a stronger connection to childhood?

I think childhood is so important. If you think back to being eleven, you're still exactly the same person and same human being – at eleven, you know much less, but you are the same person. Of course you look back and hate yourself for how embarrassing you were. I still find it difficult to differentiate between my nine-year-old self and my thirty-seven-year-old self. It's quite weird but I think that when you are young you are more open to stuff because you know a lot less and people assume a lot less of you when you are young so behave very differently around you and assume you don't understand things they're talking out. At that age we still have an ability to be shocked by what we see. But for instance with all we have seen over past four years, I think you will agree it's quite difficult to show someone an image that will haunt them as we've now seen everything. As a child, something like a photo of a shark can stay with you for five or six years and can work its way into your dreams and nightmares. I really hold on to nightmares and recurring dreams I had as a child. I try not to use dreams in my writing as they're mostly a pile of nonsense, but the atmosphere from them is something so uncanny and useful in creative work.

The type of sense of dread you have in childhood nightmares you probably never have again.

Even if you get terribly frightened by something uncanny as an adult, your rational brain kicks in. If it is a ghost, then everything I know is wrong and what can it do anyway? Or it's a person, or it's a figment of my imagination and you can sculpt reason out of it. When you're a child it's more like that thing is going to get me and chase me down. Like an elderly relative. I've recently got into podcasts, and I listened to this podcast which has been going more than ten years called Anything Ghost. It's this guy in America who started collecting people's ghost stories. Some of them he reads out and some people send in. One guy told an amazing story about the dreams he used to have as a child and there was this Baba Yaga figure who used to stalk him in his dreams. But, because he was a child, when she found him, all she would do is tickle him. As he grew up, things got worse and worse, but the feeling of dread didn't change. I find that so interesting.

Are you drawn to images that haunt a reader?

Absolutely! I'm fascinated by ghosts. I'm an atheist but I do believe that people see ghosts. I don't think they are images of the dead, I think it's even more disturbing than that. I'm interested in what it is that haunts individual people. The best ghost stories are not the sculpted, proper stories. It's the ones which are a flash of the uncanny. Not a story about relatives, but like there's an old man in the corner facing the wall, and then he's gone. Not having closure or a reason is much more interesting. Craft it too much and people will try to interpret it as a warning like someone's trying to frighten me away from changing my house or something.

You are drawn to the difficult?

Well, think about horror movies and how they make us frightened. It's a much harder ask to do that in a book with only words at your disposal, and you can only rely on the reader to imagine something and take what you want from the words you have written. The next thing I'm hoping to do is to write a truly frightening graphic novel. And how do you do that? The element of surprise is in turning the page, and there's not much more to hide behind. I don't know why I write about difficult, hard stuff other than that a novel about nice things isn't a novel. Quite often I'd get people in the bookshop I used to work in asking for a nice book for a friend who is ill without sadness or grief of death and I don't know what that is. It's a really strange thing that most novelists write about really difficult stuff to understand people and the darkest bits of people and surviving being human.

Would you be a reader of your own writing?

I guess you write books you want to read. I always end writing with a feeling of deep disappointment that that's not what I meant and start books with a feeling that this time I'm going to write the thing I really want to say but I don't know what that is. So, I have re-read my first book because I had to do a radio interview about it, and I couldn't remember it, so I listened to it on tape and I found it excruciating. Partly because I've changed as a writer a lot and partly because having your words read to you and you didn't realise how rude it was, in a male voice as well. I do like reading books about paranormal stuff: that's my bag.

Can we talk a little about the bookshop?

The bookshop is called Review and it's in Peckham. We've been open for twelve years now. It was started by Ros Simpson, an Australian who has since moved to Ireland. She opened this bookshop at the end of my road, and I wandered in and asked if she had any work going. I'm sure I was completely useless and had no customer service skills, but we got on really well. I wrote most of my first book at the counter there. This was before Peckham had become so trendy so it was very quiet. It's a curated bookshop, really. We're very small. Now Ros lives in Ireland and she comes back once a month. Our manager is a wonderful woman called Kathia. We all bring different areas of interest. Ros leads on architecture, I'm literature, and Kathia is better than any human on earth; she's good at everything and is fiercely interested in being a bookseller. Every book in there is a book we can stand behind and say you should read this because. There isn't any fluff.

Is there any relationship between your writing and working there?

It's a weird thing that I get asked a lot. It's actually worked the other way round. Being a writer has affected how I sell books. Think of being a butcher: if you butcher a pig, you're not just going to wrap it in plastic and put it in the window. It matters a great deal that the right person gets the right book. And also it matters that we don't discount books. We have a sale now and then but that's it: because literature should have a price that's worthy of the work that goes in the amount of entertainment you get. Sadly, we can't absorb through our skin the words on the shelf.

Can we talk about the graphic novel? We also haven't talked about the fact that when you were younger you divided your time between two different countries which seems important to your creativity. So let's talk about the graphic novel first, the one you wrote after All The Birds Singing.

Well, actually it was written alongside *All The Birds Singing*. We started it actually just after my first novel was published. It took seven years to complete. It's quite a slim book so seems a bit ludicrous that it took so long but we were both doing other things and we'd never done it before there was a lot of trial and error, and editing pictures is quite time consuming. Joe Sumner is one of my best friends from Bath Spa; he did the Fine Art degree there. We've been close friends since our time at Bath Spa and have collaborated on a couple of things. He once illustrated a short story I wrote called *Monkey House*. We always got so far with something and went to something else. Joe is a model maker by day and he was badgering me for something to illustrate. I gave him some memoir stuff I'd been working on. I live in Peckham and my mother is Australian so we go back frequently – at least once every two years. As a kid, I felt really Australian partly because I sided with my mother's feeling of homesickness. My father was incredibly British. An art dealer, he liked fine wines and conversation and refined things and my mother like swimming underwater with a dagger on her belt. Very different people in a lot of ways. My father didn't fit in Australia. There wasn't a way of us living there together so we lived here. It's really interesting. The way I've written my first book, second book, third book, about relatives in Australia, and now the book I'm working on now is based in England, so I don't know if I've written myself out of Australia, or what that's about. It always was my place to go to, my creative start. I remember one class at Bath with Philip Gross. He gave us an exercise to imagine ourselves somewhere and use all our senses so I imagined I was on my grandparents' veranda, and it's still the place I go to: it's always been an incredibly potent place for me. I also promised myself that I would do a book primarily about sharks as a lot of my books have sharks in them. It's about me as a seven-year-old being in Australia with my father who isn't comfortable there, and about a shark survivor – famous in Australia – called Rodney Fox. He was disemboweled by a great white whilst he was spear fishing and he's now an amazing eco-warrior, in his seventies. He takes school children out to meet great whites and works on conservation and all that good stuff. And whilst I was writing *Everything is Teeth*, it was a long process, I gave Joe some work and we'd meet up and it became a conversation about images and writing. A lot of time passed and a lot of things happened. During that book my father became very ill and died. Towards the end of writing, the end of the book, looking back at everything I had written and Joe had drawn, it showed itself to be all about my father. A reviewer kindly called it a love letter to my father. It's quite weird in all of that being about Australia and sharks, it ended up being about my very English father.

Do you daydream about Australia?

Absolutely, day and night dreams, I'd be on the veranda, butcher birds and cicadas, I could smell it, every time we passed a gum tree, I'd crunch up the leaves and it would transport me there. There's a gum tree in Dulwich park and every time I walk past it, I remember. None of it is the same as when I was a kid. My best friend from South London, Lucy, I took her out there to meet my family when we were eighteen and she stayed. She married my cousin and had his babies, which is amazing and means there's still some link, but now they live in my Grandma's house. It's very peculiar. My family are sugar cane farmers so my aunty and uncle live next door. In a way she took over the role I wanted to have on the farm but obviously I couldn't have it, because I didn't want to marry my cousin. But it's just really interesting and now I'm incredibly relieved that I didn't marry my cousin for many reasons but it's strange to still have this link and to go back and see how different it is to how I imagine it when I write. I don't know if it's to do with the people or the landscape or just growing up.

That's a great story!

I'm fine about it! It was very funny. I genuinely didn't believe her when she said she wasn't getting on the Greyhound with me.

Did it really happen that quickly?

Yeah, yeah. She was doing her degree at Goldsmiths College in Anthropology – a really smart woman, and she had a boyfriend back here and everything, but my cousin drove up with his four-wheeler with a gun slung over his shoulder and asked, 'Do any of you girls want to go hunting?' And soon they were absolutely in love with each other. He had a girlfriend he was living with in town. It's weird.

On fear in comic books: there is one bit, some Neil Gaiman bits, a subplot about two dead school boys in the final book when hell is closed and I still find it scary. I have a low threshold for that kind of thing.

I think it's a wonderful thing to have a low threshold for horror. My mum and brother have a low threshold for anything, thrillers, horror movies, they can't go near it. I've saturated myself and it's hard to find anything that actually does it for me.

But you do have a fear of monkeys and sharks.

Yes, well the shark thing was a fear, but now it's a healthy respect. I still don't want to get in the water with one, but – like a lot of English people – I had a fear that that sharks would swim up through the plughole of the swimming pool and I'm sure it's to do with *Jaws*. Sharks used to scare me so much that if I was in a boat, or an aeroplane even, I wasn't scared we'd crash and die, I was scared we'd crash land in the ocean and sharks would be waiting. It was the Indianapolis Speech from *Jaws*, basically – which I had read at my wedding. With time, it became more of a fascination with sharks. Monkeys still shit me though.

Can we talk about monkeys?

I think it's because they're so human. Chimps in particular. They're so close to us and they look like us. I find dolls creepy too. I never had a doll as a child.

Why would you want a human looking at you like that? They're like humans but seven times stronger and there'll tear your arsehole off you. They're just disgusting. Don't get me started! I watched a film about some scientists who bred a chimp with human and the baby was kept at the lab and they were going to dissect it. And two of the scientists set it free and the thing just bludgeoned people in the English countryside to death.

That could happen?

Yes, that could happen.

Notes on Contributors

NAOMI ALDERMAN is a novelist, videogame designer and broadcaster. Her novels include *Disobedience*, *The Liars' Gospel*, and *The Power*. She has won the Orange Award for New Writers and the *Sunday Times* Young Writer of the Year Award. She was selected for *Granta*'s Best of Young British Novelists in 2013 and was mentored by Margaret Atwood under the Rolex mentor and protégé initiative. She presents Science Stories on BBC Radio 4 and is the co-creator and lead writer of the bestselling smartphone audio adventure app *Zombies, Run!*. In 2017 she won the Bailey's Prize for Fiction for *The Power*.

DAVID ALMOND is the author of *Skellig*, *The Tightrope Walkers*, *A Song for Ella Grey*, *The Tale of Angelino Brown*, and many other novels, stories, picture books, opera librettos, and plays. His work is translated into 40 languages. His major awards include The Carnegie Medal, two Whitbread Awards, The Michael L Printz Award (USA), Le Prix Sorcières (France) and the Guardian Children's Fiction Prize. In 2010 he won the Hans Christian Andersen Award, the world's most prestigious prize for children's authors. He is Professor of Creative Writing.

JANINE AMOS is a children's author and literacy consultant. She writes for a variety of age ranges and in a variety of forms: picture books, series books for 5-7s, and fiction and non-fiction for 8-12s through to teens. She is a Senior Lecturer in Writing for Young People and leads the MA module in Contemporary Publishing for young people's writers at Bath Spa University. Janine is currently writing four picture books to commission, on the themes of self-expression, problem-solving, diversity, and exploring the imagination through play.

MIRANDA BARNES is a poet originally from the US, now resident in the UK. She completed her PhD in Creative Writing at Bath Spa University in 2017, which examines how poetry functions as dialogue between science and spirituality. Miranda has presented on her research at the BRLSI in Bath and the NAWE Conference. She performed experimental work on The Southwest Poetry Tour in late 2016. Her current collection, *Twelve Foundation Stones of the New Heaven*, is seeking a publisher. Her poems appear in journals in the UK and abroad. Miranda teaches Poetry and other genres at Bath Spa University.

SUSAN BEALE wrote the first draft of her Costa-Award shortlisted first novel, *The Good Guy*, while on the MA course at Bath Spa. She also co-edited the course's 2012–2013 anthology, *A Cache*. Her work has appeared in various online and print publications, including *Belle Ombre*, *Empty Sink Publishing*, and *Good Housekeeping*. A native of Cape Cod, Susan has lived most of her adult life in Europe, primarily in Brussels. She now resides in Wells with her husband and four sons.

RACHEL BENTHAM is a poet and short story writer and has written many dramas for BBC Radio 4, including *Hanging Around*, *On the Rob* and *Dolly Shepherd; Edwardian Parachute Queen*. Her poetry collections include *Let All Tongues Flower* and a haiku collection, *Trust*. She also works with businesses and NGOs on improving their writing skills, and has been a Royal Literary Fellow in five leading UK universities. She is currently editing an anthology of poetry in which women speak of themselves – *Project Boast*. She lectures in Creative Writing for Bath Spa University and University of Bristol.

GAVIN JAMES BOWER is the author of two novels and one non-fiction work, and has contributed as a journalist to the *Guardian*, the *Independent* and *Independent on Sunday*, and the *Sunday Telegraph*. He joined the writing team for *EastEnders* in 2014. He currently lectures in Creative Writing at Bath Spa University.

CELIA BRAYFIELD is an author, journalist, and cultural commentator. Her nine novels range from contemporary social comedy to international genre bestsellers while her non-fiction books include a study of celebrity culture, travel writing, and a companion to historical fiction. She has judged national literary awards and served on the management committee of the Society of Authors. As a journalist she has mostly contributed to *The Times* and the *Evening Standard*. A Senior Fellow of the Higher Education Academy, she has also chaired the Higher Education Committee of the National Association of Writers in Education.

JESS BUTTERWORTH was born in London and grew up between Bath and the Himalayas in India. She completed a Creative Writing BA (Hons) at Bath Spa University, where she won the 2011 Writing for Young People Prize. She then graduated from the Bath Spa MA in Writing for Young People in 2015. *Running on the Roof of the World* is her debut adventure novel for 9–12 year olds, published by Orion Children's Books. *When the Mountains Roared* will be published in April 2017.

LUCY CHRISTOPHER was born in Wales but grew up in Australia, living in Melbourne from the age of nine until she completed her undergraduate degree at Melbourne University. Later she moved back to the UK to earn a Creative Writing MA (with distinction) from Bath Spa University, then a PhD to explore the ways that Australian literature represents wild places, particularly in its writing for young adults. Lucy's debut novel, *Stolen*, was written as part of this PhD. She has published three novels and is soon to publish a fourth, and is a Senior Lecturer at Bath Spa University.

STEPHEN CONNOLLY graduated with an MA in Scriptwriting for Film, Theatre, Radio, and TV in 2014. His scripts have had readings and performances in Bristol, London, Salisbury, Brighton, and Gloucester, his monologues and fiction have been performed at both the Stroud and Bath Fringes. He has published a collection of short stories, *Remember My Name and Other Stories*. He is currently writing and recording drama for local radio.

SIÂN MELANGELL DAFYDD is an author, poet and translator. Her first published novel, *Y Trydydd Peth* (*The Third Thing*; Gomer, 2009), won the coveted 2009 National Eisteddfod Literature Medal. She writes in both Welsh and English and often collaborates with artists of other disciplines. She was the co-editor of the literary review *Taliesin* and *Y Neuadd* online literary magazine for six years. Her second Welsh language novel and a collection of hybrid literature, *Spitting Distance*, are forthcoming. She works with authors and poets internationally to translate literature between minority languages and is undertaking research in yoga and writing as parallel practices. She works as a lecturer in Creative Writing at the American University of Paris, France and is course leader of the MRes in Transnational Writing at Bath Spa University, England.

JAMES DAVEY graduated from Bath Spa University in 2011 with an MA in Creative Writing. His poetry has appeared in journals including *Poetry*

Wales, *New Welsh Reader*, *Stand*, *Ambit*, *The Warwick Review*, and *New Walk*. Between 2012 and 2015, James spent three years working in Catania, Sicily, as an English-language teacher. He now teaches Poetry and Flash Fiction at Bath Spa.

KELLY ANNE DORAN (*Novel in 25 Words*) is a writer and actor based in Southern California. She is a graduate of the University of California, Irvine, where she co-created a documentary style play, *Piece of Mind*, that explored mental health and mental illness. Her poetry has been featured in *San Diego Poetry Annual 2017* and *Quail Bell* magazine.

SARAH DRIVER was born on the Sussex coast and started writing as a small child. She graduated from the Bath Spa MA in Writing for Young People in 2015, after winning the 2014 United Agents prize for 'most promising writer'. She is also a qualified nurse and midwife. Her debut novel, *The Huntress: Sea*, was her MA project and is the first in a fantasy-adventure trilogy for 8–12s published by Egmont. In March 2017 *Sea* was selected for Waterstones' children's book of the month, before official publication in April. *The Huntress: Sky* will be published in September 2017.

COLIN EDWARDS taught both English and Creative Writing for over 30 years at Bath Spa, including (for 23 years) the MA 'Context' modules, Suspense Fiction and Modernism & Postmodernism. Colin has been an actor, and director, in much student drama (and film) across those years. He continues to write, and publish, critical articles on Modernists (especially Ford Madox Ford), as well as some poetry.

LUCY ENGLISH has three novels published by Fourth Estate: *Selfish People* (1998), *Children of Light* (1999), and *Our Dancing Days* (2001). She is a spoken word poet and has appeared at many literature festivals in the UK and beyond. Her collection of poetry *Prayer to Imperfection* was published by Burning Eye in 2014. She is currently creating an online poetry film project *The Book of Hours*. Films from this project have been screened in Canada, Spain, Portugal, Australia, and Germany. She is Reader in Creative Writing at BSU.

CARRIE ETTER has published three collections of poetry: *The Tethers* (Seren, 2009), winner of the London New Poetry Prize; *Divining for Starters* (Shearsman, 2011); and *Imagined Sons* (Seren, 2014), shortlisted for the Ted Hughes Award for New Work in Poetry by The Poetry Society. She also edited *Infinite Difference:*

Other Poetries by UK Women Poets (Shearsman, 2010) and Linda Lamus's posthumous collection, *A Crater the Size of Calcutta* (Mulfran, 2015). She is a Reader in Creative Writing and has taught at Bath Spa since 2004.

NATHAN FILER is the author of *The Shock of the Fall* (2013). This won numerous major awards including The Costa Book of the Year and The National Book Award for Popular Fiction. It was a *Sunday Times* bestseller and has been translated into thirty languages. He has written essays and articles for numerous publications including, the *Guardian* and the *New York Times*. In 2017 he wrote and presented an *Archive on 4* documentary for BBC Radio 4, exploring the role of the media in shaping public perceptions of mental illness. His poetry has been broadcast on BBC Radio 4's *Bespoken Word* and *Wondermentalist Cabaret* and BBC Radio 7's *Poetry Stand-up*. His short film *Oedipus* won the 2005 BBC Best New Filmmaker Award and Berlin's Zebra Poetry Film Award. His current projects include a BFI funded screenplay. He is a Reader in Creative Writing at Bath Spa University.

KYLIE FITZPATRICK has worked as a script editor in the UK, the US, and Australia after training at the Australian Film, Television and Radio school, and for the BBC and the Australian Broadcasting Commission. She is the author of four historical novels that have, between them, been published in eleven languages. Kylie is a mentor and manuscript editor for Cornerstones literary consultancy and Writer's & Artists literary consultancy at Bloomsbury publishing and a lecturer and tutor on the Creative Writing degree and MA courses at Bath Spa University, from which she received both her MA and PhD in Creative Writing.

RICHARD FRANCIS has published eleven novels, the two most recent being *The Old Spring*, which was voted Best Foreign Novel of 2011 by the Chinese Association for Foreign Literature; and *Crane Pond*, which was longlisted for this year's Walter Scott Prize for Historical Fiction. He has also written biographies and other non-fiction in the field of American social, religious, and intellectual history. He was Professor of Creative Writing at Bath Spa from 1999–2009.

CLARE GALLAGHER (*Novel in 25 Words*) is a primary school teacher from Derry, Northern Ireland. She completed a Master's degree in Creative Writing at Bath Spa University in 2015 / 16. During the MA, she wrote both poetry and fiction and her novel-in-progress was shortlisted for the Janklow & Nesbit

Prize. She received an award from Arts Council NI to assist in the completion of her debut novel.

SALLY GANDER graduated from Bath Spa in 2006 with an MA in Creative Writing and began teaching soon after. She writes novels, creative non-fiction and short stories, and is the author of the *The Big Deep*. *The Staymaker* is her novel-in-progress.

SAM GAYTON is the author of four novels with Andersen Press, and several plays with Dumbshow Theatre. He graduated from Bath Spa's MA Writing for Young People in 2009. He has been shortlisted for the UKLA award and nominated for the Carnegie medal.

MAGGIE GEE, OBE has published fourteen books, including *The Ice People*, *My Cleaner*, *The White Family*, *My Animal Life*, and *Virginia Woolf in Manhattan* (2014). In 2012 an international conference about her writing was held at St Andrew's University. Her most recent publication is a 9,000-word short story in *Protest* (2017), and she is currently writing another commissioned story in the form of twenty-one sonnets. She has represented writers' rights for the Society of Authors, PLR, and ALCS; and was the first female Chair of Council of the Royal Society of Literature, of which she is now a Vice-President.

EMMA GEEN is a PhD student at Bath Spa and the author of *The Many Selves of Katherine North* (Bloomsbury).

GIANCARLO GEMIN is the author of two novels. *Cowgirl* (Nosy Crow) Won the Tir na n-Og Award 2015 and was shortlisted for the Waterstones Prize, the Branford Boase award, and the UKLA award. It was adapted as a play by Oxford University Press. *Sweet Pizza* (Nosy Crow) won the Tir na n-Og Award 2017 and was longlisted for the *Guardian* Children's Fiction Prize 2016 and shortlisted for the Little Rebels Award 2017.

ELIANE GLASER is a senior lecturer at Bath Spa University, and a BBC radio producer and broadcaster. Her books include *Get Real: How to See Through the Hype, Spin and Lies of Modern Life* (Fourth Estate, 2013), which is about how political and financial elites legitimise themselves by co-opting 'ordinary people', authenticity, and progressive ideals. She writes opinion pieces for the *Guardian*, the *New Statesman*, and the *Independent*, among other places. She is completing a book about what's happened to politics.

JULIA GREEN has published sixteen novels including *Blue Moon* (Puffin), *Breathing Underwater*, *Drawing with Light*, *This Northern Sky* (Bloomsbury) and many short stories for young people. *The Wilderness War* (Oxford University Press) is currently shortlisted for four awards. She completed her PhD by Publication in 2015. Julia is Course Director for the MA Writing for Young People which has launched the careers of more than 30 alumni and has an international reputation for excellence.

PHILIP GROSS taught at Bath College of Higher Education / Bath Spa University College from the early days of the MA in Creative Writing until 2004, then until 2017 was Professor of Creative Writing at the University of South Wales. The sestina published here is by way of a valedictory address. Philip is the author of some twenty collections of poetry, for adults and young people, as well as radio stories, plays, and fiction for young adults. His earlier poetry up to *The Wasting Game* (shortlisted for the Whitbread Prize) is collected in *Changes of Address* (2001). Since then Bloodaxe have published seven collections including *The Water Table* (winner of the TS Eliot Prize) and most recently *A Bright Acoustic* (2017). Poetry / art collaborations *I Spy Pinhole Eye*, *The Abstract Garden* and *A Fold in the River* have appeared from Cinnamon, Old Stile Press, and Seren, respectively.

TESSA HADLEY is a graduate of the Bath Spa MA in Creative Writing. She has written six novels and three collections of short stories; her novel *The Past* won the Hawthornden Prize; *Bad Dreams and other stories* came out in 2017. She publishes short stories regularly in the *New Yorker*, reviews for the *Guardian*, and the *London Review of Books*, and was awarded a Windham Campbell Prize for Fiction in 2016.

SABRIN HASBUN is an Italian-Palestinian travel writer and blogger. Italy and Palestine are her two countries and form the focus of her writing, but in the last few years she has lived in France, Japan, and the UK, and has studied at the University of Pisa, the Sorbonne University of Paris, and Bath Spa University, where she completed her Masters and will start her PhD in October 2017. Her works have been published in several international magazines and can be found on her website www.sabrinisnothere.com

MATT HAW graduated in 2012 with an MA in Creative Writing from Bath Spa University. Since then he has published a pamphlet of poetry titled *Saint-Paul-de-Mausole* with tall-lighthouse press, penned a libretto for a piece of choral music to mark Benjamin Britten's centenary, and directed a feature length film-poem titled *Boudica* which is scheduled to appear sometime next year. He received an Eric Gregory Award in 2013 and recently completed a PhD at Lancaster University researching the relationship between poetry and film.

JULIE HAYMAN began teaching at Bath Spa University in 2002 and has also been Writer in Residence at a grammar school. Her short stories have appeared in anthologies, magazines, and on radio.

PHILIP HENSHER is the author of ten novels, including *Kitchen Venom*, *The Mulberry Empire*, *The Northern Clemency*, *Scenes from Early Life*, and *The Emperor Waltz*. His novels have won the Somerset Maugham Award and the Ondaatje Prize, and been shortlisted for the Man Booker Prize and the Commonwealth Prize, among others. His opera libretto for Thomas Ades, *Powder Her Face*, has been performed in dozens of productions worldwide. He was a Granta Best of Young British Novelist in 2003, and a Fellow of the Royal Society of Literature from 1999. He is a Professor of Creative Writing at Bath Spa University and lives in London and Geneva.

TANIA HERSHMAN's debut poetry collection, *Terms & Conditions*, is published by Nine Arches Press and her third short story collection, *Some Of Us Glow More Than Others*, by Unthank Books. Tania is also the author of a poetry chapbook, and two short story collections, and co-author of *Writing Short Stories: A Writers' & Artists' Companion* (Bloomsbury, 2014). Tania is curator of ShortStops (www.shortstops.info), celebrating short story activity across the UK & Ireland. www.taniahershman.com

JASON HEWITT's debut novel, *The Dynamite Room* (2014), was longlisted for the Desmond Elliot Prize and the Authors' Club Best First Novel Award, and shortlisted for the New Angle Prize for Literature. His second novel, *Devastation Road* (2015), was longlisted for the Walter Scott Prize for Historical Fiction. His first play, *Claustrophobia*, premiered at Edinburgh Fringe before transferring to the Hope Theatre in London. He completed his MA in Creative Writing at Bath Spa in 2005 and following a career in publishing is now Lecturer on the Publishing degree and regularly runs Creative Writing workshops at the British Library.

BEATRICE HITCHMAN is a PhD student in Creative Writing at Bath Spa. Her first novel, *Petite Mort*, was published in 2013 by Serpent's Tail, longlisted for the HWA Debut Dagger, the Desmond Elliott Prize and the Author's Club Best First Novel Prize. It was adapted as a Radio 4 *Woman's Hour Drama* serial.

ALYSSA HOLLINGSWORTH was born in small-town Milton, Florida, but life as a roving military kid soon mellowed her (unintelligibly strong) Southern accent. Wanderlust is in her blood, and she's always waiting for the wind to change. Stories remain her constant. Alyssa's debut, *The Eleventh Trade*, will launch fall 2018 with Macmillan (US) and HotKey (UK). She received her Writing for Young People MA in 2014.

STEVE HOLLYMAN is Programme Coordinator and Senior Lecturer in Creative Writing at Bath Spa University. His first novel, *Keeping Britain Tidy*, was published in 2010. He gained his PhD in 2013 and has contributed to the *Journal of Literature and Trauma Studies*, the *Routledge Companion to Critical and Cultural Theory, Convergence*, and *Brand Literary Magazine*. He is currently working on his second novel.

JEREMY HOOKER was the first Director of the MA in Creative Writing. His many books include *The Cut of the Light: Poems 1965–2005* and *Diary of a Stroke*. His *Ditch Vision:: Essays on Poetry, Nature, and Place* is forthcoming from Awen Press. He is Emeritus Professor of the University of South Wales, and Fellow of the Learned Society of Wales. His awards include a Cholmondeley Award for poetry.

MICHAEL HUNT (*Novel in 25 Words*) is an IT consultant for book distributors and publishers in the UK, Europe and the USA. A lifetime of exposure to the written word has spurred his desire to move from back-office system designer and implementer to aspiring author. He spends his spare time seeking the services of a literary agent with an appropriately themed list for his two, as yet unpublished, sci-fi novels.

CLAIRE KENDAL is a novelist and Plath scholar with expertise in the literary thriller. *The Book of You* was published in 2014 and has been translated into more than twenty languages. It was a *Sunday Times* bestseller and a Richard & Judy Book Club pick. *The Second Sister* was published in 2017. Claire began her career at Bath Spa teaching English Literature but now concentrates on working with doctoral students in Creative Writing. She will be writing two new novels for HarperCollins.

RICHARD KERRIDGE leads the MA in Creative Writing as Course Director, and co-ordinates Research and Graduate Studies in that subject. He is a nature writer and ecocritic. *Cold Blood: Adventures with Reptiles and Amphibians*, (Chatto & Windus, 2014) his nature writing memoir, was adapted for BBC national radio and broadcast as a Radio 4 Book of the Week in July 2014. Other nature writing by Richard has been broadcast on BBC Radio 4 and published in *BBC Wildlife*, *Poetry Review*, and *Granta*. He was awarded the 2012 Roger Deakin Prize by the Society of Authors, and has twice received the *BBC Wildlife* Award for Nature Writing. A leading ecocritic, he has published essays on ecocritical topics ranging from Shakespeare and Thomas Hardy to present-day fiction, poetry, nature writing, and film. He reviews new nature writing for the *Guardian*. Collaborative works include *Nearly Too Much: The Poetry of J. H. Prynne* (Liverpool UP, 1995), *Writing the Environment* (Zed Books, 1998), the first collection of ecocritical essays to be published in Britain, and *The Face of the Earth: Natural Landscapes, Science and Culture* (University of California Press, 2011). He has been an elected member of the ASLE Executive Council, and was founding Chair of ASLE-UKI. Richard is co-editor of the Bloomsbury Academic series entitled 'Environmental Cultures' – the first series of monographs in the Environmental Humanities to be published in Britain – and is on the steering committee of *New Networks for Nature*.

TIM LIARDET is a poet and critic. Twice shortlisted for the T.S. Eliot Prize, for *The World Before Snow* (Carcanet) in 2015 and *The Blood Choir* (Seren) in 2006, Tim Liardet has produced ten collections of poetry to date. He has also been longlisted for the Whitbread Poetry Prize, and has received several Poetry Book Society Recommendations, a Poetry Book Society Pamphlet Choice, an Arts Council England Writer's Award, a Society of Authors Award, a Hawthornden fellowship, two Pushcart nominations, and various other awards. *Arcimboldo's Bulldog: New and Selected Poems* is due from Carcanet. He is currently a Poetry Book Society selector and Professor of Poetry at Bath Spa University.

STEVE MAY has won awards for drama, poetry, and fiction, and has written more than 50 plays for BBC radio, including the *Higher* series (set in a struggling university). He was Head of Department, Creative Writing from 2008 to 2013.

BRITTANY MCCOMAS made her scriptwriting debut on the Royal Television Society Award winning comedy series *Liquid Soap*. She went on to script develop with the Full Tilt Theatre Company in London, and has served as an editor for the BBC. She has also written live sketch comedy as a main-stage writer for Second City, Hollywood. Her debut film, *Dr. Sugarloaf*, world premiered at the 69th Cannes Film Festival and has recently been signed for global distribution with Shorts International. While her feature film, *American Fango*, has received international acclaim as a multi-award winning film including Best Picture and Best Screenplay.

SUSAN MCMILLAN is Head of Field: Writing, Film and Digital Creativity at Bath Spa University. This field includes Creative Writing, Creative Computing, Film and Television, Media Communications, and Publishing. She holds an MA and PhD in Creative Writing from Bath Spa University, and is also an award-winning TV producer and writer with more than twenty years' experience in the industry.

PAUL MEYER is Subject Leader of Creative Writing.

STEPHEN MOSS is a naturalist, writer, and broadcaster specialising in British birds and wildlife. The first series producer of the BAFTA-award-winning TV series *Springwatch*, he has written more than 30 books, including *Wild Kingdom*, *Wild Hares and Hummingbirds*, and *Mrs Moreau's Warbler: How Birds Got Their Names*, to be published by Faber in spring 2018. He lives in Somerset, where he is President of the Somerset Wildlife Trust. He is the course leader on the MA in Travel and Nature Writing.

ROBIN MUKHERJEE has contributed extensively to television drama, both returning series and serials. He has also written for film, theatre, and radio. His first feature film, *Dance of the Wind*, premiered at Venice and won the Audience Prize at the London Film Festival. His most recent feature, *Lore*, has won numerous awards worldwide. His three part serial for CBBC, *Combat Kids*, was nominated for a BAFTA.

JOANNA NADIN has published more than seventy books for children and young adults; her latest is *The Incredible Billy Wild* (Little, Brown, 2017). Her first adult novel, *The Queen of Bloody Everything*, will be published by Macmillan in 2018. She completed her PhD on multiple self in the young adult novel in 2016.

ANTHONY NANSON is the author of the novel *Deep Time* and the story collections *Exotic Excursions*, award-winning *Gloucestershire Folk Tales*, and *Gloucestershire Ghost Tales* (co-author). He has worked widely as a storyteller, co-producing such ecobardic epics as *Arthur's Dream, Robin of the Wildwood*, and *Return to Arcadia*. His pioneering ecocritical work on storytelling practice includes *Storytelling and Ecology*, award-winning *Words of Re-enchantment*, and *Storytelling for a Greener World* (co-editor). He has lectured in Creative Writing at Bath Spa University since 2001, serves on the editorial board of *Logos*, and is the publisher of Awen Publications.

KATE PULLINGER has published ten novels, two collections of short stories, and a number of works for digital media, including the novel *The Mistress of Nothing* which won Canada's Governor General Award, and the digital war memorial *Letter to an Unknown Soldier*. Her novel for smartphones, *Jellybone*, is forthcoming in 2017, and the novel *Peg and Art* will be published by Doubleday in 2018.

JOE ROBERTS was born in Bath, where he still lives with his wife and three sons. Since the publication of his first book, *Three Quarters of A Footprint*, in 1994, he has visited India many times. He has published three books since, including *Abdul's Taxi to Kalighat* about Kolkata and a novel about Edward Lear's visit to India, *Bengal, The Cold Weather, 1873*. He has also written regularly for *The Times, Condé Nast Traveller, National Geographic Traveler*, and many other magazines. He taught life writing and narrative non-fiction at Bath Spa University for 12 years and is working on a third Indian travel book about Lucknow. His interests are broad, ranging from gastronomy – he is a contributor to *The Oxford Companion to Food* as well as several other food reference books – to art history, but his real passion is India.

DANNY ROTHSCHILD is from Italy and West Africa. He graduated from Bath Spa University in 2015 with the Les Arnold Prize. His plays have been produced off-Broadway at the Cherry Lane Theater, the Stella Adler Theater in Hollywood, and fringe festivals around the UK. His newest play, *Home, Again*, premiered at The John F. Kennedy Center in Washington D.C. He is currently in California working in the TV and film industry, still writing plays on the side.

URSULA RANI SARMA is an award-winning playwright, screenwriter and poet. She grew up in County Clare, Ireland and has a BA from University

College Cork and an MPhil from Trinity College Dublin. She has been Writer in Residence for the National Theatre Studio London, Paines Plough Theatre Company London and the Eugene O'Neill Theatre Centre. She has written for the BBC, RTE, TV3, Element Films and Company Pictures amongst many others, and she leads the MA Scriptwriting course at Bath Spa University.

C.J. SKUSE is the author of the YA novels *Pretty Bad Things*, *Rockoholic*, *Dead Romantic*, *Monster*, and *The Deviants*. She was born in 1980 in Weston-super-Mare, England. She has first class degrees in Creative Writing and Writing for Young People, both from Bath Spa, and aside from writing novels, works as a Senior Lecturer on the MA Writing for Young People. CJ's first adult title, *Sweetpea*, was published by HQ / HarperCollins in April 2017.

ROB MAGNUSON SMITH's debut novel, *The Gravedigger*, appeared in 2010 after winning the Pirate's Alley William Faulkner Award. His second novel, *Scorper* is published by Granta Books. Rob's short fiction appears widely; his story 'The Elector of Nossnearly' won the 2015 Elizabeth Jolley Prize and was longlisted for the 2016 *Sunday Times* EFG Short Story Award. He earned his MA in Creative Writing at UEA as winner of the David Higham Award and was International Doctoral Research Fellow at Bath Spa from 2010–2013. Based in Cornwall, Rob lectures in English and Creative Writing at Exeter University.

MIMI THEBO is the Carnegie-longlisted author of *Dreaming the Bear* and ten other novels for children and adults. Her work has been adapted for a BAFTA award-winning film by the BBC, translated into twelve languages and signed for deaf children by ITV. *Coyote Summer* was published in 2017 by Oxford University Press and *Hospital High* is due for publication in September 2017. After more than a decade teaching at Bath Spa University, she recently joined the University of Bristol as Reader in Creative Writing.

MICHAEL UMNEY (Evie Wyld interview) is production manager at community arts radio Resonance FM 104.4. He also produces radio features for the BBC through the Resonance production unit as well as podcasts for the Poetry Society.

STEVE VOAKE is a Senior Lecturer in Writing for Young People. He has written many books and hopes one day to write another.

TOM WEIR has published poetry which has been Highly Commended in The National Poetry Competition and the Forward Prize. He was one of the inaugural winners of the Templar IOTA Shots competition with his pamphlet *The Outsider* and his first full collection, *All That Falling*, was brought out by Templar in 2015. His poetry has appeared in various journals and magazines, including the anthology *Lung Jazz: Young British Poets for Oxfam*. He graduated from Bath Spa Univeristy with a First Class Honours Degree and an MA in Creative Writing.

FAY WELDON is an author, stage and screen playwright, journalist, and cultural commentator, who describes herself as an all-purpose writaholic. Her subject matter is the war between the sexes, now gradually being resolved. She has published some 37 novels, seven short story collections and several books of non-fiction. Her work has been translated into many languages and adapted for TV and film here and abroad. She has a CBE for Services to Literature, been Chairperson of the Booker Prize, and judged other national literary prizes. She is a Council Member of the Society of Authors, has served on the Art Council Literary Panel, and in her early days as a TV playwright, been a negotiator for the Writers Guild of Great Britain. But mostly these days she just writes novels and teaches others the craft.

ANNA WILSON writes for children. Her own kids and their friends have been an endless source of inspiration for over 30 books. Nowadays she has to hide what she has written as her kids would burn every word if they saw what she has committed to print. Her latest books are *The Parent Problem* and *The Family Fiasco*, both of which draw on the trials and tribulations of Anna's own teenage years as well as those of her nearest and dearest. (Think 'Adrian Mole' meets 'Miranda'.) Her books have been chosen as World Book Day titles, shortlisted for the Hull and Lancashire library awards, and chosen for the Richard and Judy Book Club and Summer Reading Challenge.

JACK WOLF is the author of *The Tale of Raw Head and Bloody Bones* (Chatto and Windus, 2013), which was shortlisted for the Polari Award for debut fiction and went on to win the Author's Club Best First Novel Award 2014. His non-fiction work has appeared in *Le Monde*, *Psychologies* magazine, and a few other random places. Jack's work focuses on sites of identity and transformation, and he is currently working on a multi-modal project aimed at exploring what it means to be human in the anthropocene. He blogs about this intermittently at jackwolfauthor.wordpress.com. He teaches Creative Writing at Bath Spa University.

GERARD WOODWARD is a novelist, poet, and short story writer. His trilogy of novels concerning the Jones Family (*August*, *I'll Go To Bed at Noon*, and *A Curious Earth*) have won widespread critical acclaim, including shortlistings for the Man-Booker Prize and Whitbread First Novel Award. His five poetry collections have earned him two T.S. Eliot Prize shortlistings. His most recent publications are the novel, *Vanishing*, which is set partly in Egypt and Libya during World War Two, and *Legoland*, a collection of short stories. A new novel will be published in 2018

EVIE WYLD was born in London and grew up in Australia and South London. She studied Creative Writing at Bath Spa University College and Goldsmiths College, University of London. Her first novel, *After the Fire, a Still Small Voice*, won the John Llewellyn Rhys Prize and a Betty Trask Award and was shortlisted for the Orange Prize for New Writers, the Commonwealth Prize, and the International IMPAC Dublin literary award. In 2013 she was included on *Granta* magazine's once a decade Best of Young British Novelists list. Her second novel, *All the Birds, Singing*, won the Miles Franklin Award, the Encore Award, and the Jerwood Fiction Uncovered Prize, was shortlisted for the Costa Novel Prize, the James Tait Black Prize, and the Sky Arts Times Breakthrough Award and longlisted for the Stella Prize and the Bailey's Women's Prize for Fiction.

Acknowledgements

The editors are grateful to the following publications, in whose pages some of this work first appeared: *Blue Fifth Review, Confingo, The Cresset, The Interpreter's House, Lighthouse Journal, New Walk, New Welsh Review, Poetry London*, and *Poetry Wales*. 'A Species of its Own' by Fay Weldon was first published in *The Author. Birdsong* by Ursula Rani Sarma was commissioned by the Abbey Theatre, Dublin and produced in June 2009. It was directed by Róisín McBrinn and the cast included Orla Fitzgerald and Lorcan Cranitch. 'The Buzzard and the Babe' by David Almond is an extract from his forthcoming novel *The Colour of the Sun*. The poem 'damp change' by Siân Melangell Dafydd is taken from her forthcoming collection *Spitting Distance*. 'How to Write an Award-Winning First Novel' by Nathan Filer was first published in the *Writers and Artists Yearbook*. Carrie Etter's poems from *Imagined Sons* were published by Seren in 2014. 'Mary Palmer: A Short Poetic Life' by Anthony Nanson was first published as 'Afterword' in Mary Palmer, *Iona*, 2nd edn (Awen, Stroud, 2011). 'The Midnight Bell' by Sarah Driver was first published on a website for children celebrating an exhibition of the Beau Street Hoard at the Roman Baths. *Peg and Art* by Kate Pullinger is forthcoming from Doubleday Canada. 'Village Bay' is an extract from Julia Green's new novel for children, *To the Edge of the World*, to be published by Oxford University Press in 2018 and printed here with their kind permission. An earlier draft of Matt Haw's poem 'A Vision for the Topographical Future of East Anglia' appeared in *The Rialto*. Steve Voake's poem 'My Brother Saves Things' first appeared in the anthology *Tremble: The University of Canberra Vice-Chancellor's International Poetry Prize 2016*.

We also wish to extend our gratitude to each of the contributors to this anthology and those graduates who have contributed additional reminiscences and stories to our website – in particular Professor Tessa Hadley for her enthusiasm and for taking the time to write the introduction to this anthology. We would also like to thank Penny Williams, Jane Jones, Abbi Cross and Kirsty Folan for their administrative support of this project; more than one thousand contributors to the *Novel in 25 Words* competition from across the world; the mighty Gavin James Bower for managing the text and proofreading; design and art direction by the hugely talented Matthew Robertson – Matt is the person most responsible for the lovely book you hold in your hands at the present moment; exquisite photographs of our campuses by Kellie Hindmarch; PR by Jane Wakefield, Jennifer Davis and the team at Speed Communications; judges of the *Novel in 25 Words* competition Jonathan Dent, Professor Philip Hensher and Beatrice Hitchman; a huge thank you to Kate Love, Director of Development at Bath Spa University for her advice and overall support from the very beginning of this project; Chris Wakefield for website design, hosting and additional photography; Michael Umney for conducting the audio interviews which are also available on the website; Chancellor Jeremy Irons for recording selected pieces from the anthology; and the Board of Governors at Bath Spa University for its support of our efforts.

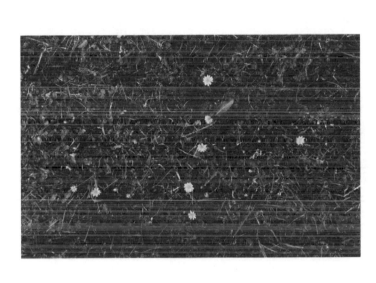